ENGINEERING

Electrical Engineering:
Principles and Applications
Penn State Edition

Pearson Learning Solutions

New York   Boston   San Francisco
London   Toronto   Sydney   Tokyo   Singapore   Madrid
Mexico City   Munich   Paris   Cape Town   Hong Kong   Montreal

Senior Vice President, Editorial and Marketing: Patrick F. Boles
Executive Marketing Manager: Nathan Wilbur
Senior Acquisition Editor: Debbie Coniglio
Development Editor: Christina Martin
Editorial Assistant: Jeanne Martin
Operations Manager: Eric M. Kenney
Production Manager: Jennifer Berry
Art Director: Renée Sartell
Cover Designer: Kristen Kiley

Cover Art: "Abstract Sphere Garden," courtesy of iStockphoto; "Abstract Scheme," courtesy of Andrey Prokhorov/iStockphoto; "Confederation Bridge," courtesy of Shaun Lowe Photographic/iStockphoto; "Rebar Reinforcements 5," courtesy of Bailey Digital Images/iStockphoto; "Airliner in Storm," courtesy of iStockphoto; "Train Passing Next to High-rise Building," courtesy of Terry Husebye/Getty Images; "Highway Intersection," courtesy of Maciej Noskowski/Getty Images; "Golden Gate Bridge Roadway and Cables," courtesy of David Sanger/Getty Images; "Geodesic Dome," courtesy of Russell Hart/Getty Images; "Bridge Architecture," courtesy of Tetra images/Getty Images.

Printed in the United States of America.

Please visit our web site at *www.pearsoncustom.com/custom-library/engineering*.

Attention bookstores: For permission to return any unsold stock, contact us at *pe-uscustomreturns@pearson.com*.

Pearson Learning Solutions, 501 Boylston Street, Suite 900, Boston, MA 02116
A Pearson Education Company
www.pearsoned.com

ISBN 10: 0-558-90521-8
ISBN 13: 978-0-558-90521-7

Contents

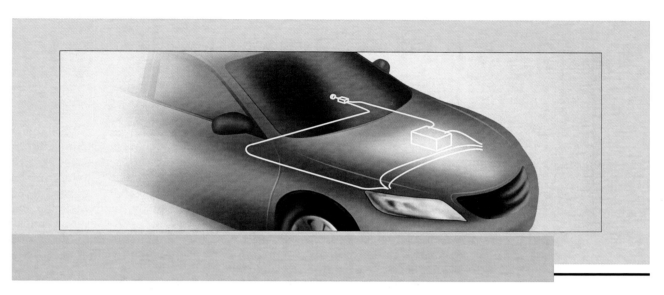

Introduction

Study of this chapter will enable you to:

- Recognize interrelationships between electrical engineering and other fields of science and engineering.

- List the major subfields of electrical engineering.

- List several important reasons for studying electrical engineering.

- Define current, voltage, and power, including their units.

- Calculate power and energy and determine whether energy is supplied or absorbed by a circuit element.

- State and apply Kirchhoff's current and voltage laws.

- Recognize series and parallel connections.

- Identify and describe the characteristics of voltage and current sources.

- State and apply Ohm's law.

- Solve for currents, voltages, and powers in simple circuits.

Introduction to this chapter:

In this chapter, we introduce electrical engineering, define circuit variables (current, voltage, power, and energy), study the laws that these circuit variables obey, and meet several circuit elements (current sources, voltage sources, and resistors).

1 OVERVIEW OF ELECTRICAL ENGINEERING

Electrical engineers design systems that have two main objectives:

1. To gather, store, process, transport, and present *information*.
2. To distribute, store, and convert *energy* between various forms.

In many electrical systems, the manipulation of energy and the manipulation of information are interdependent.

For example, numerous aspects of electrical engineering relating to information are applied in weather prediction. Data about cloud cover, precipitation, wind speed, and so on are gathered electronically by weather satellites, by land-based radar stations, and by sensors at numerous weather stations. (Sensors are devices that convert physical measurements to electrical signals.) This information is transported by electronic communication systems and processed by computers to yield forecasts that are disseminated and displayed electronically.

In electrical power plants, energy is converted from various sources to electrical form. Electrical distribution systems transport the energy to virtually every factory, home, and business in the world, where it is converted to a multitude of useful forms, such as mechanical energy, heat, and light.

No doubt you can list scores of electrical engineering applications in your daily life. Increasingly, electrical and electronic features are integrated into new products. Automobiles and trucks provide just one example of this trend. The electronic content of the average automobile is growing rapidly in value. Auto designers realize that electronic technology is a good way to provide increased functionality at lower cost. Table 1 shows some of the applications of electrical engineering in automobiles.

As another example, we note that many common household appliances contain keypads for operator control, sensors, electronic displays, and computer chips, as well as more conventional switches, heating elements, and motors. Electronics have become so intimately integrated with mechanical systems that a new name, **mechatronics**, is beginning to be used for the combination.

You may find it interesting to search the web for sites related to "mechatronics."

Unfortunately, it would seem that too many engineers are not well equipped to design mechatronic products:

> The world of engineering is like an archipelago whose inhabitants are familiar with their own islands but have only a distant view of the others and little communication with them. A comparable near-isolation impedes the productivity of engineers, whether their field is electrical and electronics, mechanical, chemical, civil, or industrial. Yet modern manufacturing systems, as well as the planes, cars, computers, and myriad other complex products of their making, depend on the harmonious blending of many different technologies. (Richard Comerford, "Mecha . . . what?" *IEEE Spectrum,* August 1994)

Subdivisions of Electrical Engineering

Next, we give you an overall picture of electrical engineering by listing and briefly discussing eight of its major areas.

1. Communication systems transport information in electrical form. Cellular phone, radio, satellite television, and the Internet are examples of communication systems. It is possible for virtually any two people (or computers) on the globe to communicate almost instantaneously. A climber on a mountaintop in Nepal can call or send e-mail to friends whether they are hiking in Alaska or sitting in a New York

Table 1. Current and Emerging Electronic/Electrical Applications in Automobiles and Trucks

Safety
    Antiskid brakes
    Inflatable restraints
    Collision warning and avoidance
    Blind-zone vehicle detection (especially for large trucks)
    Infrared night vision systems
    Heads-up displays
    Automatic accident notification

Communications and entertainment
    AM/FM radio
    Digital audio broadcasting
    CD/tape player
    Cellular phone
    Computer/e-mail
    Satellite radio

Convenience
    Electronic navigation
    Personalized seat/mirror/radio settings
    Electronic door locks

Emissions, performance, and fuel economy
    Vehicle instrumentation
    Electronic ignition
    Tire inflation sensors
    Computerized performance evaluation and maintenance scheduling
    Adaptable suspension systems

Alternative propulsion systems
    Electric vehicles
    Advanced batteries
    Hybrid vehicles

City office. This kind of connectivity affects the way we live, the way we conduct business, and the design of everything we use. For example, communication systems will change the design of highways because traffic and road-condition information collected by roadside sensors can be transmitted to central locations and used to route traffic. When an accident occurs, an electrical signal can be emitted automatically when the airbags deploy, giving the exact location of the vehicle, summoning help, and notifying traffic-control computers.

    2. Computer systems process and store information in digital form. No doubt you have already encountered computer applications in your own field. Besides the computers of which you are aware, there are many in unobvious places, such as household appliances and automobiles. A typical modern automobile contains several dozen special-purpose computers. Chemical processes and railroad switching yards are routinely controlled through computers.

    3. Control systems gather information with sensors and use electrical energy to control a physical process. A relatively simple control system is the heating/cooling system in a residence. A sensor (thermostat) compares the temperature with the desired value. Control circuits operate the furnace or air conditioner to achieve the

> Computers that are part of products such as appliances and automobiles are called *embedded computers*.

desired temperature. In rolling sheet steel, an electrical control system is used to obtain the desired sheet thickness. If the sheet is too thick (or thin), more (or less) force is applied to the rollers. The temperatures and flow rates in chemical processes are controlled in a similar manner. Control systems have even been installed in tall buildings to reduce their movement due to wind.

4. Electromagnetics is the study and application of electric and magnetic fields. The device (known as a magnetron) used to produce microwave energy in an oven is one application. Similar devices, but with much higher power levels, are employed in manufacturing sheets of plywood. Electromagnetic fields heat the glue between layers of wood so that it will set quickly. Cellular phone and television antennas are also examples of electromagnetic devices.

5. Electronics is the study and application of materials, devices, and circuits used in amplifying and switching electrical signals. The most important electronic devices are transistors of various kinds. They are used in nearly all places where electrical information or energy is employed. For example, the cardiac pacemaker is an electronic circuit that senses heart beats, and if a beat does not occur when it should, applies a minute electrical stimulus to the heart, forcing a beat. Electronic instrumentation and electrical sensors are found in every field of science and engineering. Many of the aspects of electronic amplifiers studied later in this book have direct application to the instrumentation used in your field of engineering.

Electronic devices are based on controlling electrons. Photonic devices perform similar functions by controlling photons.

6. Photonics is an exciting new field of science and engineering that promises to replace conventional computing, signal-processing, sensing, and communication devices based on manipulating electrons with greatly improved products based on manipulating photons. Photonics includes light generation by lasers and light-emitting diodes, transmission of light through optical components, as well as switching, modulation, amplification, detection, and steering light by electrical, acoustical, and photon-based devices. Current applications include readers for DVD disks, holograms, optical signal processors, and fiber-optic communication systems. Future applications include optical computers, holographic memories, and medical devices. Photonics offers tremendous opportunities for nearly all scientists and engineers.

7. Power systems convert energy to and from electrical form and transmit energy over long distances. These systems are composed of generators, transformers, distribution lines, motors, and other elements. Mechanical engineers often utilize electrical motors to empower their designs. The selection of a motor having the proper torque–speed characteristic for a given mechanical application is another example of how you can apply the information in this text.

8. Signal processing is concerned with information-bearing electrical signals. Often, the objective is to extract useful information from electrical signals derived from sensors. An application is machine vision for robots in manufacturing. Another application of signal processing is in controlling ignition systems of internal combustion engines. The timing of the ignition spark is critical in achieving good performance and low levels of pollutants. The optimum ignition point relative to crankshaft rotation depends on fuel quality, air temperature, throttle setting, engine speed, and other factors.

If the ignition point is advanced slightly beyond the point of best performance, *engine knock* occurs. Knock can be heard as a sharp metallic noise that is caused by rapid pressure fluctuations during the spontaneous release of chemical energy in the combustion chamber. A combustion-chamber pressure pulse displaying knock is shown in Figure 1. At high levels, knock will destroy an engine in a very short time. Prior to the advent of practical signal-processing electronics for this application,

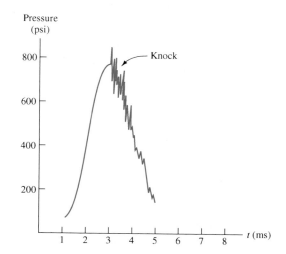

Figure 1 Pressure versus time for an internal combustion engine experiencing knock. Sensors convert pressure to an electrical signal that is processed to adjust ignition timing for minimum pollution and good performance.

engine timing needed to be adjusted for distinctly suboptimum performance to avoid knock under varying combinations of operating conditions.

By connecting a sensor through a tube to the combustion chamber, an electrical signal proportional to pressure is obtained. Electronic circuits process this signal to determine whether the rapid pressure fluctuations characteristic of knock are present. Then electronic circuits continuously adjust ignition timing for optimum performance while avoiding knock.

Why You Need to Study Electrical Engineering

As a reader of this text, you may be majoring in another field of engineering or science and taking a required course in electrical engineering. Your immediate objective is probably to meet the course requirements for a degree in your chosen field. However, there are several other good reasons to learn and retain some basic knowledge of electrical engineering:

1. *To pass the Fundamentals of Engineering (FE) Examination as a first step in becoming a Registered Professional Engineer.* In the United States, before performing engineering services for the public, you will need to become registered as a Professional Engineer (PE). This text gives you the knowledge to answer questions relating to electrical engineering on the registration examinations. Save this text and course notes to review for the FE examination.

Save this text and course notes to review for the FE exam.

2. *To have a broad enough knowledge base so that you can lead design projects in your own field.* Increasingly, electrical engineering is interwoven with nearly all scientific experiments and design projects in other fields of engineering. Industry has repeatedly called for engineers who can see the big picture and work effectively in teams. Engineers or scientists who narrow their focus strictly to their own field are destined to be directed by others. (Electrical engineers are somewhat fortunate in this respect because the basics of structures, mechanisms, and chemical processes are familiar from everyday life. On the other hand, electrical engineering concepts are somewhat more abstract and hidden from the casual observer.)

3. *To be able to operate and maintain electrical systems, such as those found in control systems for manufacturing processes.* The vast majority of electrical-circuit malfunctions can be readily solved by the application of basic electrical-engineering principles. You will be a much more versatile and valuable engineer or scientist if you can apply electrical-engineering principles in practical situations.

4. *To be able to communicate with electrical-engineering consultants.* Very likely, you will often need to work closely with electrical engineers in your career.

2 CIRCUITS, CURRENTS, AND VOLTAGES

Overview of an Electrical Circuit

Before we carefully define the terminology of electrical circuits, let us gain some basic understanding by considering a simple example: the headlight circuit of an automobile. This circuit consists of a battery, a switch, the headlamps, and wires connecting them in a closed path, as illustrated in Figure 2.

The battery voltage is a measure of the energy gained by a unit of charge as it moves through the battery.

Chemical forces in the battery cause electrical charge (electrons) to flow through the circuit. The charge gains energy from the chemicals in the battery and delivers energy to the headlamps. The battery voltage (nominally, 12 volts) is a measure of the energy gained by a unit of charge as it moves through the battery.

Electrons readily move through copper but not through plastic insulation.

The wires are made of an excellent electrical conductor (copper) and are insulated from one another (and from the metal auto body) by electrical insulation (plastic) coating the wires. Electrons readily move through copper but not through the plastic insulation. Thus, the charge flow (electrical current) is confined to the wires until it reaches the headlamps. Air is also an insulator.

The switch is used to control the flow of current. When the conducting metallic parts of the switch make contact, we say that the switch is **closed** and current flows through the circuit. On the other hand, when the conducting parts of the switch do not make contact, we say that the switch is **open** and current does not flow.

Electrons experience collisions with the atoms of the tungsten wires, resulting in heating of the tungsten.

The headlamps contain special tungsten wires that can withstand high temperatures. Tungsten is not as good an electrical conductor as copper, and the electrons experience collisions with the atoms of the tungsten wires, resulting in heating of

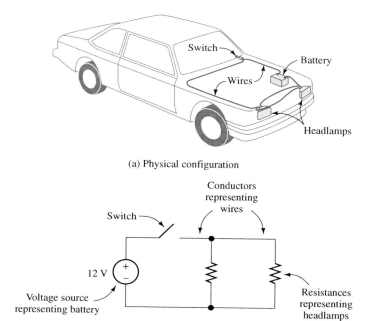

(a) Physical configuration

(b) Circuit diagram

Figure 2 The headlight circuit. (a) The actual physical layout of the circuit. (b) The circuit diagram.

the tungsten. We say that the tungsten wires have electrical resistance. Thus, energy is transferred by the chemical action in the battery to the electrons and then to the tungsten, where it appears as heat. The tungsten becomes hot enough so that copious light is emitted. We will see that the power transferred is equal to the product of current (rate of flow of charge) and the voltage (also called electrical potential) applied by the battery.

> Energy is transferred by the chemical action in the battery to the electrons and then to the tungsten.

(Actually, the simple description of the headlight circuit we have given is most appropriate for older cars. In more modern automobiles, sensors provide information to an embedded computer about the ambient light level, whether or not the ignition is energized, and whether the transmission is in park or drive. The dashboard switch merely inputs a logic level to the computer, indicating the intention of the operator with regard to the headlights. Depending on these inputs, the computer controls the state of an electronic switch in the headlight circuit. When the ignition is turned off and if it is dark, the computer keeps the lights on for a few minutes so the passengers can see to exit and then turns them off to conserve energy in the battery. This is typical of the trend to use highly sophisticated electronic and computer technology to enhance the capabilities of new designs in all fields of engineering.)

Fluid-Flow Analogy

Electrical circuits are analogous to fluid-flow systems. The battery is analogous to a pump, and charge is analogous to the fluid. Conductors (usually copper wires) correspond to frictionless pipes through which the fluid flows. Electrical current is the counterpart of the flow rate of the fluid. Voltage corresponds to the pressure differential between points in the fluid circuit. Switches are analogous to valves. Finally, the electrical resistance of a tungsten headlamp is analogous to a constriction

> The fluid-flow analogy can be very helpful initially in understanding electrical circuits.

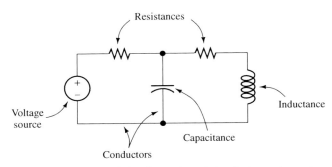

Figure 3 An electrical circuit consists of circuit elements, such as voltage sources, resistances, inductances, and capacitances, connected in closed paths by conductors.

in a fluid system that results in turbulence and conversion of energy to heat. Notice that current is a measure of the flow of charge *through* the cross section of a circuit element, whereas voltage is measured *across* the ends of a circuit element or *between* any other two points in a circuit.

Now that we have gained a basic understanding of a simple electrical circuit, we will define the concepts and terminology more carefully.

Electrical Circuits

An electrical circuit consists of various types of circuit elements connected in closed paths by conductors.

An **electrical circuit** consists of various types of circuit elements connected in closed paths by conductors. An example is illustrated in Figure 3. The circuit elements can be resistances, inductances, capacitances, and voltage sources, among others. The symbols for some of these elements are illustrated in the figure. Eventually, we will carefully discuss the characteristics of each type of element.

Charge flows easily through conductors.

Charge flows easily through conductors, which are represented by lines connecting circuit elements. Conductors correspond to connecting wires in physical circuits. Voltage sources create forces that cause charge to flow through the conductors and other circuit elements. As a result, energy is transferred between the circuit elements, resulting in a useful function.

Electrical Current

Current is the time rate of flow of electrical charge. Its units are amperes (A), which are equivalent to coulombs per second (C/s).

Electrical current is the time rate of flow of electrical charge through a conductor or circuit element. The units are amperes (A), which are equivalent to coulombs per second (C/s). (The charge on an electron is -1.602×10^{-19} C.)

Conceptually, to find the current for a given circuit element, we first select a cross section of the circuit element roughly perpendicular to the flow of current. Then, we select a **reference direction** along the direction of flow. Thus, the reference direction points from one side of the cross section to the other. This is illustrated in Figure 4.

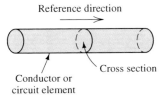

Figure 4 Current is the time rate of charge flow through a cross section of a conductor or circuit element.

Next, suppose that we keep a record of the net charge flow through the cross section. Positive charge crossing in the reference direction is counted as a positive contribution to net charge. Positive charge crossing opposite to the reference is counted as a negative contribution. Furthermore, negative charge crossing in the reference direction is counted as a negative contribution, and negative charge against the reference direction is a positive contribution to charge.

Thus, in concept, we obtain a record of the net charge in coulombs as a function of time in seconds denoted as $q(t)$. The electrical current flowing through the element

8

in the reference direction is given by

$$i(t) = \frac{dq(t)}{dt}$$ (1)

Colored shading is used to indicate key equations.

A constant current of one ampere means that one coulomb of charge passes through the cross section each second.

To find charge given current, we must integrate. Thus, we have

$$q(t) = \int_{t_0}^{t} i(t)\, dt + q(t_0)$$ (2)

in which t_0 is some initial time at which the charge is known. (We assume that time t is in seconds unless stated otherwise.)

Current flow is the same for all cross sections of a circuit element. The current that enters one end flows through the element and exits through the other end.

Determining Current Given Charge

Suppose that charge versus time for a given circuit element is given by

$$q(t) = 0 \qquad \text{for } t < 0$$

and

$$q(t) = 2 - 2e^{-100t}\, \text{C} \qquad \text{for } t > 0$$

Sketch $q(t)$ and $i(t)$ to scale versus time.

Solution   First we use Equation 1 to find an expression for the current:

$$i(t) = \frac{dq(t)}{dt}$$
$$= 0 \qquad \text{for } t < 0$$
$$= 200e^{-100t}\, \text{A} \qquad \text{for } t > 0$$

Plots of $q(t)$ and $i(t)$ are shown in Figure 5. ∎

Reference Directions

In analyzing electrical circuits, we may not initially know the *actual direction* of current flow in a particular circuit element. Therefore, we start by assigning current variables and arbitrarily selecting a *reference direction* for each current of interest. It is customary to use the letter i for currents and subscripts to distinguish different currents. This is illustrated by the example in Figure 6, in which the boxes labeled A, B, and so on represent circuit elements. After we solve for the current values, we may find that some currents have negative values. For example, suppose that $i_1 = -2$ A in the circuit of Figure 6. Because i_1 has a negative value, we know that current actually flows in the direction opposite to the reference initially selected for i_1. Thus, the actual current is 2 A flowing downward through element A.

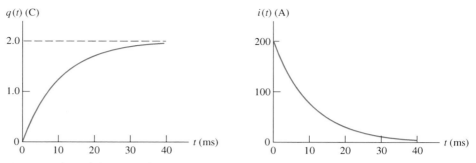

Figure 5 Plots of charge and current versus time for Example 1. *Note*: The time scale is in milliseconds (ms). One millisecond is equivalent to 10^{-3} seconds.

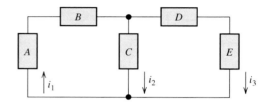

Figure 6 In analyzing circuits, we frequently start by assigning current variables i_1, i_2, i_3, and so forth.

Direct Current and Alternating Current

Dc currents are constant with respect to time, whereas ac currents vary with time.

When a current is constant with time, we say that we have **direct current**, abbreviated as dc. On the other hand, a current that varies with time, reversing direction periodically, is called **alternating current**, abbreviated as ac. Figure 7 shows the values of a dc current and a sinusoidal ac current versus time. When $i_b(t)$ takes a negative value, the actual current direction is opposite to the reference direction for $i_b(t)$. The designation ac is used for other types of time-varying currents, such as the triangular and square waveforms shown in Figure 8.

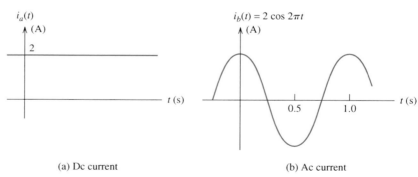

(a) Dc current

(b) Ac current

Figure 7 Examples of dc and ac currents versus time.

Double-Subscript Notation for Currents

So far we have used arrows alongside circuit elements or conductors to indicate reference directions for currents. Another way to indicate the current and reference direction for a circuit element is to label the ends of the element and use double subscripts to define the reference direction for the current. For example, consider the resistance of Figure 9. The current denoted by i_{ab} is the current through the element

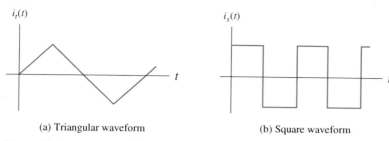

(a) Triangular waveform   (b) Square waveform

Figure 8 Ac currents can have various waveforms.

Figure 9 Reference directions can be indicated by labeling the ends of circuit elements and using double subscripts on current variables. The reference direction for i_{ab} points from a to b. On the other hand, the reference direction for i_{ba} points from b to a.

with its reference direction pointing from a to b. Similarly, i_{ba} is the current with its reference directed from b to a. Of course, i_{ab} and i_{ba} are the same in magnitude and opposite in sign, because they denote the same current but with opposite reference directions. Thus, we have

$$i_{ab} = -i_{ba}$$

Exercise 1 A constant current of 2 A flows through a circuit element. In 10 seconds (s), how much net charge passes through the element?
Answer 20 C. ☐

Exercise 2 The charge that passes through a circuit element is given by $q(t) = 0.01 \sin(200t)$ C, in which the angle is in radians. Find the current as a function of time.
Answer $i(t) = 2 \cos(200t)$ A. ☐

Exercise 3 In Figure 6, suppose that $i_2 = 1$ A and $i_3 = -3$ A. Assuming that the current consists of positive charge, in which direction (upward or downward) is charge moving in element C? In element E?
Answer Downward in element C and upward in element E. ☐

Voltages

When charge moves through circuit elements, energy can be transferred. In the case of automobile headlights, stored chemical energy is supplied by the battery and absorbed by the headlights where it appears as heat and light. The **voltage** associated with a circuit element is the energy transferred per unit of charge that flows through the element. The units of voltage are volts (V), which are equivalent to joules per coulomb (J/C).

For example, consider the storage battery in an automobile. The voltage across its terminals is (nominally) 12 V. This means that 12 J are transferred to or from the battery for each coulomb that flows through it. When charge flows in one direction, energy is supplied by the battery, appearing elsewhere in the circuit as heat or light or perhaps as mechanical energy at the starter motor. If charge moves through the battery in the opposite direction, energy is absorbed by the battery, where it appears as stored chemical energy.

Voltages are assigned polarities that indicate the direction of energy flow. If positive charge moves from the positive polarity through the element toward the negative polarity, the element absorbs energy that appears as heat, mechanical energy, stored chemical energy, or as some other form. On the other hand, if positive charge moves from the negative polarity toward the positive polarity, the element supplies energy. This is illustrated in Figure 10. For negative charge, the direction of energy transfer is reversed.

Voltage is a measure of the energy transferred per unit of charge when charge moves from one point in an electrical circuit to a second point.

Notice that voltage is measured across the ends of a circuit element, whereas current is a measure of charge flow through the element.

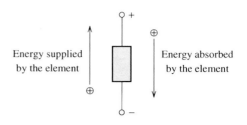

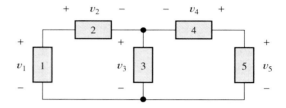

Figure 10 Energy is transferred when charge flows through an element having a voltage across it.

Figure 11 If we do not know the voltage values and polarities in a circuit, we can start by assigning voltage variables choosing the reference polarities arbitrarily. (The boxes represent unspecified circuit elements.)

Reference Polarities

When we begin to analyze a circuit, we often do not know the actual polarities of some of the voltages of interest in the circuit. Then, we simply assign voltage variables choosing *reference* polarities arbitrarily. (Of course, the *actual* polarities are not arbitrary.) This is illustrated in Figure 11. Next, we apply circuit principles (discussed later), obtaining equations that are solved for the voltages. If a given voltage has an actual polarity opposite to our arbitrary choice for the reference polarity, we obtain a negative value for the voltage. For example, if we find that $v_3 = -5$ V in Figure 11, we know that the voltage across element 3 is 5 V in magnitude and its actual polarity is opposite to that shown in the figure (i.e., the actual polarity is positive at the bottom end of element 3 and negative at the top).

In circuit analysis, we frequently assign reference polarities for voltages arbitrarily. If we find at the end of the analysis that the value of a voltage is negative, then we know that the true polarity is opposite of the polarity selected initially.

We usually do not put much effort into trying to assign "correct" references for current directions or voltage polarities. If we have doubt about them, we make arbitrary choices and use circuit analysis to determine true directions and polarities (as well as the magnitudes of the currents and voltages).

Voltages can be constant with time or they can vary. Constant voltages are called **dc voltages**. On the other hand, voltages that change in magnitude and alternate in polarity with time are said to be **ac voltages**. For example,

$$v_1(t) = 10 \text{ V}$$

is a dc voltage. It has the same magnitude and polarity for all time. On the other hand,

$$v_2(t) = 10 \cos(200\pi t)\text{V}$$

is an ac voltage that varies in magnitude and polarity. When $v_2(t)$ assumes a negative value, the actual polarity is opposite the reference polarity.

Double-Subscript Notation for Voltages

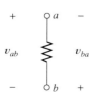

Figure 12 The voltage v_{ab} has a reference polarity that is positive at point *a* and negative at point *b*.

Another way to indicate the reference polarity of a voltage is to use double subscripts on the voltage variable. We use letters or numbers to label the terminals between which the voltage appears, as illustrated in Figure 12. For the resistance shown in the figure, v_{ab} represents the voltage between points *a* and *b* with the positive reference at point a. The two subscripts identify the points between which the voltage appears, and the first subscript is the positive reference. Similarly, v_{ba} is the voltage between a and b with the positive reference at point b. Thus, we can write

$$v_{ab} = -v_{ba} \tag{3}$$

because v_{ba} has the same magnitude as v_{ab} but has opposite polarity.

Still another way to indicate a voltage and its reference polarity is to use an arrow, as shown in Figure 13. The positive reference corresponds to the head of the arrow.

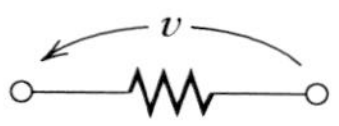

Figure 13 The positive reference for v is at the head of the arrow.

Switches

Switches control the currents in circuits. When an ideal switch is open, the current through it is zero and the voltage across it is determined by the remainder of the circuit. When an ideal switch is closed, the voltage across it is zero and the current through it is determined by the remainder of the circuit.

Exercise 4 The voltage across a given circuit element is $v_{ab} = 20$ V. A positive charge of 2 C moves through the circuit element from terminal b to terminal a. How much energy is transferred? Is the energy supplied by the circuit element or absorbed by it?
Answer 40 J are supplied by the circuit element. ☐

3 POWER AND ENERGY

Consider the circuit element shown in Figure 14. Because the current i is the rate of flow of charge and the voltage v is a measure of the energy transferred per unit of charge, the product of the current and the voltage is the rate of energy transfer. In other words, the product of current and voltage is power:

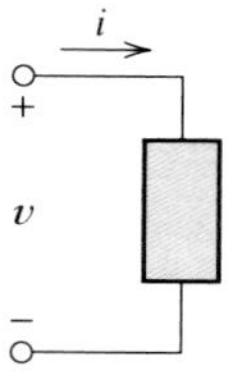

$$p = vi \tag{4}$$

The physical units of the quantities on the right-hand side of this equation are

$$\text{volts} \times \text{amperes} =$$
$$(\text{joules/coulomb}) \times (\text{coulombs/second}) =$$
$$\text{joules/second} =$$
$$\text{watts}$$

Figure 14 When current flows through an element and voltage appears across the element, energy is transferred. The rate of energy transfer is $p = vi$.

Passive Reference Configuration

Now we may ask whether the power calculated by Equation 4 represents energy supplied by or absorbed by the element. Refer to Figure 14 and notice that the current reference enters the positive polarity of the voltage. We call this arrangement the **passive reference configuration**. Provided that the references are picked in this manner, a positive result for the power calculation implies that energy is being absorbed by the element. On the other hand, a negative result means that the element is supplying energy to other parts of the circuit.

If the current reference enters the negative end of the reference polarity, we compute the power as

$$p = -vi \tag{5}$$

Then, as before, a positive value for p indicates that energy is absorbed by the element, and a negative value shows that energy is supplied by the element.

If the circuit element happens to be an electrochemical battery, positive power means that the battery is being charged. In other words, the energy absorbed by the battery is being stored as chemical energy. On the other hand, negative power indicates that the battery is being discharged. Then the energy supplied by the battery is delivered to some other element in the circuit.

Sometimes currents, voltages, and powers are functions of time. To emphasize this fact, we can write Equation 4 as

$$p(t) = v(t)i(t) \tag{6}$$

Power Calculations

Consider the circuit elements shown in Figure 15. Calculate the power for each element. If each element is a battery, is it being charged or discharged?

Solution In element A, the current reference enters the positive reference polarity. This is the passive reference configuration. Thus, power is computed as

$$p_a = v_a i_a = 12 \text{ V} \times 2 \text{ A} = 24 \text{ W}$$

Because the power is positive, energy is absorbed by the device. If it is a battery, it is being charged.

In element B, the current reference enters the negative reference polarity. (Recall that the current that enters one end of a circuit element must exit from the other end, and vice versa.) This is opposite to the passive reference configuration. Hence, power is computed as

$$p_b = -v_b i_b = -(12 \text{ V}) \times 1 \text{ A} = -12 \text{ W}$$

Since the power is negative, energy is supplied by the device. If it is a battery, it is being discharged.

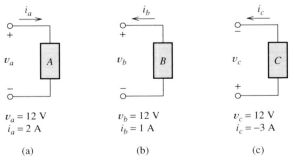

Figure 15 Circuit elements for Example 2.

In element C, the current reference enters the positive reference polarity. This is the passive reference configuration. Thus, we compute power as

$$p_c = v_c i_c = 12 \text{ V} \times (-3 \text{ A}) = -36 \text{ W}$$

Since the result is negative, energy is supplied by the element. If it is a battery, it is being discharged. (Notice that since i_c takes a negative value, current actually flows downward through element C.) ∎

Energy Calculations

To calculate the energy w delivered to a circuit element between time instants t_1 and t_2, we integrate power:

$$w = \int_{t_1}^{t_2} p(t)\, dt \qquad (7)$$

Here we have explicitly indicated that power can be a function of time by using the notation $p(t)$.

Energy Calculation

Find an expression for the power for the voltage source shown in Figure 16. Compute the energy for the interval from $t_1 = 0$ to $t_2 = \infty$.

Solution   The current reference enters the positive reference polarity. Thus, we compute power as

$$\begin{aligned} p(t) &= v(t)i(t) \\ &= 12 \times 2e^{-t} \\ &= 24e^{-t} \text{ W} \end{aligned}$$

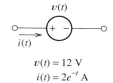

$v(t) = 12$ V
$i(t) = 2e^{-t}$ A

Figure 16 Circuit element for Example 3.

Subsequently, the energy transferred is given by

$$\begin{aligned} w &= \int_0^\infty p(t)\, dt \\ &= \int_0^\infty 24e^{-t}\, dt \\ &= \left[-24e^{-t}\right]_0^\infty = -24e^{-\infty} - (-24e^0) = 24 \text{ J} \end{aligned}$$

Because the energy is positive, it is absorbed by the source. ∎

Prefixes

In electrical engineering, we encounter a tremendous range of values for currents, voltages, powers, and other quantities. We use the prefixes shown in Table 2 when working with very large or small quantities. For example, 1 milliampere (1 mA) is equivalent to 10^{-3} A, 1 kilovolt (1 kV) is equivalent to 1000 V, and so on.

Table 2. Prefixes Used for Large or Small Physical Quantities

Prefix	Abbreviation	Scale Factor
giga-	G	10^9
meg- or mega-	M	10^6
kilo-	k	10^3
milli-	m	10^{-3}
micro-	μ	10^{-6}
nano-	n	10^{-9}
pico-	p	10^{-12}
femto-	f	10^{-15}

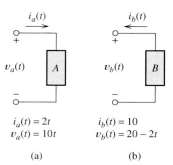

$i_a(t) = 2t$ $\qquad$ $i_b(t) = 10$
$v_a(t) = 10t$ $\qquad$ $v_b(t) = 20 - 2t$

Figure 17 See Exercise 6. $\qquad$ (a) $\qquad$ (b)

Exercise 5 The ends of a circuit element are labeled a and b, respectively. Are the references for i_{ab} and v_{ab} related by the passive reference configuration? Explain.

Answer The reference direction for i_{ab} enters terminal a, which is also the positive reference for v_{ab}. Therefore, the current reference direction enters the positive reference polarity, so we have the passive reference configuration. $\square$

Exercise 6 Compute the power as a function of time for each of the elements shown in Figure 17. Find the energy transferred between $t_1 = 0$ and $t_2 = 10$ s. In each case is energy supplied or absorbed by the element?

Answer **a.** $p_a(t) = 20t^2$ W, $w_a = 6667$ J; since w_a is positive, energy is absorbed by element A. **b.** $p_b(t) = 20t - 200$ W, $w_b = -1000$ J; since w_b is negative, energy is supplied by element B. $\square$

4 KIRCHHOFF'S CURRENT LAW

Kirchhoff's current law states that the net current entering a node is zero.

A **node** in an electrical circuit is a point at which two or more circuit elements are joined together. Examples of nodes are shown in Figure 18.

An important principle of electrical circuits is **Kirchhoff's current law**: *The net current entering a node is zero.* To compute the *net* current entering a node, we add the currents entering and subtract the currents leaving. For illustration, consider the nodes of Figure 18. Then, we can write:

$$\text{Node } a: \quad i_1 + i_2 - i_3 = 0$$
$$\text{Node } b: \quad i_3 - i_4 = 0$$
$$\text{Node } c: \quad i_5 + i_6 + i_7 = 0$$

16

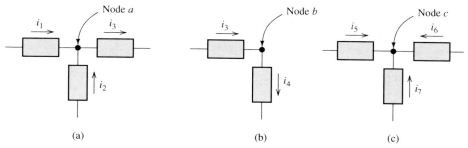

Figure 18 Partial circuits showing one node each to illustrate Kirchhoff's current law.

Notice that for node b, Kirchhoff's current law requires that $i_3 = i_4$. In general, if only two circuit elements are connected at a node, their currents must be equal. The current flows into the node through one element and out through the other. Usually, we will recognize this fact and assign a single current variable for both circuit elements.

For node c, either all of the currents are zero or some are positive while others are negative.

We abbreviate Kirchhoff's current law as KCL. There are two other equivalent ways to state KCL. One way is: *The net current leaving a node is zero.* To compute the net current leaving a node, we add the currents leaving and subtract the currents entering. For the nodes of Figure 18, this yields the following:

$$\text{Node } a: \quad -i_1 - i_2 + i_3 = 0$$
$$\text{Node } b: \quad -i_3 + i_4 = 0$$
$$\text{Node } c: \quad -i_5 - i_6 - i_7 = 0$$

Of course, these equations are equivalent to those obtained earlier.

Another way to state KCL is: *The sum of the currents entering a node equals the sum of the currents leaving a node.* Applying this statement to Figure 18, we obtain the following set of equations:

An alternative way to state Kirchhoff's current law is that the sum of the currents entering a node is equal to the sum of the currents leaving a node.

$$\text{Node } a: \quad i_1 + i_2 = i_3$$
$$\text{Node } b: \quad i_3 = i_4$$
$$\text{Node } c: \quad i_5 + i_6 + i_7 = 0$$

Again, these equations are equivalent to those obtained earlier.

Physical Basis for Kirchhoff's Current Law

An appreciation of why KCL is true can be obtained by considering what would happen if it were violated. Suppose that we could have the situation shown in Figure 18(a), with $i_1 = 3$ A, $i_2 = 2$ A, and $i_3 = 4$ A. Then, the net current entering the node would be

$$i_1 + i_2 - i_3 = 1 \text{ A} = 1 \text{ C/s}$$

In this case, 1 C of charge would accumulate at the node during each second. After 1 s, we would have $+1$ C of charge at the node, and -1 C of charge somewhere else in the circuit.

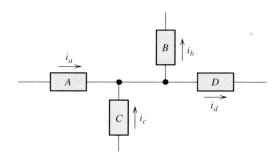

Figure 19 Elements A, B, C, and D can be considered to be connected to a common node, because all points in a circuit that are connected directly by conductors are electrically equivalent to a single point.

Suppose that these charges are separated by a distance of one meter (m). Recall that unlike charges experience a force of attraction. The resulting force turns out to be approximately 8.99×10^9 newtons (N) (equivalent to 2.02×10^9 pounds). Very large forces are generated when charges of this magnitude are separated by moderate distances. In effect, KCL states that such forces prevent charge from accumulating at the nodes of a circuit.

All points in a circuit that are connected directly by conductors can be considered to be a single node. For example, in Figure 19, elements A, B, C, and D are connected to a common node. Applying KCL, we can write

All points in a circuit that are connected directly by conductors can be considered to be a single node.

$$i_a + i_c = i_b + i_d$$

Series Circuits

We make frequent use of KCL in analyzing circuits. For example, consider the elements A, B, and C shown in Figure 20. When elements are connected end to end, we say that they are connected in **series**. *In order for elements A and B to be in series, no other path for current can be connected to the node joining A and B. Thus, all elements in a series circuit have identical currents.* For example, writing Kirchhoff's current law at node 1 for the circuit of Figure 20, we have

$$i_a = i_b$$

At node 2, we have

$$i_b = i_c$$

Thus, we have

$$i_a = i_b = i_c$$

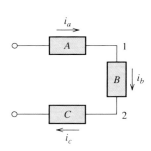

Figure 20 Elements A, B, and C are connected in series.

The current that enters a series circuit must flow through each element in the circuit.

Exercise 7 Use KCL to determine the values of the unknown currents shown in Figure 21.
Answer $i_a = 4 \, \text{A}, i_b = -2 \, \text{A}, i_c = -8 \, \text{A}$. ☐

Exercise 8 Consider the circuit of Figure 22. Identify the groups of circuit elements that are connected in series.
Answer Elements A and B are in series; elements E, F, and G form another series combination. ☐

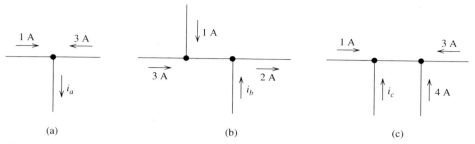

(a)   (b)   (c)

Figure 21 See Exercise 7.

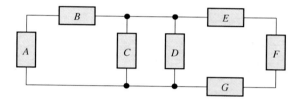

Figure 22 Circuit for Exercise 8.

5 KIRCHHOFF'S VOLTAGE LAW

A **loop** in an electrical circuit is a closed path starting at a node and proceeding through circuit elements, eventually returning to the starting node. Frequently, several loops can be identified for a given circuit. For example, in Figure 22, one loop consists of the path starting at the top end of element A and proceeding clockwise through elements B and C, returning through A to the starting point. Another loop starts at the top of element D and proceeds clockwise through E, F, and G, returning to the start through D. Still another loop exists through elements A, B, E, F, and G around the periphery of the circuit.

Kirchhoff's voltage law (KVL) states: *The algebraic sum of the voltages equals zero for any closed path (loop) in an electrical circuit.* In traveling around a loop, we encounter various voltages, some of which carry a positive sign while others carry a negative sign in the algebraic sum. A convenient convention is to use the first polarity mark encountered for each voltage to decide if it should be added or subtracted in the algebraic sum. If we go through the voltage from the positive polarity reference to the negative reference, it carries a plus sign. If the polarity marks are encountered in the opposite direction (minus to plus), the voltage carries a negative sign. This is illustrated in Figure 23.

For the circuit of Figure 24, we obtain the following equations:

$$\text{Loop 1:} \quad -v_a + v_b + v_c = 0$$

$$\text{Loop 2:} \quad -v_c - v_d + v_e = 0$$

$$\text{Loop 3:} \quad v_a - v_b + v_d - v_e = 0$$

Notice that v_a is subtracted for loop 1, but it is added for loop 3, because the direction of travel is different for the two loops. Similarly, v_c is added for loop 1 and subtracted for loop 2.

Kirchhoff's voltage law (KVL) states that the algebraic sum of the voltages equals zero for any closed path (loop) in an electrical circuit.

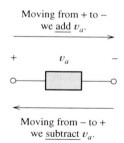

Figure 23 In applying KVL to a loop, voltages are added or subtracted depending on their reference polarities relative to the direction of travel around the loop.

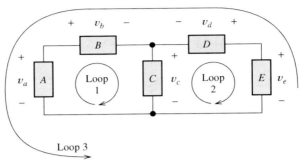

Figure 24 Circuit used for illustration of Kirchhoff's voltage law.

Kirchhoff's Voltage Law Related to Conservation of Energy

KVL is a consequence of the law of energy conservation. Consider the circuit shown in Figure 25. This circuit consists of three elements connected in series. Thus, the same current i flows through all three elements. The power for each of the elements is given by

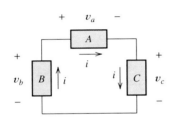

Figure 25 In this circuit, conservation of energy requires that $v_b = v_a + v_c$.

$$\text{Element } A: \quad p_a = v_a i$$
$$\text{Element } B: \quad p_b = -v_b i$$
$$\text{Element } C: \quad p_c = v_c i$$

Notice that the current and voltage references have the passive configuration (the current reference enters the plus polarity mark) for elements A and C. For element B, the relationship is opposite to the passive reference configuration. That is why we have a negative sign in the calculation of p_b.

At a given instant, the sum of the powers for all of the elements in a circuit must be zero. Otherwise, for an increment of time taken at that instant, more energy would be absorbed than is supplied by the circuit elements (or vice versa):

$$p_a + p_b + p_c = 0$$

Substituting for the powers, we have

$$v_a i - v_b i + v_c i = 0$$

Canceling the current i, we obtain

$$v_a - v_b + v_c = 0$$

This is exactly the same equation that is obtained by adding the voltages around the loop and setting the sum to zero for a clockwise loop in the circuit of Figure 25.

One way to check our results after solving for the currents and voltages in a circuit is the check to see that the power adds to zero for all of the elements.

Parallel Circuits

Two circuit elements are connected in parallel if both ends of one element are connected directly (i.e., by conductors) to corresponding ends of the other.

We say that two circuit elements are connected in **parallel** if both ends of one element are connected directly (i.e., by conductors) to corresponding ends of the other. For

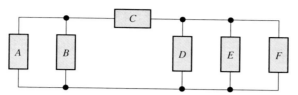

Figure 26 In this circuit, elements A and B are in parallel. Elements D, E, and F form another parallel combination.

example, in Figure 26, elements A and B are in parallel. Similarly, we say that the three circuit elements D, E, and F are in parallel. Element B is *not* in parallel with D because the top end of B is not *directly* connected to the top end of D.

The voltages across parallel elements are equal in magnitude and have the same polarity. For illustration, consider the partial circuit shown in Figure 27. Here elements A, B, and C are connected in parallel. Consider a loop from the bottom end of A upward and then down through element B back to the bottom of A. For this clockwise loop, we have $-v_a + v_b = 0$. Thus, KVL requires that

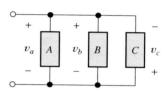

Figure 27 For this circuit, we can show that $v_a = v_b = -v_c$. Thus, the magnitudes and *actual* polarities of all three voltages are the same.

$$v_a = v_b$$

Next, consider a clockwise loop through elements A and C. For this loop, KVL requires that

$$-v_a - v_c = 0$$

This implies that $v_a = -v_c$. In other words, v_a and v_c have opposite algebraic signs. Furthermore, one or the other of the two voltages must be negative (unless both are zero). Therefore, one of the voltages has an actual polarity opposite to the reference polarity shown in the figure. Thus, the actual polarities of the voltages are the same (either both are positive at the top of the circuit or both are positive at the bottom).

Usually, when we have a parallel circuit, we simply use the same voltage variable for all of the elements as illustrated in Figure 28.

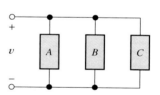

Figure 28 Analysis is simplified by using the same voltage variable and reference polarity for elements that are in parallel.

Exercise 9 Use repeated application of KVL to find the values of v_c and v_e for the circuit of Figure 29.

Answer $v_c = 8\,\text{V}, v_e = -2\,\text{V}$. □

Exercise 10 Identify elements that are in parallel in Figure 29. Identify elements in series.

Answer Elements E and F are in parallel; elements A and B are in series. □

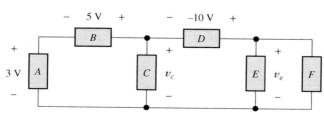

Figure 29 Circuit for Exercises 9 and 10.

6 INTRODUCTION TO CIRCUIT ELEMENTS

In this section, we carefully define several types of ideal circuit elements:

Conductors
Voltage sources
Current sources
Resistors

Later in the book, we will encounter additional elements, including inductors and capacitors. Eventually, we will be able to use these idealized circuit elements to describe (model) complex real-world electrical devices.

Conductors

We have already encountered conductors. Ideal conductors are represented in circuit diagrams by unbroken lines between the ends of other circuit elements. We define ideal circuit elements in terms of the relationship between the voltage across the element and the current through it.

The voltage between the ends of an ideal conductor is zero regardless of the current flowing through the conductor. When two points in a circuit are connected together by an ideal conductor, we say that the points are **shorted** together. Another term for an ideal conductor is **short circuit**. All points in a circuit that are connected by ideal conductors can be considered as a single node.

If no conductors or other circuit elements are connected between two parts of a circuit, we say that an **open circuit** exists between the two parts of the circuit. No current can flow through an ideal open circuit.

> The voltage between the ends of an ideal conductor is zero regardless of the current flowing through the conductor.
>
> All points in a circuit that are connected by ideal conductors can be considered as a single node.

Independent Voltage Sources

An **ideal independent voltage source** maintains a specified voltage across its terminals. The voltage across the source is independent of other elements that are connected to it and of the current flowing through it. We use a circle enclosing the reference polarity marks to represent independent voltage sources. The value of the voltage is indicated alongside the symbol. The voltage can be constant or it can be a function of time. Several voltage sources are shown in Figure 30.

In Figure 30(a), the voltage across the source is constant. Thus, we have a dc voltage source. On the other hand, the source shown in Figure 30(b) is an ac voltage source having a sinusoidal variation with time. We say that these are *independent* sources because the voltages across their terminals are independent of all other voltages and currents in the circuit.

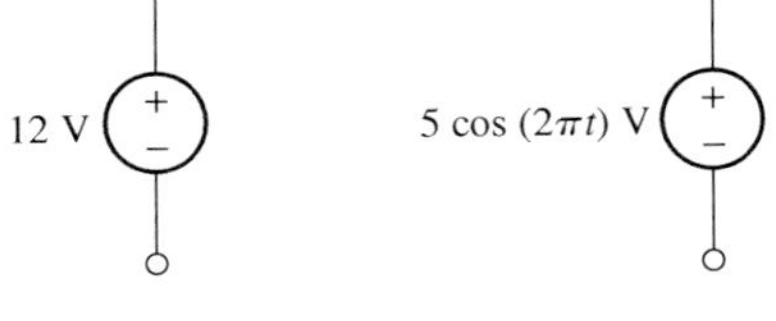

> An ideal independent voltage source maintains a specified voltage across its terminals.

12 V ⊕⊖ $5 \cos (2\pi t) \text{ V}$ ⊕⊖

(a) Constant or dc voltage source

(b) Ac voltage source

Figure 30 Independent voltage sources.

Ideal Circuit Elements versus Reality

Here we are giving definitions of *ideal* circuit elements. It is possible to draw ideal circuits in which the definitions of various circuit elements conflict. For example, Figure 31 shows a 12-V voltage source with a conductor connected across its terminals. In this case, the definition of the voltage source requires that $v_x = 12$ V. On the other hand, the definition of an ideal conductor requires that $v_x = 0$. In our study of ideal circuits, we avoid such conflicts.

In the real world, an automobile battery is nearly an ideal 12-V voltage source, and a short piece of heavy-gauge copper wire is nearly an ideal conductor. If we place the wire across the terminals of the battery, a very large current flows through the wire, stored chemical energy is converted to heat in the wire at a very high rate, and the wire will probably melt or the battery be destroyed.

When we encounter a contradictory idealized circuit model, we often have an undesirable situation (such as a fire or destroyed components) in the real-world counterpart to the model. In any case, a contradictory circuit model implies that we have not been sufficiently careful in choosing circuit models for the real circuit elements. For example, an automobile battery is not exactly modeled as an ideal voltage source. We will see that a better model (particularly if the currents are very large) is an ideal voltage source in series with a resistance. (We will discuss resistance very soon.) A short piece of copper wire is not modeled well as an ideal conductor, in this case. Instead, we will see that it is modeled better as a small resistance. If we have done a good job at picking circuit models for real-world circuits, we will not encounter contradictory circuits, and the results we calculate using the model will match reality very well.

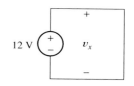

Figure 31 We avoid self-contradictory circuit diagrams such as this one.

Dependent Voltage Sources

A **dependent** or **controlled voltage source** is similar to an independent source except that the voltage across the source terminals is a function of other voltages or currents in the circuit. Instead of a circle, it is customary to use a diamond to represent controlled sources in circuit diagrams. Two examples of dependent sources are shown in Figure 32.

A **voltage-controlled voltage source** is a voltage source having a voltage equal to a constant times the voltage across a pair of terminals elsewhere in the network.

A voltage-controlled voltage source maintains a voltage across its terminals equal to a constant times a voltage elsewhere in the circuit.

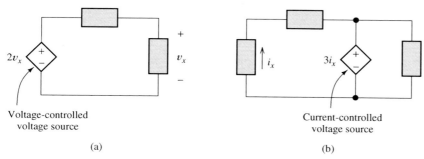

Voltage-controlled voltage source

(a)

Current-controlled voltage source

(b)

Figure 32 Dependent voltage sources (also known as controlled voltage sources) are represented by diamond-shaped symbols. The voltage across a controlled voltage source depends on a current or voltage that appears elsewhere in the circuit.

An example is shown in Figure 32(a). The dependent voltage source is the diamond symbol. The reference polarity of the source is indicated by the marks inside the diamond. The voltage v_x determines the value of the voltage produced by the source. For example, if it should turn out that $v_x = 3$ V, the source voltage is $2v_x = 6$ V. If v_x should equal -7 V, the source produces $2v_x = -14$ V (in which case, the actual positive polarity of the source is at the bottom end).

> A current-controlled voltage source maintains a voltage across its terminals equal to a constant times a current flowing through some other element in the circuit.

A **current-controlled voltage source** is a voltage source having a voltage equal to a constant times the current through some other element in the circuit. An example is shown in Figure 32(b). In this case, the source voltage is three times the value of the current i_x. The factor multiplying the current is called the **gain parameter**. We assume that the voltage has units of volts and the current is in amperes. Thus, the gain parameter [which is 3 in Figure 32(b)] has units of volts per ampere (V/A). (Shortly, we will see that the units V/A are the units of resistance and are called ohms.)

Returning our attention to the voltage-controlled voltage source in Figure 32(a), we note that the gain parameter is 2 and is unitless (or we could say that the units are V/V).

Independent Current Sources

> An ideal independent current source forces a specified current to flow through itself.

An ideal **independent current source** forces a specified current to flow through itself. The symbol for an independent current source is a circle enclosing an arrow that gives the reference direction for the current. The current through an independent current source is independent of the elements connected to it and of the voltage across it. Figure 33 shows the symbols for a dc current source and for an ac current source.

If an open circuit exists across the terminals of a current source, we have a contradictory circuit. For example, consider the 2-A dc current source shown in Figure 33(a). This current source is shown with an open circuit across its terminals. By definition, the current flowing into the top node of the source is 2 A. Also by definition, no current can flow through the open circuit. Thus, KCL is not satisfied at this node. In good models for actual circuits, this situation does not occur. Thus, we will avoid current sources with open-circuited terminals in our discussion of ideal networks.

A battery is a good example of a voltage source, but an equally familiar example does not exist for a current source. However, current sources are useful in constructing theoretical models. Later, we will see that a good approximation to an ideal current source can be achieved with electronic amplifiers.

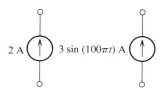

Figure 33 Independent current sources.

(a) Dc current source

(b) Ac current source

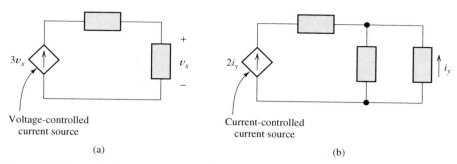

Figure 34 Dependent current sources. The current through a dependent current source depends on a current or voltage that appears elsewhere in the circuit.

Dependent Current Sources

The current flowing through a **dependent current source** is determined by a current or voltage elsewhere in the circuit. The symbol is a diamond enclosing an arrow that indicates the reference direction. Two types of controlled current sources are shown in Figure 34.

In Figure 34(a), we have a **voltage-controlled current source**. The current through the source is three times the voltage v_x. The gain parameter of the source (3 in this case) has units of A/V (which we will soon see are equivalent to siemens or inverse ohms). If it turns out that v_x has a value of 5 V, the current through the controlled current source is $3v_x = 15$ A.

Figure 34(b) illustrates a **current-controlled current source**. In this case, the current through the source is twice the value of i_y. The gain parameter, which has a value of 2 in this case, has units of A/A (i.e., it is unitless).

Like controlled voltage sources, controlled current sources are useful in constructing circuit models for many types of real-world devices, such as electronic amplifiers, transistors, transformers, and electrical machines. If a controlled source is needed for some application, it can be implemented by using electronic amplifiers. In sum, these are the four kinds of controlled sources:

1. Voltage-controlled voltage sources

2. Current-controlled voltage sources

3. Voltage-controlled current sources

4. Current-controlled current sources

> The current flowing through a dependent current source is determined by a current or voltage elsewhere in the circuit.

Resistors and Ohm's Law

The voltage v across an ideal **resistor** is proportional to the current i through the resistor. The constant of proportionality is the resistance R. The symbol used for a resistor is shown in Figure 35(a). Notice that the current reference and voltage polarity reference conform to the passive reference configuration. In other words, the reference direction for the current is into the positive polarity mark and out of the negative polarity mark. In equation form, the voltage and current are related by **Ohm's law**:

$$v = iR$$

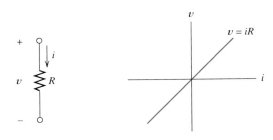

(a) Resistance symbol   (b) Ohm's law

Figure 35 Voltage is proportional to current in an ideal resistor. Notice that the references for v and i conform to the passive reference configuration.

The units of resistance are V/A, which are called ohms. The uppercase Greek letter omega (Ω) represents ohms. In practical circuits, we encounter resistances ranging from milliohms (mΩ) to megohms (MΩ).

Except for rather unusual situations, the resistance R assumes positive values. (In certain types of electronic circuits, we can encounter negative resistance, but for now we assume that R is positive.) In situations for which the current reference direction enters the *negative* reference of the voltage, Ohm's law becomes

$$v = -iR$$

This is illustrated in Figure 36.

Figure 36 If the references for v and i are opposite to the passive configuration, we have $v = -Ri$.

The relationship between current direction and voltage polarity can be neatly included in the equation for Ohm's law if double-subscript notation is used. (Recall that to use double subscripts, we label the ends of the element under consideration, which is a resistance in this case.) If the order of the subscripts is the same for the current as for the voltage (i_{ab} and v_{ab}, for example), the current reference direction enters the first terminal and the positive voltage reference is at the first terminal. Thus, we can write

$$v_{ab} = i_{ab}R$$

On the other hand, if the order of the subscripts is not the same, we have

$$v_{ab} = -i_{ba}R$$

Conductance

Solving Ohm's law for current, we have

$$i = \frac{1}{R}v$$

We call the quantity $1/R$ a **conductance**. It is customary to denote conductances with the letter G:

$$G = \frac{1}{R} \tag{8}$$

Conductances have the units of inverse ohms (Ω^{-1}), which are called siemens (abbreviated S). Thus, we can write Ohm's law as

$$i = Gv \qquad (9)$$

Resistors

It turns out that we can construct nearly ideal resistors by attaching terminals to many types of conductive materials. This is illustrated in Figure 37. Conductive materials that can be used to construct resistors include most metals, their alloys, and carbon.

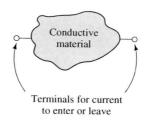

Figure 37 We construct resistors by attaching terminals to a piece of conductive material.

On a microscopic level, current in metals consists of electrons moving through the material. (On the other hand, in solutions of ionic compounds, current is carried partly by positive ions.) The applied voltage creates an electric field that accelerates the electrons. The electrons repeatedly collide with the atoms of the material and lose their forward momentum. Then they are accelerated again. The net effect is a constant average velocity for the electrons. At the macroscopic level, we observe a current that is proportional to the applied voltage.

Resistance Related to Physical Parameters

The dimensions and geometry of the resistor as well as the particular material used to construct a resistor influence its resistance. We consider only resistors that take the form of a long cylinder or bar with terminals attached at the ends, as illustrated in Figure 38. The cross-sectional area A is constant along the length of the cylinder or bar. If the length L of the resistor is much greater than the dimensions of its cross section, the resistance is approximately given by

$$R = \frac{\rho L}{A} \qquad (10)$$

in which ρ is the *resistivity* of the material used to construct the resistor. The units of resistivity are ohm meters (Ωm).

Materials can be classified as conductors, semiconductors, or insulators, depending on their resistivity. **Conductors** have the lowest resistivity and easily conduct electrical current. **Insulators** have very high resistivity and conduct very little current (at least for moderate voltages). **Semiconductors** fall between conductors and insulators. Certain semiconductors are very useful in constructing electronic devices. Table 3 gives approximate values of resistivity for several materials.

Figure 38 Resistors often take the form of a long cylinder (or bar) in which current enters one end and flows along the length.

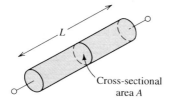

Cross-sectional area A

Table 3. Resistivity Values (Ωm) for Selected Materials at 300 K

Conductors	
Aluminum	2.73×10^{-8}
Carbon (amorphous)	3.5×10^{-5}
Copper	1.72×10^{-8}
Gold	2.27×10^{-8}
Nichrome	1.12×10^{-6}
Silver	1.63×10^{-8}
Tungsten	5.44×10^{-8}
Semiconductors	
Silicon (device grade)	10^{-5} to 1
depends on impurity concentration	
Insulators	
Fused quartz	$> 10^{21}$
Glass (typical)	1×10^{12}
Teflon	1×10^{19}

Example 4   Resistance Calculation

Compute the resistance of a copper wire having a diameter of 2.05 mm and a length of 10 m.

Solution   First, we compute the cross-sectional area of the wire:

$$A = \frac{\pi d^2}{4} = \frac{\pi (2.05 \times 10^{-3})^2}{4} = 3.3 \times 10^{-6} \text{ m}^2$$

Then, the resistance is given by

$$R = \frac{\rho L}{A} = \frac{1.72 \times 10^{-8} \times 10}{3.3 \times 10^{-6}} = 0.052 \ \Omega$$

These are the approximate dimensions of a piece of 12-gauge copper wire that we might find connecting an electrical outlet to the distribution box in a residence. Of course, two wires are needed for a complete circuit. ∎

Power Calculations for Resistances

Recall that we compute power for a circuit element as the product of the current and voltage:

$$p = vi \tag{11}$$

If v and i have the passive reference configuration, a positive sign for power means that energy is being absorbed by the device. Furthermore, a negative sign means that energy is being supplied by the device.

If we use Ohm's law to substitute for v in Equation 11, we obtain

$$p = Ri^2 \tag{12}$$

On the other hand, if we solve Ohm's law for i and substitute into Equation 11, we obtain

$$p = \frac{v^2}{R} \qquad (13)$$

Notice that power for a resistance is positive regardless of the sign of v or i (assuming that R is positive, which is ordinarily the case). Thus, power is absorbed by resistances. If the resistance results from collisions of electrons with the atoms of the material composing a resistor, this power shows up as heat.

Some applications for conversion of electrical power into heat are heating elements for ovens, water heaters, cooktops, and space heaters. In a typical space heater, the heating element consists of a nichrome wire that becomes red hot in operation. (Nichrome is an alloy of nickel, chromium, and iron.) To fit the required length of wire in a small space, it is coiled rather like a spring.

Using Resistance to Measure Strain

Civil and mechanical engineers routinely employ the dependence of resistance on physical dimensions of a conductor to measure strain. These measurements are important in experimental stress–strain analysis of mechanisms and structures. (Strain is defined as fractional change in length, given by $\epsilon = \Delta L / L$.)

A typical resistive strain gauge consists of nickel–copper alloy foil that is photoetched to obtain multiple conductors aligned with the direction of the strain to be measured. This is illustrated in Figure PA1. Typically, the conductors are bonded to a thin polyimide (a tough flexible plastic) backing, which in turn is attached to the structure under test by a suitable adhesive, such as cyanoacrylate cement.

The resistance of a conductor is given by

$$R = \frac{\rho L}{A}$$

As strain is applied, the length and area change, resulting in changes in resistance. The strain and the change in resistance are related by the gauge factor:

$$G = \frac{\Delta R / R_0}{\epsilon}$$

in which R_0 is the resistance of the gauge before strain. A typical gauge has $R_0 = 350\ \Omega$ and $G = 2.0$. Thus, for a strain of 1%, the change in resistance is $\Delta R = 7\ \Omega$. Usually, a Wheatstone bridge is used to measure the small changes in resistance associated with accurate strain determination.

Sensors for force, torque, and pressure are constructed by using resistive strain gauges.

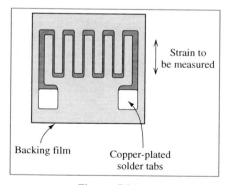

Figure PA1

Resistors versus Resistances

As an aside, we mention that resistance is often useful in modeling devices in which electrical power is converted into forms other than heat. For example, a loudspeaker appears to have a resistance of 8 Ω. Part of the power delivered to the loudspeaker is converted to acoustic power. Another example is a transmitting antenna having a resistance of 50 Ω. The power delivered to an antenna is radiated, traveling away as an electromagnetic wave.

There is a slight distinction between the terms *resistor* and *resistance*. A resistor is a two-terminal device composed of a conductive material. Resistance is a circuit property for which voltage is proportional to current. Thus, resistors have the property of resistance. However, resistance is also useful in modeling antennas and loudspeakers, which are quite different from resistors. Often, we are not careful about this distinction in using these terms.

Example 1   Determining Resistance for Given Power and Voltage Ratings

A certain electrical heater is rated for 1500 W when operated from 120 V. Find the resistance of the heater element and the operating current. (Resistance depends on temperature, and we will find the resistance at the operating temperature of the heater.)

Solution   Solving Equation 13 for resistance, we obtain

$$R = \frac{v^2}{p} = \frac{120^2}{1500} = 9.6 \ \Omega$$

Then, we use Ohm's law to find the current:

$$i = \frac{v}{R} = \frac{120}{9.6} = 12.5 \ \text{A}$$ ∎

Exercise 11   The 9.6-Ω resistance of Example 5 is in the form of a nichrome wire having a diameter of 1.6 mm. Find the length of the wire. (*Hint:* The resistivity of nichrome is given in Table 3.)
Answer $L = 17.2$ m. □

Exercise 12   An electric light bulb is rated for 100 W and 120 V. Find its resistance (at operating temperature) and operating current.
Answer $R = 144 \ \Omega, i = 0.833$ A. □

Exercise 13   A 1-kΩ resistor used in a television receiver is rated for a maximum power of 1/4 W. Find the current and voltage when the resistor is operated at maximum power.
Answer $v_{max} = 15.8$ V, $i_{max} = 15.8$ mA. □

7 INTRODUCTION TO CIRCUITS

In this chapter, we have defined electrical current and voltage, discussed Kirchhoff's laws, and introduced several ideal circuit elements: voltage sources, current sources, and resistances. Now we illustrate these concepts by considering a few relatively simple circuits.

Consider the circuit shown in Figure 39(a). Suppose that we want to know the current, voltage, and power for each element. To obtain these results, we apply

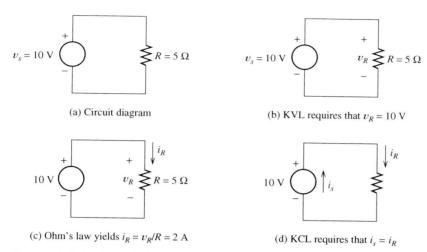

(a) Circuit diagram

(b) KVL requires that $v_R = 10$ V

(c) Ohm's law yields $i_R = v_R/R = 2$ A

(d) KCL requires that $i_s = i_R$

Figure 39 A circuit consisting of a voltage source and a resistance.

the basic principles introduced in this chapter. At first, we proceed in small, methodical steps. Furthermore, for ease of understanding, we initially select reference polarities and directions that agree with the actual polarities and current directions.

KVL requires that the sum of the voltages around the circuit shown in Figure 39 must equal zero. Thus, traveling around the circuit clockwise, we have $v_R - v_s = 0$. Consequently, $v_R = v_s$, and the voltage across the resistor v_R must have an actual polarity that is positive at the top end and a magnitude of 10 V.

An alternative way of looking at the voltages in this circuit is to notice that the voltage source and the resistance are in parallel. (The top ends of the voltage source and the resistance are connected, and the bottom ends are also connected.) Recall that when elements are in parallel, the voltage magnitude and polarity are the same for all elements.

Now consider Ohm's law. Because 10 V appears across the 5-Ω resistance, the current is $i_R = 10/5 = 2$ A. This current flows through the resistance from the positive polarity to the negative polarity. Thus, $i_R = 2$ A flows downward through the resistance, as shown in Figure 39(c).

According to KCL, the sum of the currents entering a given node must equal the sum of the currents leaving. There are two nodes for the circuit of Figure 39: one at the top and one at the bottom. The current i_R leaves the top node through the resistance. Thus, an equal current must enter the top node through the voltage source. The actual direction of current flow is upward through the voltage source, as shown in Figure 39(d).

Another way to see that the currents i_s and i_R are equal is to notice that the voltage source and the resistance are in series. In a series circuit, the current that flows in one element must continue through the other element. (Notice that for this circuit the voltage source and the resistance are in parallel and they are also in series. A two-element circuit is the only case for which this occurs. If more than two elements are interconnected, a pair of elements that are in parallel cannot also be in series, and vice versa.)

Notice that in Figure 39, the current in the voltage source flows from the negative polarity toward the positive polarity. It is only for resistances that the current is required to flow from plus to minus. For a voltage source, the current can flow in either direction, depending on the circuit to which the source is connected.

It is only for resistances that the current is required to flow from plus to minus. Current may flow in either direction for a voltage source depending on the other elements in the circuit.

Now let us calculate the power for each element. For the resistance, we have several ways to compute power:

$$p_R = v_R i_R = 10 \times 2 = 20 \text{ W}$$
$$p_R = i_R^2 R = 2^2 \times 5 = 20 \text{ W}$$
$$p_R = \frac{v_R^2}{R} = \frac{10^2}{5} = 20 \text{ W}$$

Of course, all the calculations yield the same result. Energy is delivered to the resistance at the rate of 20 J/s.

To find the power for the voltage source, we have

$$p_s = -v_s i_s$$

where the minus sign is used because the reference direction for the current enters the negative voltage reference (opposite to the passive reference configuration). Substituting values, we obtain

$$p_s = -v_s i_s = -10 \times 2 = -20 \text{ W}$$

Because p_s is negative, we understand that energy is being delivered by the voltage source.

As a check, if we add the powers for all the elements in the circuit, the result should be zero, because energy is neither created nor destroyed in an electrical circuit. Instead, it is transported and changed in form. Thus, we can write

$$p_s + p_R = -20 + 20 = 0$$

Using Arbitrary References

In the previous discussion, we selected references that agree with actual polarities and current directions. This is not always possible at the start of the analysis of more complex circuits. Fortunately, it is not necessary. We can pick the references in an arbitrary manner. Application of circuit laws will tell us not only the magnitudes of the currents and voltages but the true polarities and current directions as well.

Example 6   Circuit Analysis Using Arbitrary References

Analyze the circuit of Figure 39 using the current and voltage references shown in Figure 40. Verify that the results are in agreement with those found earlier.

Solution   Traveling clockwise and applying KVL, we have

$$-v_s - v_x = 0$$

This yields $v_x = -v_s = -10$ V. Since v_x assumes a negative value, the actual polarity is opposite to the reference. Thus, as before, we conclude that the voltage across the resistance is actually positive at the top end.

According to Ohm's law,

$$i_x = -\frac{v_x}{R}$$

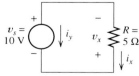

Figure 40 Circuit for Example 6.

where the minus sign appears because v_x and i_x have references opposite to the passive reference configuration. Substituting values, we get

$$i_x = -\frac{-10}{5} = 2 \text{ A}$$

Since i_x assumes a positive value, the actual current direction is downward through the resistance.

Next, applying KCL at the bottom node of the circuit, we have

$$\text{total current entering} = \text{total current leaving}$$
$$i_y + i_x = 0$$

Thus, $i_y = -i_x = -2$ A, and we conclude that a current of 2 A actually flows upward through the voltage source.

The power for the voltage source is

$$p_s = v_s i_y = 10 \times (-2) = -20 \text{ W}$$

Finally, the power for the resistance is given by

$$p_R = -v_x i_x$$

where the minus sign appears because the references for v_x and i_x are opposite to the passive reference configuration. Substituting, we find that $p_R = -(-10) \times (2) = 20$ W. Because p_R has a positive value, we conclude that energy is delivered to the resistance. ∎

Sometimes circuits can be solved by repeated application of Kirchhoff's laws and Ohm's law. We illustrate with an example.

Example 7 Using KVL, KCL, and Ohm's Law to Solve a Circuit

Solve for the source voltage in the circuit of Figure 41 in which we have a current controlled current source and we know that the voltage across the 5-Ω resistance is 15 V.

Solution First, we use Ohm's Law to determine the value of i_y:

$$i_y = \frac{15 \text{ V}}{5 \text{ }\Omega} = 3 \text{ A}$$

Next, we apply KCL at the top end of the controlled source:

$$i_x + 0.5i_x = i_y$$

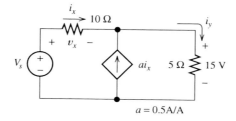

Figure 41 Circuit for Example 7.

$a = 0.5\text{A/A}$

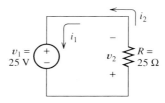

Figure 42 Circuit for Exercise 14.

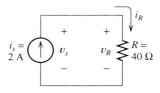

Figure 43 Circuit for Exercise 15.

Substituting the value found for i_y and solving, we determine that $i_x = 2$ A. Then Ohm's law yields $v_x = 10i_x = 20$ V. Applying KCL around the periphery of the circuit gives

$$V_s = v_x + 15$$

Finally, substituting the value found for v_x yields $V_s = 35$ V. ■

Exercise 14 Analyze the circuit shown in Figure 42 to find the values of i_1, i_2, and v_2. Use the values found to compute the power for each element.
Answer $i_1 = i_2 = -1$ A, $v_2 = -25$ V, $p_R = 25$ W, $p_s = -25$ W. □

Exercise 15 Figure 43 shows an independent current source connected across a resistance. Analyze to find the values of i_R, v_R, v_s, and the power for each element.
Answer $i_R = 2$ A, $v_s = v_R = 80$ V, $p_s = -160$ W, $p_R = 160$ W. □

Summary

1. Electrical and electronic features are increasingly integrated into the products and systems designed by engineers in other fields. Furthermore, instrumentation in all fields of engineering and science is based on the use of electrical sensors, electronics, and computers.

2. Some of the main areas of electrical engineering are communication systems, computer systems, control systems, electromagnetics, photonics, electronics, power systems, and signal processing.

3. Some important reasons to learn basic electrical engineering principles are to pass the Fundamentals of Engineering Examination, to have a broad enough knowledge base to lead design projects in your own field, to be able to identify and correct simple malfunctions in electrical systems, and to be able to communicate efficiently with electrical engineering consultants.

4. Current is the time rate of flow of electrical charge. Its units are amperes (A), which are equivalent to coulombs per second (C/s).

5. The voltage associated with a circuit element is the energy transferred per unit of charge that flows through the element. The units of voltages are volts (V), which are equivalent to joules per coulomb (J/C). If positive charge moves from the positive reference to the negative reference, energy is absorbed by the circuit element. If the charge moves in the opposite direction, energy is delivered by the element.

6. In the passive reference configuration, the current reference direction enters the positive reference polarity.

7. If the references have the passive configuration, power for a circuit element is computed as the product of the current through the element and the voltage across it:

$$p = vi$$

If the references are opposite to the passive configuration, we have

$$p = -vi$$

In either case, if p is positive, energy is being absorbed by the element.

8. A node in an electrical circuit is a point at which two or more circuit elements are joined together. All points joined by ideal conductors are electrically equivalent and constitute a single node.

9. Kirchhoff's current law (KCL) states that the sum of the currents entering a node equals the sum of the currents leaving.

10. Elements connected end to end are said to be in series. For two elements to be in series, no other current path can be connected to their common node. The current is identical for all elements in a series connection.

11. A loop in an electrical circuit is a closed path starting at a node and proceeding through circuit elements eventually returning to the starting point.

12. Kirchhoff's voltage law (KVL) states that the algebraic sum of the voltages in a loop must equal zero. If the positive polarity of a voltage is encountered first in going around the loop, the voltage carries a plus sign in the sum. On the other hand, if the negative polarity is encountered first, the voltage carries a minus sign.

13. Two elements are in parallel if both ends of one element are directly connected to corresponding ends of the other element. The voltages of parallel elements are identical.

14. The voltage between the ends of an ideal conductor is zero regardless of the current flowing through the conductor. All points in a circuit that are connected by ideal conductors can be considered as a single point.

15. An ideal independent voltage source maintains a specified voltage across its terminals independent of other elements that are connected to it and of the current flowing through it.

16. For a controlled voltage source, the voltage across the source terminals depends on other voltages or currents in the circuit. A voltage-controlled voltage source is a voltage source having a voltage equal to a constant times the voltage across a pair of terminals elsewhere in the network. A current-controlled voltage source is a voltage source having a voltage equal to a constant times the current through some other element in the circuit.

17. An ideal independent current source forces a specified current to flow through itself, independent of other elements that are connected to it and of the voltage across it.

18. For a controlled current source, the current depends on other voltages or currents in the circuit. A voltage-controlled current source produces a current equal to a constant times the voltage across a pair of terminals elsewhere in the network. A current-controlled current source produces a current equal to a constant times the current through some other element in the circuit.

19. For constant resistances, voltage is proportional to current. If the current and voltage references have the passive configuration, Ohm's law states that $v = Ri$. For references opposite to the passive configuration, $v = -Ri$.

Problems

Section 1: Overview of Electrical Engineering

P1. What are four reasons that other engineering students need to learn the fundamentals of electrical engineering?

P2. Broadly speaking, what are the two main objectives of electrical systems?

P3. Name eight subdivisions of electrical engineering.

P4. Write a few paragraphs describing an interesting application of electrical engineering in your field. Consult engineering journals and trade magazines such as the *IEEE Spectrum, Automotive Engineering, Chemical Engineering*, or *Civil Engineering* for ideas.

Section 2: Circuits, Currents, and Voltages

P5. Carefully define or explain each of the following terms in your own words giving units where appropriate: **a.** electrical current; **b.** voltage; **c.** an open switch; **d.** a closed switch; **e.** direct current; **f.** alternating current.

P6. In the fluid-flow analogy for electrical circuits, what is analogous to: **a.** a conductor; **b.** an open switch; **c.** a resistance; **d.** a battery?

*P7. The ends of a length of wire are labeled a and b. If the current in the wire is $i_{ab} = -3$ A, are electrons moving toward a or b? How much charge passes through a cross section of the wire in 3 seconds?

---

* Denotes that answers are contained in the Student Solutions files.

P8. The charge of an electron is 1.60×10^{-19} C. A current of 2 A flows in a wire carried by electrons. How many electrons pass through a cross section of the wire each second?

*__P9.__ The net charge through a cross section of a circuit element is given by $q(t) = 2t + t^2$ C. As usual, t is in seconds. Find the current through the element in amperes.

P10. The circuit element shown in Figure P10 has $v = -10$ V and $i_{ba} = 3$ A. What is the value of v_{ba}? Be sure to give the correct algebraic sign. What is the value of i? Is energy delivered to the element or taken from it?

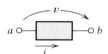

Figure P10

P11. For current to flow through the headlight circuit of Figure 2, should the switch be open or closed? In the fluid-flow analogy for the circuit, would the valve corresponding to the switch be open or closed? What state for a valve, open or closed, is analogous to an open switch?

*__P12.__ The current through a given circuit element is given by $i(t) = 2e^{-t}$ A. As usual, time t is in seconds. Find the net charge that passes through the element in the interval from $t = 0$ to $t = \infty$. (*Hint:* Current is the rate of flow of charge. Thus, to find charge, we must integrate current with respect to time.)

P13. The current through a particular circuit element is given by $i(t) = 10 \sin(200\pi t)$ A in which t is in seconds and the angle is in radians. **a.** Sketch $i(t)$ to scale versus time for t ranging from 0 to 15 ms. **b.** Determine the net charge that passes through the element between $t = 0$ and $t = 10$ ms. **c.** Repeat for the interval from $t = 0$ to $t = 15$ ms.

*__P14.__ A certain lead acid storage battery has a mass of 30 kg. Starting from a fully charged state, it can supply 5 A for 24 hours with a terminal voltage of 12 V before it is totally discharged. **a.** If the energy stored in the fully charged battery is used to lift the battery with 100-percent efficiency, what height is attained?

Assume that the acceleration due to gravity is $9.8 \, \text{m/s}^2$ and is constant with height. **b.** If the stored energy is used to accelerate the battery with 100-percent efficiency, what velocity is attained? **c.** Gasoline contains about 4.5×10^7 J/kg. Compare this with the energy content per unit mass for the fully charged battery.

P15. The net charge through a cross section of a certain circuit element is given by $q(t) = 2t + \exp(-2t)$ C with time t in seconds. Determine the current through the element as a function of time.

P16. A copper wire has a diameter of 2.05 mm and carries a current of 5 A due solely to electrons. (These values are common in residential wiring.) Each electron has a charge of 1.60×10^{-19} C. Given that the free electron (these are the electrons capable of moving through the copper) concentration in copper is 10^{29} electrons/m^3, find the average velocity of the electrons in the wire.

*__P17.__ A typical "deep-cycle" battery (used for electric trolling motors for fishing boats) is capable of delivering 12.6 V and 10 A for a period of 10 hours. How much charge flows through the battery in this interval? How much energy does the battery deliver?

P18. We have a circuit element with terminals a and b. Furthermore, the element has $v_{ab} = 5$ V and $i_{ab} = 2$ A. Over a period of 10 seconds, how much charge moves through the element? If electrons carry the charge, which terminal do they enter? How much energy is transferred? Is it delivered to the element or taken from it?

P19. The charge carried by an electron is 1.9×10^{-19} C. Suppose that an electron moves through a voltage of 120 V from the positive polarity to the negative polarity. How much energy is transferred? Does the electron gain or lose energy?

Section 3: Power and Energy

*__P20.__ Compute the power for each element shown in Figure P20. For each element, state whether energy is being absorbed by the element or supplied by it.

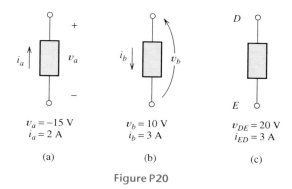

$v_a = -15$ V
$i_a = 2$ A

(a)

$v_b = 10$ V
$i_b = 3$ A

(b)

$v_{DE} = 20$ V
$i_{ED} = 3$ A

(c)

Figure P20

P21. What does the term *passive reference config-uration* imply? When do we have this config-uration when using double subscript notation for an element having terminals a and b?

*P22. A certain battery has terminals labeled a and b. The battery voltage is $v_{ab} = 12$ V. To increase the chemical energy stored in the battery by 600 J, how much charge must move through the battery? Should electrons move from a to b or from b to a?

P23. Suppose that the terminals of an electrical device are labeled a and b. If $v_{ab} = -15$ V, how much energy is exchanged when a posi-tive charge of 4 C moves through the device from a to b? Is the energy delivered to the device or taken from the device?

*P24. Suppose that the cost of electrical energy is $0.12 per kilowatt hour and that your elec-trical bill for 30 days is $60. Assume that the power delivered is constant over the entire 30 days. What is the power in watts? If a volt-age of 120 V supplies this power, what current flows? Part of your electrical load is a 60-W light that is on continuously. By what percent-age can your energy consumption be reduced by turning this light off?

P25. The element shown in Figure P25 has $v(t) = 10$ V, and $i(t) = 3e^{-t}$ A. Compute the power

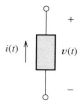

Figure P25

for the circuit element. Find the energy trans-ferred between $t = 0$ and $t = \infty$. Is this energy absorbed by the element or supplied by it?

P26. The current and voltage of an electrical device are $i_{ab}(t) = 5$ A and $v_{ab}(t) = 10\sin(200\pi t)$ V in which the angle is in radians. **a.** Find the power delivered to the device and sketch it to scale versus time for t ranging from 0 to 15 ms. **b.** Determine the energy delivered to the device for the interval from $t = 0$ to $t = 2.5$ ms. **c.** Repeat for the interval from $t = 0$ to $t = 10$ ms.

*P27. Figure P27 shows an ammeter (AM) and voltmeter (VM) connected to measure the current and voltage, respectively, for circuit element A. When current actually enters the + terminal of the ammeter, the reading is positive, and when current leaves the + ter-minal, the reading is negative. If the actual voltage polarity is positive at the + terminal of the VM, the reading is positive; otherwise, it is negative. (Actually, for the connection shown, the ammeter reads the sum of the cur-rent in element A and the very small current taken by the voltmeter. For purposes of this problem, assume that the current taken by the voltmeter is negligible.) Find the power for element A and state whether energy is being delivered to element A or taken from it if **a.** the ammeter reading is $+2$ A and the voltmeter reading is -25 V; **b.** the ammeter reading is -2 A and the voltmeter reading is $+25$ V; **c.** the ammeter reading is -2 A and the voltmeter reading is -25 V.

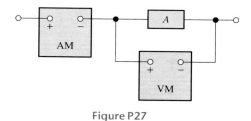

Figure P27

P28. Repeat Problem P27 with the meters con-nected as shown in Figure P28.

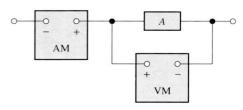

Figure P28

P29. The electronics aboard a certain sailboat consume 25 W when operated from a 12.6-V source. If a certain fully charged deep-cycle lead acid storage battery is rated for 12.6 V and 80 ampere-hours, for how many hours can the electronics be operated from the battery without recharging? (The ampere-hour rating of the battery is the operating time to discharge the battery multiplied by the current.) How much energy in kilowatt hours is initially stored in the battery? If the battery costs $85 and has a life of 250 charge–discharge cycles, what is the cost of the energy in dollars per kilowatt hour? Neglect the cost of recharging the battery.

P30. A typical alkaline 9-V "transistor" battery that costs $1.95 is capable of delivering a current of 50 mA for a period of 10 hours. Determine the cost of the energy delivered by this battery per kilowatt hour. (For comparison, the approximate cost of energy purchased from electric utilities in the United States is $0.12 per kilowatt hour.)

Section 4: Kirchhoff's Current Law

P31. In your own words, explain KCL. Why is it true?

P32. Define the term *node* as it applies in electrical circuits. Identify the nodes in the

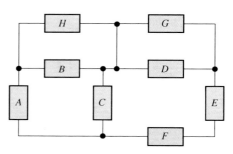

Figure P32

circuit of Figure P32. Keep in mind that all points connected by ideal conductors are considered to be a single node in electrical circuits.

P33. Suppose that three electrical elements are connected in series. What can you say about the currents through the elements?

***P34.** Identify elements that are in series in the circuit of Figure P32.

P35. Suppose that, in the fluid-flow analogy for an electrical circuit, the analog of electrical current is volumetric flow rate with units of cm^3/s. For a proper analogy to electrical circuits, must the fluid be compressible or incompressible? Must the walls of the pipes be elastic or inelastic? Explain your answers.

***P36.** Use KCL to find the values of $i_a, i_c,$ and i_d for the circuit of Figure P36. Which elements are connected in series in this circuit?

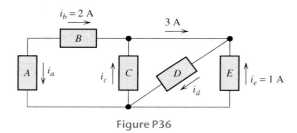

Figure P36

***P37.** Given that $i_a = 2\,A, i_b = 3\,A, i_d = -5\,A,$ and $i_h = 4\,A,$ determine the values of the other currents in Figure P37.

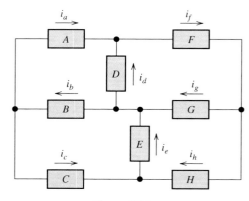

Figure P37

P38. **a.** Which elements are in series in Figure P38? **b.** What is the relationship between i_d and i_c? **c.** Given that $i_a = 4\,\text{A}$ and $i_c = -1\,\text{A}$, determine the values of i_b and i_d.

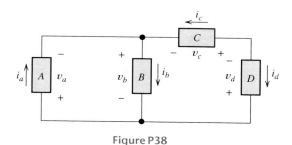

Figure P38

P39. Given that $i_a = 1\,\text{A}, i_c = -2\,\text{A}, i_g = 7\,\text{A}$, and $i_h = 2\,\text{A}$, determine the values of the other currents in Figure P37.

Section 5: Kirchhoff's Voltage Law

P40. In your own words, explain KVL. Why is it true?

*P41. Use KVL to solve for the voltages v_a, v_b, and v_c in Figure P41.

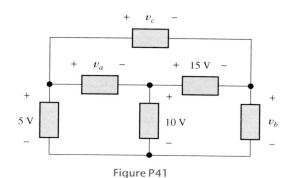

Figure P41

*P42. Use KVL and KCL to solve for the labeled currents and voltages in Figure P42. Compute the power for each element and show that power is conserved (i.e., the algebraic sum of the powers is zero).

P43. Consider the circuit shown in Figure P38. **a.** Which elements are in parallel? **b.** What is the relationship between v_a and v_b? **c.** Given that $v_a = 12\,\text{V}$ and $v_c = 7\,\text{V}$, determine the values of v_b and v_d.

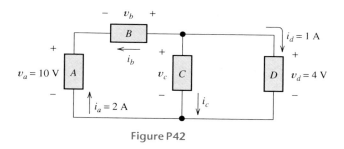

Figure P42

P44. Identify the nodes in Figure P44. Which elements are in series? In parallel?

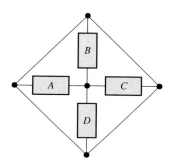

Figure P44

P45. Given that $v_a = 15\,\text{V}, v_b = -7\,\text{V}, v_f = 10\,\text{V}$, and $v_h = 4\,\text{V}$, solve for the other voltages shown in Figure P45.

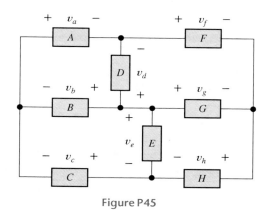

Figure P45

P46. We have a circuit containing four nodes labeled a, b, c, and d. Furthermore, we know that $v_{ab} = 15\,\text{V}, v_{cb} = -7\,\text{V}$, and $v_{da} = 10\,\text{V}$. Determine the values of v_{ac} and v_{cd}.

(*Hint:* Draw a picture showing the nodes and the known voltages.)

P47. Identify elements that are in parallel **a.** in Figure P36; **b.** in Figure P42; **c.** in Figure P45.

P48. A typical golf cart uses a number of 6-V batteries (which for the purposes of this problem can be modeled as ideal 6-V voltage sources). If the motor requires 36 V, what is the minimum number of batteries needed? How should they be connected? Sketch a diagram for the battery connections showing the polarity of each battery.

Section 6: Introduction to Circuit Elements

P49. Define these terms in your own words: **a.** an ideal conductor; **b.** an ideal voltage source; **c.** an ideal current source; **d.** short circuit; **e.** open circuit.

P50. Explain Ohm's law in your own words, including references.

P51. Name four types of dependent sources and give the units for the gain parameter of each type.

*P52. Draw a circuit that contains a 5-Ω resistance, a 10-V independent voltage source, and a 2-A independent current source. Connect all three elements in series. (Because the polarity of the voltage source and reference direction for the current source are not specified, several correct answers are possible.)

P53. Repeat Problem P52, placing all three elements in parallel.

P54. We know that the resistance of a certain copper wire is 1.5 Ω. Determine the resistance of a tungsten wire having the same dimensions as the copper wire.

P55. Suppose that a certain wire has a resistance of 10 Ω. Find the new resistance **a.** if the length of the wire is doubled; **b.** if the diameter of the wire is doubled.

P56. Sketch the diagram of a circuit that contains a 5-Ω resistor, a 10-V voltage source, and a voltage-controlled voltage source having a gain constant of 0.5 V/V. Assume that the voltage across the resistor is the control voltage for the controlled source. Place all three

elements in series. Several answers are possible, depending on the polarities chosen for the sources and the control voltage.

P57. Sketch the diagram of a circuit that contains a 5-Ω resistor, a 10-V voltage source, and a current-controlled voltage source having a gain constant of 2 Ω. Assume that the current through the resistor is the control current for the controlled source. Place all three elements in series. Several answers are possible, depending on the polarities chosen for the sources and the reference direction for the control current.

*P58. A power of 100 W is delivered to a certain resistor when the applied voltage is 100 V. Find the resistance. Suppose that the voltage is reduced by 10 percent (to 90 V). By what percentage is the power reduced? Assume that the resistance remains constant.

P59. We know that the current through a 10-Ω resistor is given by $i(t) = \exp(-3t)$ A. Determine the energy delivered to the resistor between $t = 0$ and $t = \infty$.

P60. Given that the voltage across a 20-Ω resistor is given by $v(t) = 10\sin(2\pi t)$ V, calculate the energy delivered to the resistor between $t = 0$ and $t = 2$ s. The argument of the sine function, $2\pi t$, is in radians.

Section 7: Introduction to Circuits

P61. Sketch a plot to scale showing i_{ab} versus v_{ab} to scale for each of the parts of Figure P61.

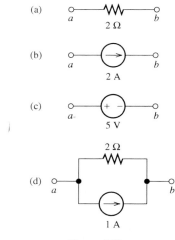

Figure P61

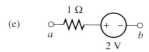

(e)

Figure P61 (Cont.)

*P62. Which of the following are self-contradictory combinations of circuit elements? **a.** A 12-V voltage source in parallel with a 2-A current source. **b.** A 2-A current source in series with a 3-A current source. **c.** A 2-A current source in parallel with a short circuit. **d.** A 2-A current source in series with an open circuit. **e.** A 5-V voltage source in parallel with a short circuit.

*P63. Consider the circuit shown in Figure P63. Find the current i_R flowing through the resistor. Find the power for each element in the circuit. Which elements are absorbing power?

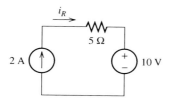

Figure P63

*P64. Consider the circuit shown in Figure P64. Use repeated applications of Ohm's law, KVL, and KCL to eventually find V_x.

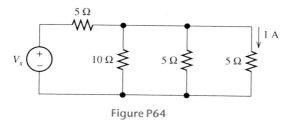

Figure P64

P65. Given the circuit shown in Figure P65, find the power for each source. Which source is absorbing power? Which is delivering power?

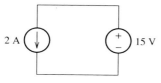

Figure P65

P66. Consider the circuit shown in Figure P66. Find the current i_R flowing through the resistor. Find the power for each element in the circuit. Which elements are absorbing energy?

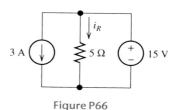

Figure P66

P67. Use repeated applications of Ohm's law, KVL, and KCL to eventually find the value of I_x in the circuit of Figure P67.

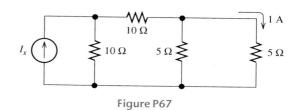

Figure P67

P68. Consider the circuit shown in Figure P68. **a.** Which elements are in series? **b.** Which elements are in parallel? **c.** Apply Ohm's and Kirchhoff's laws to solve for V_x.

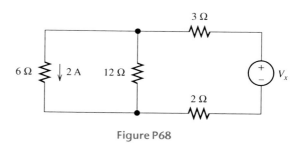

Figure P68

*P69. The circuit shown in Figure P69 contains a voltage-controlled voltage source. **a.** Use KVL to write an equation relating the voltages and solve for v_x. **b.** Use Ohm's law to find the current i_x. **c.** Find the power for each element in the circuit and verify that power is conserved.

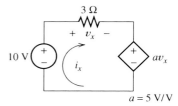

Figure P69

*P70. What type of controlled source is shown in the circuit of Figure P70? Solve for v_s.

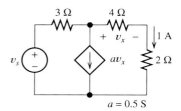

Figure P70

P71. Figure P71 is the electrical model for an electronic megaphone, in which the 8-Ω resistance models a loudspeaker, the source I_x and the 5-Ω resistance represent a microphone, and the remaining elements model an amplifier. What is the name of the type of controlled source shown? Given that the power delivered to the 8-Ω resistance is 8 W, determine the current flowing in the controlled source. Also, determine the value of the microphone current I_x.

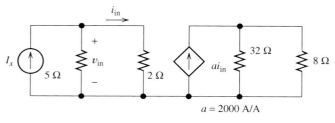

Figure P71

P72. Consider the circuit shown in Figure P72. **a.** Which elements are in series? **b.** Which elements are in parallel? **c.** Apply Ohm's and Kirchhoff's laws to solve for R_x.

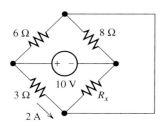

Figure P72

P73. Solve for the currents shown in Figure P73.

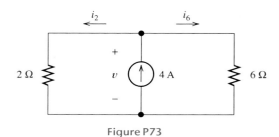

Figure P73

P74. What type of controlled source appears in the circuit of Figure P74? Determine the values of v_x and i_y.

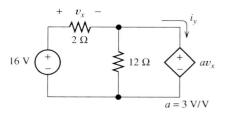

Figure P74

P75. A 10-V independent voltage source is in series with a 2-A independent current source. What single source is equivalent to this series combination? Give the type and value of the equivalent source.

P76. A 10-V independent voltage source is in parallel with a 2-A independent current source.

What single source is equivalent to this parallel combination? Give the type and value of the equivalent source.

P77. Consider the circuit shown in Figure P77 given $R_1 = 4\,\Omega$, $R_2 = 6\,\Omega$, and $V_s = 20\,\text{V}$. **a.** Use KVL to write an equation relating the voltages. **b.** Use Ohm's law to write equations relating v_1 and v_2 to the current i. **c.** Substitute the equations from part (b) into the equation from part (a) and solve for i. **d.** Find the power for each element in the circuit and verify that power is conserved.

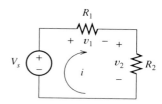

Figure P77

P78. Consider the circuit shown in Figure P78 given $R_1 = 5\,\Omega$, $R_2 = 10\,\Omega$, and $I_s = 3\,\text{A}$. **a.** Use KCL to write an equation relating the currents. **b.** Use Ohm's law to write equations relating i_1 and i_2 to the voltage v. **c.** Substitute the equations from part (b) into the equation from part (a) and solve for v. **d.** Find the power for each element in the circuit and verify that power is conserved.

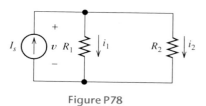

Figure P78

P79. What types of sources are present in the circuit shown in Figure P79? Solve for i_s.

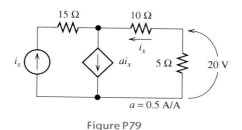

Figure P79

P80. What types of sources are present in the circuit of Figure P80? Solve for the current i_x.

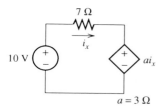

Figure P80

Practice Test

Here is a practice test you can use to check your comprehension of the most important concepts in this chapter. Answers can be found at the end of this chapter and complete solutions are included in the Student Solutions files.

T1. Match each entry in Table T1(a) with the best choice from the list given in Table T1(b). [Items in Table T1(b) may be used more than once or not at all.]

T2. Consider the circuit of Figure T2 with $I_s = 3\,\text{A}$, $R = 2\,\Omega$, and $V_s = 10\,\text{V}$. **a.** Determine the value of v_R. **b.** Determine the magnitude of the power for the voltage source and state whether the voltage source is absorbing energy or delivering it. **c.** How many nodes does this circuit have? **d.** Determine the magnitude of the power for the current source and state whether the current source is absorbing energy or delivering it.

Table T1

Item	Best Match

(a)

a. Node
b. Loop
c. KVL
d. KCL
e. Ohm's law
f. Passive reference configuration
g. Ideal conductor
h. Open circuit
i. Current source
j. Parallel connected elements
k. Controlled source
l. Units for voltage
m. Units for current
n. Units for resistance
o. Series connected elements

(b)

1. $v_{ab} = Ri_{ab}$
2. The current reference for an element enters the positive voltage reference
3. A path through which no current can flow
4. Points connected by ideal conductors
5. An element that carries a specified current
6. An element whose current or voltage depends on a current or voltage elsewhere in the circuit
7. A path starting at a node and proceeding from node to node back to the starting node
8. An element for which the voltage is zero
9. A/V
10. V/A
11. J/C
12. C/V
13. C/s
14. Elements connected so their currents must be equal
15. Elements connected so their voltages must be equal
16. The algebraic sum of voltages for a closed loop is zero
17. The algebraic sum of the voltages for elements connected to a node is zero
18. The sum of the currents entering a node equals the sum of those leaving

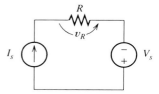

Figure T2

T3. The circuit of Figure T3 has $I_1 = 3\,\text{A}, I_2 = 1\,\text{A}, R_1 = 12\,\Omega$, and $R_2 = 6\,\Omega$. **a.** Determine the value of v_{ab}. **b.** Determine the power for each current source and state whether it is absorbing energy or delivering it. **c.** Compute the power absorbed by R_1 and by R_2.

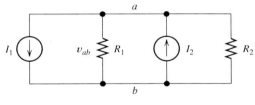

Figure T3

T4. The circuit shown in Figure T4 has $V_s = 12\,$V, $v_2 = 4\,$V, and $R_1 = 4\,\Omega$. **a.** Find the values of: **a.** v_1; **b.** i; **c.** R_2.

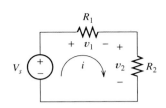

Figure T4

T5. We are given $V_s = 15\,$V, $R = 10\,\Omega$, and $a = 0.3\,$S for the circuit of Figure T5. Find the value of the current i_{sc} flowing through the short circuit.

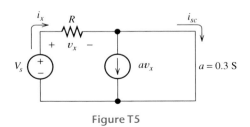

Figure T5

Answers for the Practice Test

T1. a. 4; **b.** 7; **c.** 16; **d.** 18; **e.** 1; **f.** 2; **g.** 8; **h.** 3; **i.** 5; **j.** 15; **k.** 6; **l.** 11; **m.** 13; **n.** 9; **o.** 14.

T2. a. $v_R = -6\,$V. **b.** The voltage source is delivering 30 W. **c.** There are 3 nodes. **d.** The current source is absorbing 12 W.

T3. a. $v_{ab} = -8\,$V. **b.** Source I_1 is supplying 24 W. Source I_2 is absorbing 8 W. **c.** $P_{R1} = 5.33\,$W and $P_{R2} = 10.67\,$W.

T4. a. $v_1 = 8\,$V; **b.** $i = 2\,$A; **c.** $R_2 = 2\,\Omega$.

T5. $i_{sc} = -3\,$A.

Resistive Circuits

From Chapter 2 of *Electrical Engineering: Principles and Applications*, Fifth Edition, Allan R. Hambley. Copyright © 2011 by Pearson Education, Inc. Published by Pearson Prentice Hall. All rights reserved.

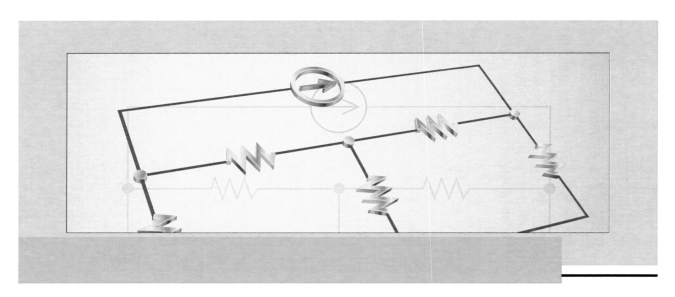

Resistive Circuits

Study of this chapter will enable you to:

- Solve circuits (i.e., find currents and voltages of interest) by combining resistances in series and parallel.

- Apply the voltage-division and current-division principles.

- Solve circuits by the node-voltage technique.

- Solve circuits by the mesh-current technique.

- Find Thévenin and Norton equivalents and apply source transformations.

- Use MATLAB® to solve circuit equations numerically and symbolically.

- Apply the superposition principle.

- Draw the circuit diagram and state the principles of operation for the Wheatstone bridge.

Introduction to this chapter:

In applications of electrical engineering, we often face circuit-analysis problems for which the structure of a circuit, including element values, is known and the currents, voltages, and powers need to be found. In this chapter, we examine techniques for analyzing circuits composed of resistances, voltage sources, and current sources. Later, we extend many of these concepts to circuits containing inductance and capacitance.

Over the years, you will meet many applications of electrical engineering in your field of engineering or science. This chapter will give you the skills needed to work effectively with the electronic instrumentation and other circuits that you will encounter. The material in this text will help you to answer questions on the Fundamentals of Engineering Examination and become a Registered Professional Engineer.

1 RESISTANCES IN SERIES AND PARALLEL

In this section, we show how to replace series or parallel combinations of resistances by equivalent resistances. Then, we demonstrate how to use this knowledge in solving circuits.

Series Resistances

Consider the series combination of three resistances shown in Figure 1(a). Recall that in a series circuit the elements are connected end to end and that the same current flows through all of the elements. By Ohm's law, we can write

$$v_1 = R_1 i \tag{1}$$

$$v_2 = R_2 i \tag{2}$$

and

$$v_3 = R_3 i \tag{3}$$

Using KVL, we can write

$$v = v_1 + v_2 + v_3 \tag{4}$$

Substituting Equations 1, 2, and 3 into Equation 4, we obtain

$$v = R_1 i + R_2 i + R_3 i \tag{5}$$

Factoring out the current i, we have

$$v = (R_1 + R_2 + R_3)i \tag{6}$$

Now, we define the equivalent resistance R_{eq} to be the sum of the resistances in series:

$$R_{eq} = R_1 + R_2 + R_3 \tag{7}$$

Using this to substitute into Equation 6, we have

$$v = R_{eq}i \tag{8}$$

Thus, we conclude that the three resistances in series can be replaced by the equivalent resistance R_{eq} shown in Figure 1(b) with no change in the relationship between

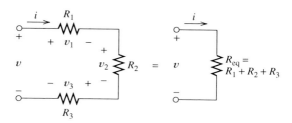

Figure 1 Series resistances can be combined into an equivalent resistance.

(a) Three resistances in series

(b) Equivalent resistance

the voltage v and current i. If the three resistances are part of a larger circuit, replacing them by a single equivalent resistance would make no changes in the currents or voltages in other parts of the circuit.

This analysis can be applied to any number of resistances. For example, two resistances in series can be replaced by a single resistance equal to the sum of the original two. To summarize, *a series combination of resistances has an equivalent resistance equal to the sum of the original resistances.*

A series combination of resistances has an equivalent resistance equal to the sum of the original resistances.

Parallel Resistances

Figure 2(a) shows three resistances in parallel. In a parallel circuit, the voltage across each element is the same. Applying Ohm's law in Figure 2(a), we can write

$$i_1 = \frac{v}{R_1} \tag{9}$$

$$i_2 = \frac{v}{R_2} \tag{10}$$

$$i_3 = \frac{v}{R_3} \tag{11}$$

The top ends of the resistors in Figure 2(a) are connected to a single node. (Recall that all points in a circuit that are connected by conductors constitute a node.) Thus, we can apply KCL to the top node of the circuit and obtain

$$i = i_1 + i_2 + i_3 \tag{12}$$

Now using Equations 9, 10, and 11 to substitute into Equation 12, we have

$$i = \frac{v}{R_1} + \frac{v}{R_2} + \frac{v}{R_3} \tag{13}$$

Factoring out the voltage, we obtain

$$i = \left(\frac{1}{R_1} + \frac{1}{R_2} + \frac{1}{R_3} \right) v \tag{14}$$

Now, we define the equivalent resistance as

$$R_{eq} = \frac{1}{1/R_1 + 1/R_2 + 1/R_3} \tag{15}$$

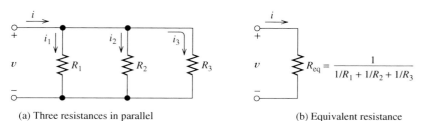

(a) Three resistances in parallel   (b) Equivalent resistance

Figure 2 Parallel resistances can be combined into an equivalent resistance.

In terms of the equivalent resistance, Equation 14 becomes

$$i = \frac{1}{R_{eq}}v \qquad (16)$$

Comparing Equations 14 and 16, we see that i and v are related in the same way by both equations provided that R_{eq} is given by Equation 15. Therefore, a parallel combination of resistances can be replaced by its equivalent resistance without changing the currents and voltages in other parts of the circuit. The equivalence is illustrated in Figure 2(b).

A parallel combination of resistances can be replaced by its equivalent resistance without changing the currents and voltages in other parts of the circuit.

This analysis can be applied to any number of resistances in parallel. For example, if four resistances are in parallel, the equivalent resistance is

$$R_{eq} = \frac{1}{1/R_1 + 1/R_2 + 1/R_3 + 1/R_4} \qquad (17)$$

Similarly, for two resistances, we have

$$R_{eq} = \frac{1}{1/R_1 + 1/R_2} \qquad (18)$$

This can be put into the form

$$R_{eq} = \frac{R_1 R_2}{R_1 + R_2} \qquad (19)$$

(Notice that Equation 19 applies only for two resistances. The product over the sum does not apply for more than two resistances.)

The product over the sum does not apply for more than two resistances.

Sometimes, resistive circuits can be reduced to a single equivalent resistance by repeatedly combining resistances that are in series or parallel.

Combining Resistances in Series and Parallel

Find a single equivalent resistance for the network shown in Figure 3(a).

Solution   First, we look for a combination of resistances that is in series or in parallel. In Figure 3(a), R_3 and R_4 are in series. (In fact, as it stands, no other two resistances in this network are either in series or in parallel.) Thus, our first step is to combine R_3 and R_4, replacing them by their equivalent resistance. Recall that for a series combination, the equivalent resistance is the sum of the resistances in series:

1. Find a series or parallel combination of resistances.

$$R_{eq1} = R_3 + R_4 = 5 + 15 = 20 \ \Omega$$

2. Combine them.

3. Repeat until the network is reduced to a single resistance (if possible).

Figure 3(b) shows the network after replacing R_3 and R_4 by their equivalent resistance. Now we see that R_2 and R_{eq1} are in parallel. The equivalent resistance for this combination is

$$R_{eq2} = \frac{1}{1/R_{eq1} + 1/R_2} = \frac{1}{1/20 + 1/20} = 10 \ \Omega$$

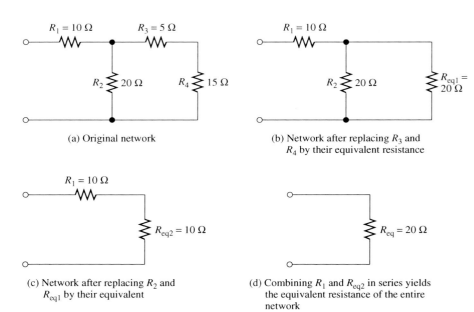

(a) Original network

(b) Network after replacing R_3 and R_4 by their equivalent resistance

(c) Network after replacing R_2 and R_{eq1} by their equivalent

(d) Combining R_1 and R_{eq2} in series yields the equivalent resistance of the entire network

Figure 3 Resistive network for Example 1.

Making this replacement gives the equivalent network shown in Figure 3(c).

Finally, we see that R_1 and R_{eq2} are in series. Thus, the equivalent resistance for the entire network is

$$R_{eq} = R_1 + R_{eq2} = 10 + 10 = 20 \; \Omega$$ ∎

Exercise 1 Find the equivalent resistance for each of the networks shown in Figure 4. [*Hint for part (b): R_3 and R_4 are in parallel.*]
Answer **a.** 3 Ω; **b.** 5 Ω; **c.** 52.1 Ω; **d.** 1.5 kΩ. ☐

Conductances in Series and Parallel

Recall that conductance is the reciprocal of resistance. Using this fact to change resistances to conductances for a series combination of n elements, we readily obtain:

Combine conductances in series as you would resistances in parallel. Combine conductances in parallel as you would resistances in series.

$$G_{eq} = \frac{1}{1/G_1 + 1/G_2 + \cdots + 1/G_n} \tag{20}$$

Thus, we see that conductances in series combine as do resistances in parallel. For two conductances in series, we have:

$$G_{eq} = \frac{G_1 G_2}{G_1 G_2}$$

For n conductances in parallel, we can show that

$$G_{eq} = G_1 + G_2 + \cdots + G_n \tag{21}$$

Conductances in parallel combine as do resistances in series.

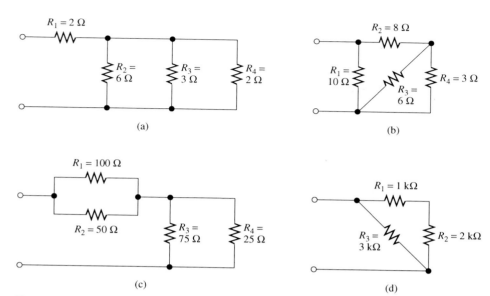

Figure 4 Resistive networks for Exercise 1.

Series versus Parallel Circuits

An element such as a toaster or light bulb that absorbs power is called a **load**. When we want to distribute power from a single voltage source to various loads, we usually place the loads in parallel. A switch in series with each load can break the flow of current to that load without affecting the voltage supplied to the other loads.

Sometimes, to save wire, strings of Christmas lights consist of bulbs connected in series. The bulbs tend to fail or "burn out" by becoming open circuits. Then the entire string is dark and the defective bulb can be found only by trying each in turn. If several bulbs are burned out, it can be very tedious to locate the failed units. In a parallel connection, only the failed bulbs are dark.

When we want to distribute power from a single voltage source to various loads, we usually place the loads in parallel.

2 NETWORK ANALYSIS BY USING SERIES AND PARALLEL EQUIVALENTS

An electrical **network** (or electrical circuit) consists of circuit elements, such as resistances, voltage sources, and current sources, connected together to form closed paths. **Network analysis** is the process of determining the current, voltage, and power for each element, given the circuit diagram and the element values. In this and the sections that follow, we study several useful techniques for network analysis.

Sometimes, we can determine the currents and voltages for each element in a resistive circuit by repeatedly replacing series and parallel combinations of resistances by their equivalent resistances. Eventually, this may reduce the circuit sufficiently that the equivalent circuit can be solved easily. The information gained from the simplified circuit is transferred to the previous steps in the chain of equivalent circuits. In the end, we gain enough information about the original circuit to determine all the currents and voltages.

An electrical network consists of circuit elements, such as resistances, voltage sources, and current sources, connected together to form closed paths.

Circuit Analysis Using Series/Parallel Equivalents

Here are the steps in solving circuits using series/parallel equivalents:

Some good advice for beginners: Don't try to combine steps. Be very methodical and do one step at a time. Take the time to redraw each equivalent carefully and label unknown currents and voltages consistently in the various circuits. The slow methodical approach will be faster and more accurate when you are learning. Walk now—later you will be able to run.

1. Begin by locating a combination of resistances that are in series or parallel. Often the place to start is farthest from the source.

2. Redraw the circuit with the equivalent resistance for the combination found in step 1.

3. Repeat steps 1 and 2 until the circuit is reduced as far as possible. Often (but not always) we end up with a single source and a single resistance.

4. Solve for the currents and voltages in the final equivalent circuit. Then, transfer results back one step and solve for additional unknown currents and voltages. Again transfer the results back one step and solve. Repeat until all of the currents and voltages are known in the original circuit.

5. Check your results to make sure that KCL is satisfied at each node, KVL is satisfied for each loop, and the powers add to zero.

Example 2 Circuit Analysis Using Series/Parallel Equivalents

Find the current, voltage, and power for each element of the circuit shown in Figure 5(a).

Steps 1, 2, and 3.

Solution First, we combine resistances in series and parallel. For example, in the original circuit, R_2 and R_3 are in parallel. Replacing R_2 and R_3 by their parallel equivalent, we obtain the circuit shown in Figure 5(b). Next, we see that R_1 and R_{eq1} are in series. Replacing these resistances by their sum, we obtain the circuit shown in Figure 5(c).

After we have reduced a network to an equivalent resistance connected across the source, we solve the simplified network. Then, we transfer results back through the chain of equivalent circuits. We illustrate this process in Figure 6. (Figure 6 is identical to Figure 5, except for the currents and voltages shown in Figure 6.

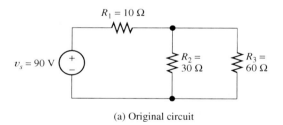

(a) Original circuit

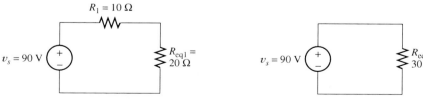

(b) Circuit after replacing R_2 and R_3 by their equivalent

(c) Circuit after replacing R_1 and R_{eq1} by their equivalent

Figure 5 A circuit and its simplified versions. See Example 2.

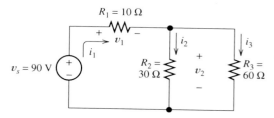

(a) Third, we use known values of i_1 and v_2
to solve for the remaining currents and voltages

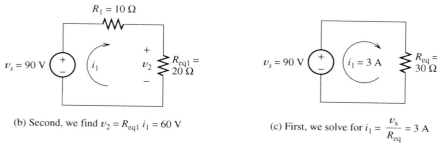

(b) Second, we find $v_2 = R_{eq1} i_1 = 60$ V

(c) First, we solve for $i_1 = \dfrac{v_s}{R_{eq}} = 3$ A

Figure 6 After reducing the circuit to a source and an equivalent resistance, we solve the simplified circuit. Then, we transfer results back to the original circuit. Notice that the logical flow in solving for currents and voltages starts from the simplified circuit in (c).

Usually, in solving a network by this technique, we first draw the chain of equivalent networks and then write results on the same drawings. However, this might be confusing in our first example.)

First, we solve the simplified network shown in Figure 6(c). Because R_{eq} is in parallel with the 90-V voltage source, the voltage across R_{eq} must be 90 V, with its positive polarity at the top end. Thus, the current flowing through R_{eq} is given by

Step 4.

$$i_1 = \frac{v_s}{R_{eq}} = \frac{90 \text{ V}}{30 \text{ }\Omega} = 3 \text{ A}$$

We know that this current flows downward (from plus to minus) through R_{eq}. Since v_s and R_{eq} are in series in Figure 6(c), the current must also flow upward through v_s. Thus, $i_1 = 3$ A flows clockwise around the circuit, as shown in Figure 6(c).

Because R_{eq} is the equivalent resistance seen by the source in all three parts of Figure 6, the current through v_s must be $i_1 = 3$ A, flowing upward in all three equivalent circuits. In Figure 6(b), we see that i_1 flows clockwise through v_s, R_1, and R_{eq1}. The voltage across R_{eq1} is given by

$$v_2 = R_{eq1} i_1 = 20 \text{ }\Omega \times 3 \text{ A} = 60 \text{ V}$$

Because R_{eq1} is the equivalent resistance for the parallel combination of R_2 and R_3, the voltage v_2 also appears across R_2 and R_3 in the original network.

At this point, we have found that the current through v_s and R_1 is $i_1 = 3$ A. Furthermore, the voltage across R_2 and R_3 is 60 V. This information is shown in

Figure 6(a). Now, we can compute the remaining values desired:

$$i_2 = \frac{v_2}{R_2} = \frac{60 \text{ V}}{30 \text{ }\Omega} = 2 \text{ A}$$

$$i_3 = \frac{v_2}{R_3} = \frac{60 \text{ V}}{60 \text{ }\Omega} = 1 \text{ A}$$

(As a check, we can use KCL to verify that $i_1 = i_2 + i_3$.)

Next, we can use Ohm's law to compute the value of v_1:

$$v_1 = R_1 i_1 = 10 \text{ }\Omega \times 3 \text{ A} = 30 \text{ V}$$

Step 5.

(As a check, we use KVL to verify that $v_s = v_1 + v_2$.)

Now, we compute the power for each element. For the voltage source, we have

$$p_s = -v_s i_1$$

We have included the minus sign because the references for v_s and i_1 are opposite to the passive configuration. Substituting values, we have

$$p_s = -(90 \text{ V}) \times 3 \text{ A} = -270 \text{ W}$$

Because the power for the source is negative, we know that the source is supplying energy to the other elements in the circuit.

The powers for the resistances are

$$p_1 = R_1 i_1^2 = 10 \text{ }\Omega \times (3 \text{ A})^2 = 90 \text{ W}$$

$$p_2 = \frac{v_2^2}{R_2} = \frac{(60 \text{ V})^2}{30 \text{ }\Omega} = 120 \text{ W}$$

$$p_3 = \frac{v_2^2}{R_3} = \frac{(60 \text{ V})^2}{60 \text{ }\Omega} = 60 \text{ W}$$

(As a check, we verify that $p_s + p_1 + p_2 + p_3 = 0$, showing that power is conserved.) ∎

Power Control by Using Heating Elements in Series or Parallel

Resistances are commonly used as heating elements for the reaction chamber of chemical processes. For example, the catalytic converter of an automobile is not effective until its operating temperature is achieved. Thus, during engine warm-up, large amounts of pollutants are emitted. Automotive engineers have proposed and studied the use of electrical heating elements to heat the converter more quickly, thereby reducing pollution. By using several heating elements that can be operated individually, in series, or in parallel, several power levels can be achieved. This is useful in controlling the temperature of a chemical process.

Exercise 2   Find the currents labeled in Figure 7 by combining resistances in series and parallel.

Answer   **a.** $i_1 = 1.04 \text{ A}$, $i_2 = 0.480 \text{ A}$, $i_3 = 0.320 \text{ A}$, $i_4 = 0.240 \text{ A}$; **b.** $i_1 = 1 \text{ A}$, $i_2 = 1$ A; **c.** $i_1 = 1 \text{ A}$, $i_2 = 0.5 \text{ A}$, $i_3 = 0.5 \text{ A}$. ☐

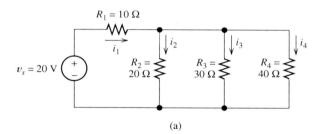

(a)

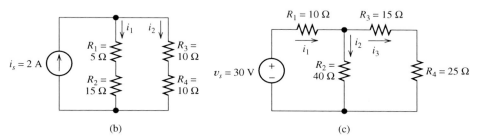

(b)   (c)

Figure 7 Circuits for Exercise 2.

3 VOLTAGE-DIVIDER AND CURRENT-DIVIDER CIRCUITS

Voltage Division

When a voltage is applied to a series combination of resistances, a fraction of the voltage appears across each of the resistances. Consider the circuit shown in Figure 8. The equivalent resistance seen by the voltage source is

$$R_{eq} = R_1 + R_2 + R_3 \qquad (22)$$

The current is the total voltage divided by the equivalent resistance:

$$i = \frac{v_{total}}{R_{eq}} = \frac{v_{total}}{R_1 + R_2 + R_3} \qquad (23)$$

Furthermore, the voltage across R_1 is

$$v_1 = R_1 i = \frac{R_1}{R_1 + R_2 + R_3} v_{total} \qquad (24)$$

Similarly, we have

$$v_2 = R_2 i = \frac{R_2}{R_1 + R_2 + R_3} v_{total} \qquad (25)$$

and

$$v_3 = R_3 i = \frac{R_3}{R_1 + R_2 + R_3} v_{total} \qquad (26)$$

We can summarize these results by the statement: *Of the total voltage, the fraction that appears across a given resistance in a series circuit is the ratio of the given resistance to the total series resistance.* This is known as the **voltage-division principle**.

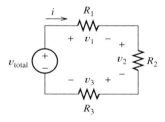

Figure 8 Circuit used to derive the voltage-division principle.

Of the total voltage, the fraction that appears across a given resistance in a series circuit is the ratio of the given resistance to the total series resistance.

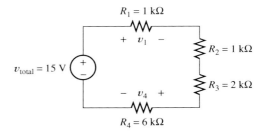

Figure 9   Circuit for Example 3.

We have derived the voltage-division principle for three resistances in series, but it applies for any number of resistances as long as they are connected in series.

Example 3   Application of the Voltage-Division Principle

Find the voltages v_1 and v_4 in Figure 9.

Solution   Using the voltage-division principle, we find that v_1 is the total voltage times the ratio of R_1 to the total resistance:

$$v_1 = \frac{R_1}{R_1 + R_2 + R_3 + R_4} v_{\text{total}}$$

$$= \frac{1000}{1000 + 1000 + 2000 + 6000} \times 15 = 1.5 \text{ V}$$

Similarly,

$$v_4 = \frac{R_4}{R_1 + R_2 + R_3 + R_4} v_{\text{total}}$$

$$= \frac{6000}{1000 + 1000 + 2000 + 6000} \times 15 = 9 \text{ V}$$

Notice that the largest voltage appears across the largest resistance in a series circuit.   ■

Current Division

The total current flowing into a parallel combination of resistances divides, and a fraction of the total current flows through each resistance. Consider the circuit shown in Figure 10. The equivalent resistance is given by

$$R_{\text{eq}} = \frac{R_1 R_2}{R_1 + R_2} \qquad (27)$$

The voltage across the resistances is given by

$$v = R_{\text{eq}} i_{\text{total}} = \frac{R_1 R_2}{R_1 + R_2} i_{\text{total}} \qquad (28)$$

Now, we can find the current in each resistance:

$$i_1 = \frac{v}{R_1} = \frac{R_2}{R_1 + R_2} i_{\text{total}} \qquad (29)$$

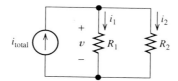

Figure 10 Circuit used to derive the current-division principle.

and

$$i_2 = \frac{v}{R_2} = \frac{R_1}{R_1 + R_2} i_{total} \qquad (30)$$

We can summarize these results by stating the **current-division principle**: *For two resistances in parallel, the fraction of the total current flowing in a resistance is the ratio of the other resistance to the sum of the two resistances.* Notice that this principle applies only for two resistances. If we have more than two resistances in parallel, we should combine resistances so we only have two before applying the current-division principle.

For two resistances in parallel, the fraction of the total current flowing in a resistance is the ratio of the other resistance to the sum of the two resistances.

An alternative approach is to work with conductances. For *n* conductances in parallel, it can be shown that

$$i_1 = \frac{G_1}{G_1 + G_2 + \cdots + G_n} i_{total}$$

Current division using conductances uses a formula with the same form as the formula for voltage division using resistances.

$$i_2 = \frac{G_2}{G_1 + G_2 + \cdots + G_n} i_{total}$$

and so forth. In other words, current division using conductances uses a formula with the same form as the formula for voltage division using resistances.

Applying the Current- and Voltage-Division Principles

Use the voltage-division principle to find the voltage v_x in Figure 11(a). Then find the source current i_s and use the current-division principle to compute the current i_3.

Solution The voltage-division principle applies only for resistances in series. Therefore, we first must combine R_2 and R_3. The equivalent resistance for the parallel

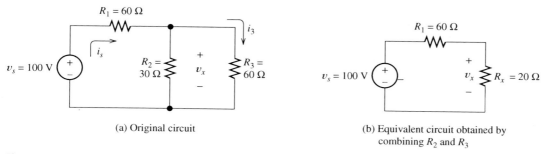

(a) Original circuit

(b) Equivalent circuit obtained by combining R_2 and R_3

Figure 11 Circuit for Example 4.

combination of R_2 and R_3 is

$$R_x = \frac{R_2 R_3}{R_2 + R_3} = \frac{30 \times 60}{30 + 60} = 20 \ \Omega$$

The equivalent network is shown in Figure 11(b).

Now, we can apply the voltage-division principle to find v_x. The voltage v_x is equal to the total voltage times R_x divided by the total series resistance:

$$v_x = \frac{R_x}{R_1 + R_x} v_s = \frac{20}{60 + 20} \times 100 = 25 \ \text{V}$$

The source current i_s is given by

$$i_s = \frac{v_s}{R_1 + R_x} = \frac{100}{60 + 20} = 1.25 \ \text{A}$$

Now, we can use the current-division principle to find i_3. The fraction of the source current i_s that flows through R_3 is $R_2/(R_2 + R_3)$. Thus, we have

$$i_3 = \frac{R_2}{R_2 + R_3} i_s = \frac{30}{30 + 60} \times 1.25 = 0.417 \ \text{A}$$

As a check, we can also compute i_3 another way:

$$i_3 = \frac{v_x}{R_3} = \frac{25}{60} = 0.417 \ \text{A} \qquad \blacksquare$$

Example 5   **Application of the Current-Division Principle**

The current-division principle applies for two resistances in parallel. Therefore, our first step is to combine R_2 and R_3.

Use the current-division principle to find the current i_1 in Figure 12(a).

Solution   The current-division principle applies for two resistances in parallel. Therefore, our first step is to combine R_2 and R_3:

$$R_{\text{eq}} = \frac{R_2 R_3}{R_2 + R_3} = \frac{30 \times 60}{30 + 60} = 20 \ \Omega$$

The resulting equivalent circuit is shown in Figure 12(b). Applying the current-division principle, we have

$$i_1 = \frac{R_{\text{eq}}}{R_1 + R_{\text{eq}}} i_s = \frac{20}{10 + 20} 15 = 10 \ \text{A}$$

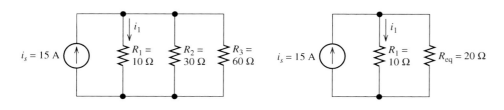

(a) Original circuit   (b) Circuit after combining R_2 and R_3

Figure 12 Circuit for Example 5.

Reworking the calculations using conductances, we have

$$G_1 = \frac{1}{R_1} = 100\,\text{mS}, \quad G_2 = \frac{1}{R_2} = 33.33\,\text{mS}, \quad \text{and} \quad G_3 = \frac{1}{R_3} = 16.67\,\text{mS}$$

Then, we compute the current

$$i_1 = \frac{G_1}{G_1 + G_2 + G_3}\, i_s = \frac{100}{100 + 33.33 + 16.67}15 = 10\,\text{A}$$

which is the same value that we obtained working with resistances. ∎

Position Transducers Based on the Voltage-Division Principle

Transducers are used to produce a voltage (or sometimes a current) that is proportional to a physical quantity of interest, such as distance, pressure, or temperature. For example, Figure 13 shows how a voltage that is proportional to the rudder angle of a boat or aircraft can be obtained. As the rudder turns, a sliding contact moves along a resistance such that R_2 is proportional to the rudder angle θ. The total resistance $R_1 + R_2$ is fixed. Thus, the output voltage is

$$v_o = v_s \frac{R_2}{R_1 + R_2} = K\theta$$

where K is a constant of proportionality that depends on the source voltage v_s and the construction details of the transducer. Many examples of transducers such as this are employed in all areas of science and engineering.

Exercise 3 Use the voltage-division principle to find the voltages labeled in Figure 14.
Answer **a.** $v_1 = 10$ V, $v_2 = 20$ V, $v_3 = 30$ V, $v_4 = 60$ V; **b.** $v_1 = 6.05$ V, $v_2 = 5.88$ V, $v_4 = 8.07$ V. □

Exercise 4 Use the current-division principle to find the currents labeled in Figure 15.
Answer **a.** $i_1 = 1$ A, $i_3 = 2$ A; **b.** $i_1 = i_2 = i_3 = 1$ A. □

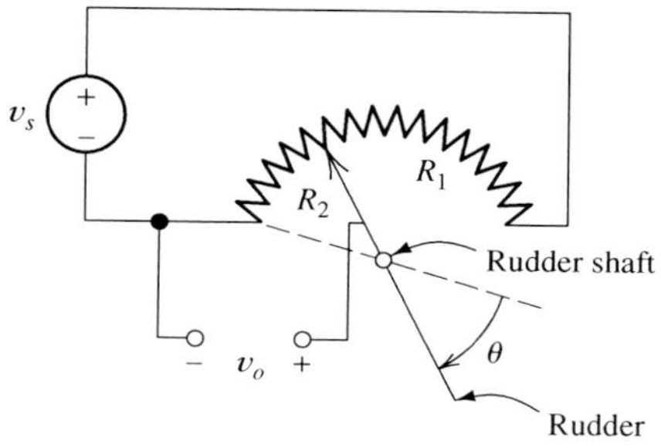

Figure 13 The voltage-division principle forms the basis for some position sensors. This figure shows a transducer that produces an output voltage v_o proportional to the rudder angle θ.

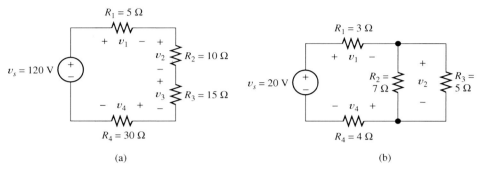

(a)

(b)

Figure 14 Circuits for Exercise 3.

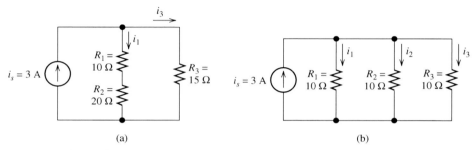

(a)

(b)

Figure 15 Circuits for Exercise 4.

4 NODE-VOLTAGE ANALYSIS

Although they are very important concepts, series/parallel equivalents and the current/voltage division principles are not sufficient to solve all circuits.

The network analysis methods that we have studied so far are useful, but they do not apply to all networks. For example, consider the circuit shown in Figure 16. We cannot solve this circuit by combining resistances in series and parallel because no series or parallel combination of resistances exists in the circuit. Furthermore, the voltage-division and current-division principles cannot be applied to this circuit. In this section, we learn **node-voltage analysis**, which is a general technique that can be applied to any circuit.

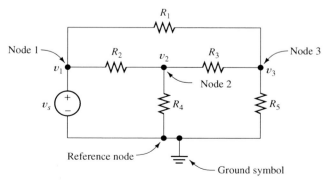

Figure 16 The first step in node analysis is to select a reference node and label the voltages at each of the other nodes.

Selecting the Reference Node

A **node** is a point at which two or more circuit elements are joined together. In node-voltage analysis, we first select one of the nodes as the **reference node**. In principle, any node can be picked to be the reference node. However, the solution is usually facilitated by selecting one end of a voltage source as the reference node. We will see why this is true as we proceed.

For example, the circuit shown in Figure 16 has four nodes. Let us select the bottom node as the reference node. We mark the reference node by the **ground symbol**, as shown in the figure.

Assigning Node Voltages

Next, we label the voltages at each of the other nodes. For example, the voltages at the three nodes are labeled v_1, v_2, and v_3 in Figure 16. The voltage v_1 is the voltage between node 1 and the reference node. The reference polarity for v_1 is positive at node 1 and negative at the reference node. Similarly, v_2 is the voltage between node 2 and the reference node. The reference polarity for v_2 is positive at node 2 and negative at the reference node. *In fact, the negative reference polarity for each of the node voltages is at the reference node.* We say that v_1 is the voltage at node 1 with respect to the reference node.

The negative reference polarity for each of the node voltages is at the reference node.

Finding Element Voltages in Terms of the Node Voltages

In node-voltage analysis, we write equations and eventually solve for the node voltages. Once the node voltages have been found, it is relatively easy to find the current, voltage, and power for each element in the circuit.

For example, suppose that we know the values of the node voltages and we want to find the voltage across R_3 with its positive reference on the left-hand side. To avoid additional labels in Figure 16, we have made a second drawing of the circuit, which is shown in Figure 17. The node voltages and the voltage v_x across R_3 are shown in Figure 17, where we have used arrows to indicate reference polarities. (Recall that the positive reference is at the head of the arrow.) Notice that v_2, v_x, and v_3 are the voltages encountered in traveling around the closed path through R_4, R_3, and R_5. Thus, these voltages must obey Kirchhoff's voltage law. Traveling around the loop

Once the node voltages have been determined, it is relatively easy to determine other voltages and currents in the circuit.

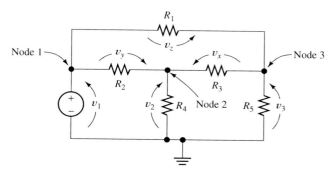

This is the same circuit shown in Figure 16. We have redrawn it simply to avoid cluttering the original diagram with the voltages v_x, v_y, and v_z that are not involved in the final node equations.

Figure 17 Assuming that we can determine the node voltages v_1, v_2, and v_3, we can use KVL to determine v_x, v_y, and v_z. Then using Ohm's law, we can find the current in each of the resistances. Thus, the key problem is in determining the node voltages.

clockwise and summing voltages, we have

$$-v_2 + v_x + v_3 = 0$$

Solving for v_x, we obtain

$$v_x = v_2 - v_3$$

Thus, we can find the voltage across any element in the network as the difference between node voltages. (If one end of an element is connected to the reference node, the voltage across the element is a node voltage.)

After the voltages are found, Ohm's law and KCL can be used to find the current in each element. Then, power can be computed by taking the product of the voltage and current for each element.

Exercise 5 In the circuit of Figure 17, find expressions for v_y and v_z in terms of the node voltages $v_1, v_2,$ and v_3.

Answer $v_y = v_2 - v_1, v_z = v_3 - v_1$. □

Writing KCL Equations in Terms of the Node Voltages

After choosing the reference node and assigning the voltage variables, we write equations that can be solved for the node voltages.

After choosing the reference node and assigning the voltage variables, we write equations that can be solved for the node voltages. We demonstrate by continuing with the circuit of Figure 16.

In Figure 16, the voltage v_1 is the same as the source voltage v_s:

$$v_1 = v_s$$

(In this case, one of the node voltages is known without any effort. This is the advantage in selecting the reference node at one end of an independent voltage source.)

Therefore, we need to determine the values of v_2 and v_3, and we must write two independent equations. We usually start by trying to write current equations at each of the nodes corresponding to an unknown node voltage. For example, at node 2 in Figure 16, the current leaving through R_4 is given by

$$\frac{v_2}{R_4}$$

This is true because v_2 is the voltage across R_4 with its positive reference at node 2. Thus, the current v_2/R_4 flows from node 2 toward the reference node, which is away from node 2.

Next, referring to Figure 17, we see that the current flowing out of node 2 through R_3 is given by v_x/R_3. However, we found earlier that $v_x = v_2 - v_3$. Thus, the current flowing out of node 2 through R_3 is given by

$$\frac{v_2 - v_3}{R_3}$$

To find the current flowing out of node n through a resistance toward node k, we subtract the voltage at node k from the voltage at node n and divide the difference by the resistance.

At this point, we pause in our analysis to make a useful observation. *To find the current flowing out of node n through a resistance toward node k, we subtract the voltage at node k from the voltage at node n and divide the difference by the resistance.*

Thus, if v_n and v_k are the node voltages and R is the resistance connected between the nodes, the current flowing from node n toward node k is given by

$$\frac{v_n - v_k}{R}$$

Applying this observation in Figure 16 to find the current flowing out of node 2 through R_2, we have

$$\frac{v_2 - v_1}{R_2}$$

[In Exercise 5, we found that $v_y = v_2 - v_1$. (See Figure 17.) The current flowing to the left through R_2 is v_y/R_2. Substitution yields the aforementioned expression.]

Of course, if the resistance is connected between node n and the reference node, the current away from node n toward the reference node is simply the node voltage v_n divided by the resistance. For example, as we noted previously, the current leaving node 2 through R_4 is given by v_2/R_4.

Now we apply KCL, adding all of the expressions for the currents leaving node 2 and setting the sum to zero. Thus, we obtain

$$\frac{v_2 - v_1}{R_2} + \frac{v_2}{R_4} + \frac{v_2 - v_3}{R_3} = 0$$

Writing the current equation at node 3 is similar. We try to follow the same pattern in writing each equation. Then, the equations take a familiar form, and mistakes are less frequent. We usually write expressions for the currents leaving the node under consideration and set the sum to zero. Applying this approach at node 3 of Figure 16, we have

$$\frac{v_3 - v_1}{R_1} + \frac{v_3}{R_5} + \frac{v_3 - v_2}{R_3} = 0$$

In many networks, we can obtain all of the equations needed to solve for the node voltages by applying KCL to the nodes at which the unknown voltages appear.

Example 6   Node-Voltage Analysis

Write equations that can be solved for the node voltages v_1, v_2, and v_3 shown in Figure 18.

Solution   We use KCL to write an equation at node 1:

$$\frac{v_1}{R_1} + \frac{v_1 - v_2}{R_2} + i_s = 0$$

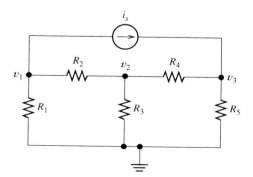

Figure 18 Circuit for Example 6.

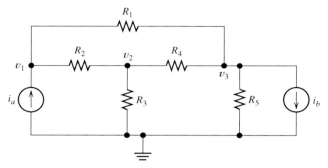

Figure 19 Circuit for Exercise 6.

Each term on the left-hand side of this equation represents a current leaving node 1. Summing the currents leaving node 2, we have

$$\frac{v_2 - v_1}{R_2} + \frac{v_2}{R_3} + \frac{v_2 - v_3}{R_4} = 0$$

Similarly, at node 3, we get

$$\frac{v_3}{R_5} + \frac{v_3 - v_2}{R_4} = i_s$$

Here, the currents leaving node 3 are on the left-hand side and the current entering is on the right-hand side. ■

Exercise 6 Use KCL to write equations at each node (except the reference node) for the circuit shown in Figure 19.
Answer

$$\text{Node 1:} \quad \frac{v_1 - v_3}{R_1} + \frac{v_1 - v_2}{R_2} = i_a$$

$$\text{Node 2:} \quad \frac{v_2 - v_1}{R_2} + \frac{v_2}{R_3} + \frac{v_2 - v_3}{R_4} = 0$$

$$\text{Node 3:} \quad \frac{v_3}{R_5} + \frac{v_3 - v_2}{R_4} + \frac{v_3 - v_1}{R_1} + i_b = 0$$

Circuit Equations in Standard Form

Once we have written the equations needed to solve for the node voltages, we put the equations into standard form. We group the node-voltage variables on the left-hand sides of the equations and place terms that do not involve the node voltages on the right-hand sides. For two node voltages, this eventually puts the node-voltage equations into the following form:

$$g_{11}v_1 + g_{12}v_2 = i_1 \tag{31}$$

$$g_{21}v_1 + g_{22}v_2 = i_2 \tag{32}$$

If we have three unknown node voltages, the equations can be put into the form

$$g_{11}v_1 + g_{12}v_2 + g_{13}v_3 = i_1 \tag{33}$$

$$g_{21}v_1 + g_{22}v_2 + g_{23}v_3 = i_2 \tag{34}$$

$$g_{31}v_1 + g_{32}v_2 + g_{33}v_3 = i_3 \tag{35}$$

We have chosen the letter g for the node-voltage coefficients because they are often (but not always) conductances with units of siemens. Similarly, we have used i for the terms on the right-hand sides of the equations because they are often currents.

In matrix form, the equations can be written as

$$\mathbf{GV} = \mathbf{I}$$

in which we have

$$\mathbf{G} = \begin{bmatrix} g_{11} & g_{12} \\ g_{21} & g_{22} \end{bmatrix} \quad \text{or} \quad \mathbf{G} = \begin{bmatrix} g_{11} & g_{12} & g_{13} \\ g_{21} & g_{22} & g_{23} \\ g_{31} & g_{32} & g_{33} \end{bmatrix}$$

depending on whether we have two or three unknown node voltages. Also, $\mathbf{V}$ and $\mathbf{I}$ are column vectors:

$$\mathbf{V} = \begin{bmatrix} v_1 \\ v_2 \end{bmatrix} \quad \text{or} \quad \mathbf{V} = \begin{bmatrix} v_1 \\ v_2 \\ v_3 \end{bmatrix} \quad \text{and} \quad \mathbf{I} = \begin{bmatrix} i_1 \\ i_2 \end{bmatrix} \quad \text{or} \quad \mathbf{I} = \begin{bmatrix} i_1 \\ i_2 \\ i_3 \end{bmatrix}$$

As the number of nodes and node voltages increases, the dimensions of the matrices increase.

One way to solve for the node voltages is to find the inverse of $\mathbf{G}$ and then compute the solution vector as:

$$\mathbf{V} = \mathbf{G}^{-1}\mathbf{I}$$

A Shortcut to Writing the Matrix Equations

If we put the node equations for the circuit of Exercise 6 (Figure 19) into matrix form, we obtain

$$\begin{bmatrix} \frac{1}{R_1} + \frac{1}{R_2} & -\frac{1}{R_2} & -\frac{1}{R_1} \\ -\frac{1}{R_2} & \frac{1}{R_2} + \frac{1}{R_3} + \frac{1}{R_4} & -\frac{1}{R_4} \\ -\frac{1}{R_1} & -\frac{1}{R_4} & \frac{1}{R_1} + \frac{1}{R_4} + \frac{1}{R_5} \end{bmatrix} \begin{bmatrix} v_1 \\ v_2 \\ v_3 \end{bmatrix} = \begin{bmatrix} i_a \\ 0 \\ -i_b \end{bmatrix}$$

Let us take a moment to compare the circuit in Figure 19 with the elements in this equation. First, look at the elements on the diagonal of the $\mathbf{G}$ matrix, which are

$$g_{11} = \frac{1}{R_1} + \frac{1}{R_2} \quad g_{22} = \frac{1}{R_2} + \frac{1}{R_3} + \frac{1}{R_4} \quad \text{and} \quad g_{33} = \frac{1}{R_1} + \frac{1}{R_4} + \frac{1}{R_5}$$

We see that the diagonal elements of $\mathbf{G}$ are equal to the sums of the conductances connected to the corresponding nodes. Next, notice the off diagonal terms:

$$g_{12} = -\frac{1}{R_2} \quad g_{13} = -\frac{1}{R_1} \quad g_{21} = -\frac{1}{R_2} \quad g_{23} = -\frac{1}{R_4} \quad g_{31} = -\frac{1}{R_1} \quad g_{32} = -\frac{1}{R_4}$$

In each case, g_{jk} is equal to the negative of the conductance connected between node j and k. The terms in the **I** matrix are the currents pushed into the corresponding nodes by the current sources. These observations hold whenever the network consists of resistances and independent current sources, assuming that we follow our usual pattern in writing the equations.

Thus, if a circuit consists of resistances and independent current sources, we can use the following steps to rapidly write the node equations directly in matrix form.

1. Make sure that the circuit contains only resistances and independent current sources.

2. The diagonal terms of **G** are the sums of the conductances connected to the corresponding nodes.

3. The off diagonal terms of **G** are the negatives of the conductances connected between the corresponding nodes.

4. The elements of **I** are the currents pushed into the corresponding nodes by the current sources.

This is a shortcut way to write the node equations in matrix form, provided that the circuit contains only resistances and independent current sources.

Keep in mind that if the network contains voltage sources or controlled sources this pattern does not hold.

Exercise 7 Working directly from Figure 18, write its node-voltage equation in matrix form.
Answer

$$
\begin{bmatrix}
\frac{1}{R_1} + \frac{1}{R_2} & -\frac{1}{R_2} & 0 \\
-\frac{1}{R_2} & \frac{1}{R_2} + \frac{1}{R_3} + \frac{1}{R_4} & -\frac{1}{R_4} \\
0 & -\frac{1}{R_4} & \frac{1}{R_4} + \frac{1}{R_5}
\end{bmatrix}
\begin{bmatrix}
v_1 \\
v_2 \\
v_3
\end{bmatrix}
=
\begin{bmatrix}
-i_s \\
0 \\
i_s
\end{bmatrix}
$$

☐

Example 7   Node-Voltage Analysis

Write the node-voltage equations in matrix form for the circuit of Figure 20.

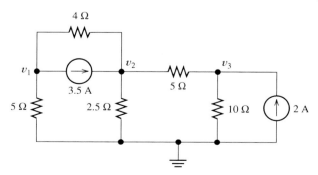

Figure 20 Circuit for Example 7.

Solution Writing KCL at each node, we have

$$\frac{v_1}{5} + \frac{v_1 - v_2}{4} + 3.5 = 0$$

$$\frac{v_2 - v_1}{4} + \frac{v_2}{2.5} + \frac{v_2 - v_3}{5} = 3.5$$

$$\frac{v_3 - v_2}{5} + \frac{v_3}{10} = 2$$

Manipulating the equations into standard form, we have

$$0.45v_1 - 0.25v_2 = -3.5$$

$$-0.25v_1 + 0.85v_2 - 0.2v_3 = 3.5$$

$$-0.2v_2 + 0.35v_3 = 2$$

Then, in matrix form, we obtain

$$\begin{bmatrix} 0.45 & -0.25 & 0 \\ -0.25 & 0.85 & -0.20 \\ 0 & -0.20 & 0.30 \end{bmatrix} \begin{bmatrix} v_1 \\ v_2 \\ v_3 \end{bmatrix} = \begin{bmatrix} -3.5 \\ 3.5 \\ 2 \end{bmatrix} \qquad (36)$$

Because the circuit contains no voltage sources or controlled sources, we could have used the shortcut method to write the matrix form directly. For example, $g_{11} = 0.45$ is the sum of the conductances connected to node 1, $g_{12} = -0.25$ is the negative of the conductance connected between nodes 1 and 2, $i_3 = 2$ is the current pushed into node 3 by the 2-A current source, and so forth. ∎

Solving the Network Equations

After we have obtained the equations in standard form, we can solve them by a variety of methods, including substitution, Gaussian elimination, and determinants. As an engineering student, you may own a powerful calculator such as the TI-84 or TI-89 that has the ability to solve systems of linear equations. You should learn to do this by practice on the exercises and the problems at the end of this chapter.

In some situations, you may not be allowed to use one of the more advanced calculators or a notebook computer. For example, only fairly simple scientific calculators are allowed on the Fundamentals of Engineering (FE) Examination, which is the first step in becoming a registered professional engineer in the United States. The calculator policy for the professional engineering examinations can be found at http://www.ncees.org/exams/calculators/. Thus, even if you own an advanced calculator, you may wish to practice with one of those allowed in the FE Examination.

Exercise 8 Use your calculator to solve Equation 36.
Answer $v_1 = -5\,\text{V}$, $v_2 = 5\,\text{V}$, $v_3 = 10\,\text{V}$. □

Using MATLAB to Solve Network Equations

When you have access to a computer and MATLAB software, you have a very powerful system for engineering and scientific calculations. This software is available to students at many engineering schools and is very likely to be encountered in some of your other courses.

In this chapter, we begin to illustrate the application of MATLAB to various aspects of circuit analysis, but we cannot possibly cover all of its many useful features in this text. If you are new to MATLAB, and it is available to you, use the video and/or getting started documentation that appear at the top of the command screen and/or in the Help menu to gain some initial familiarity with the software. Furthermore, you can gain access to a variety of online interactive tutorials at http://www.mathworks.com/academia/student_center/tutorials/register.html. If you have already used the program, the MATLAB commands we present may be familiar to you. In either case, you should be able to easily modify the examples we present to work out similar circuit problems.

Next, we illustrate the solution for Equation 36 using MATLAB. Instead of using $\mathbf{V} = \mathbf{G}^{-1}\mathbf{I}$ to compute node voltages, MATLAB documentation recommends using the command V = G\I which invokes a more accurate algorithm for computing solutions to systems of linear equations.

The comments following the % sign are ignored by MATLAB. For improved clarity, we use a **bold** font for the input commands, a regular font for comments, and a color font for the responses from MATLAB, otherwise the following has the appearance of the MATLAB command screen for this problem. ($>>$ is the MATLAB command prompt.)

```
>> clear  % First we clear the work space.
>> % Then, we enter the coefficient matrix of Equation 36 with
>> % spaces between elements in each row and semicolons between rows.
>> G = [0.45 -0.25 0; -0.25 0.85 -0.2; 0 -0.2 0.30]
G =
    0.4500   -0.2500         0
   -0.2500    0.8500   -0.2000
         0   -0.2000    0.3000
>> % Next, we enter the column vector for the right-hand side.
>> I = [-3.5; 3.5; 2]
I =
   -3.5000
    3.5000
    2.0000
>>  % The MATLAB documentation recommends computing the node
>>  % voltages using V = G\I instead of using V = inv(G)*I.
>> V = G\I
V =
   -5.0000
    5.0000
   10.0000
```

Thus, we have $v_1 = -5\,\text{V}$, $v_2 = 5\,\text{V}$, and $v_3 = 10\,\text{V}$, as you found when working Exercise 8 with your calculator.

LabVIEW MathScript

As an alternative in solving numerical network equations, you can install LabVIEW and use its MathScript features. To do this, first start LabVIEW and left click on **Blank VI**. This will bring up two windows: a Block Diagram window and a Front Panel window. Left click on **Tools** in the menu bar of either window and then left click on **MathScript Window**…, which will open a window in which you can use many commands identical to those of MATLAB. At this point, you can close the Block Diagram and Front Panel windows. Enter the commands in the Command

Window, and the results will appear in the Output Window. If you wish to try this software alternative, start by trying to duplicate the solution to the example of the previous several pages. Simply enter the commands

```
clear
G = [0.45 -0.25 0; -0.25 0.85 -0.2; 0 -0.2 0.30]
I = [-3.5; 3.5; 2]
V = G\I
```

in the Command Window and the results will appear in the Output Window.

Example 8 | Node-Voltage Analysis

Solve for the node voltages shown in Figure 21 and determine the value of the current i_x.

Solution Our first step in solving a circuit is to select the reference node and assign the node voltages. This has already been done, as shown in Figure 21.

Next, we write equations. In this case, we can write a current equation at each node. This yields

$$\text{Node 1:} \quad \frac{v_1}{10} + \frac{v_1 - v_2}{5} + \frac{v_1 - v_3}{20} = 0$$

$$\text{Node 2:} \quad \frac{v_2 - v_1}{5} + \frac{v_2 - v_3}{10} = 10$$

$$\text{Node 3:} \quad \frac{v_3}{5} + \frac{v_3 - v_2}{10} + \frac{v_3 - v_1}{20} = 0$$

Next, we place these equations into standard form:

$$0.35v_1 - 0.2v_2 - 0.05v_3 = 0$$
$$-0.2v_1 + 0.3v_2 - 0.10v_3 = 10$$
$$-0.05v_1 - 0.10v_2 + 0.35v_3 = 0$$

In matrix form, the equations are

$$\begin{bmatrix} 0.35 & -0.2 & -0.05 \\ -0.2 & 0.3 & -0.1 \\ -0.05 & -0.1 & 0.35 \end{bmatrix} \begin{bmatrix} v_1 \\ v_2 \\ v_3 \end{bmatrix} = \begin{bmatrix} 0 \\ 10 \\ 0 \end{bmatrix}$$

or $\quad \mathbf{GV = I}$

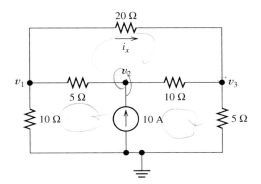

Figure 21 Circuit for Example 8.

---

in which **G** represents the coefficient matrix of conductances, **V** is the column vector of node voltages, and **I** is the column vector of currents on the right-hand side.

Here again, we could write the equations directly in standard or matrix form using the short cut method because the circuit contains only resistances and independent current sources.

The MATLAB solution is:

```
>> clear
>> G = [0.35 -0.2 -0.05; -0.2 0.3 -0.1; -0.05 -0.1 0.35];
>> % A semicolon at the end of a command suppresses the
>> % MATLAB response.
>> I = [0; 10; 0];
>> V = G\I
V =
   45.4545
   72.7273
   27.2727
>> % Finally, we calculate the current.
>> Ix = (V(1) - V(3))/20
Ix =
    0.9091
```

Alternatively, you can use the same commands with LabVIEW MathScript to obtain the answers. ∎

Exercise 9 Repeat the analysis of the circuit of Example 8, using the reference node and node voltages shown in Figure 22. **a.** First write the network equations. **b.** Put the network equations into standard form. **c.** Solve for v_1, v_2, and v_3. (The values will be different than those we found in Example 8 because v_1, v_2, and v_3 are not the same voltages in the two figures.) **d.** Find i_x. (Of course, i_x is the same in both figures, so it should have the same value.)

Answer

a.

$$\frac{v_1 - v_3}{20} + \frac{v_1}{5} + \frac{v_1 - v_2}{10} = 0$$

$$\frac{v_2 - v_1}{10} + 10 + \frac{v_2 - v_3}{5} = 0$$

$$\frac{v_3 - v_1}{20} + \frac{v_3}{10} + \frac{v_3 - v_2}{5} = 0$$

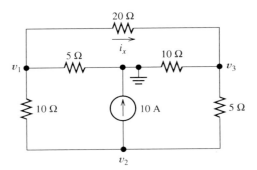

Figure 22 Circuit of Example 8 with a different choice for the reference node. See Exercise 9.

b.

$$0.35v_1 - 0.10v_2 - 0.05v_3 = 0$$
$$-0.10v_1 + 0.30v_2 - 0.20v_3 = -10$$
$$-0.05v_1 - 0.20v_2 + 0.35v_3 = 0$$

c. $v_1 = -27.27$; $v_2 = -72.73$; $v_3 = -45.45$

d. $i_x = 0.909$ A

$\square$

Circuits with Voltage Sources

When a circuit contains a single voltage source, we can often pick the reference node at one end of the source, and then we have one less unknown node voltage for which to solve.

Example 9   Node-Voltage Analysis

Write the equations for the network shown in Figure 23 and put them into standard form.

Solution   Notice that we have selected the reference node at the bottom end of the voltage source. Thus, the voltage at node 3 is known to be 10 V, and we do not need to assign a variable for that node.

Writing current equations at nodes 1 and 2, we obtain

$$\frac{v_1 - v_2}{5} + \frac{v_1 - 10}{2} = 1$$

$$\frac{v_2}{5} + \frac{v_2 - 10}{10} + \frac{v_2 - v_1}{5} = 0$$

Now if we group terms and place the constants on the right-hand sides of the equations, we have

$$0.7v_1 - 0.2v_2 = 6$$
$$-0.2v_1 + 0.5v_2 = 1$$

Thus, we have obtained the equations needed to solve for v_1 and v_2 in standard form. $\blacksquare$

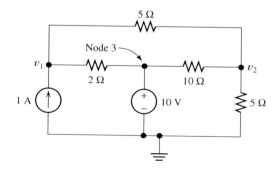

Figure 23   Circuit for Example 9.

Exercise 10 Solve the equations of Example 9 for v_1 and v_2.
Answer $v_1 = 10.32$ V; $v_2 = 6.129$ V. □

Exercise 11 Solve for the node voltages v_1 and v_2 in the circuit of Figure 24.
Answer $v_1 = 6.77$ V, $v_2 = 4.19$ V. □

Sometimes, the pattern for writing node-voltage equations that we have illustrated so far must be modified. For example, consider the network and node voltages shown in Figure 25. Notice that $v_3 = -15$ V because of the 15-V source connected between node 3 and the reference node. Therefore, we need two equations relating the unknowns v_1 and v_2.

If we try to write a current equation at node 1, we must include a term for the current through the 10-V source. We could assign an unknown for this current, but then we would have a higher-order system of equations to solve. Especially if we are solving the equations manually, we want to minimize the number of unknowns. For this circuit, it is not possible to write a current equation in terms of the node voltages for any single node (even the reference node) because a voltage source is connected to each node.

Another way to obtain a current equation is to form a **supernode**. This is done by drawing a dashed line around several nodes, including the elements connected between them. This is shown in Figure 25. Two supernodes are indicated, one enclosing each of the voltage sources.

We can state Kirchhoff's current law in a slightly more general form than we have previously: *The net current flowing through any closed surface must equal zero.* Thus, we can apply KCL to a supernode. For example, for the supernode enclosing

Another way to state Kirchhoff's current law is that the net current flowing through any closed surface must equal zero.

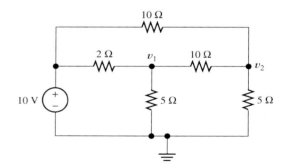

Figure 24 Circuit for Exercise 11.

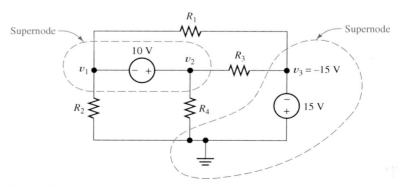

Figure 25 A supernode is formed by drawing a dashed line enclosing several nodes and any elements connected between them.

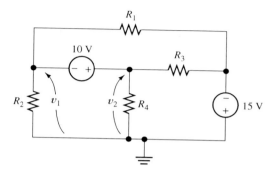

Figure 26 Node voltages v_1 and v_2 and the 10-V source form a closed loop to which KVL can be applied. (This is the same circuit as that of Figure 25.)

the 10-V source, we sum currents leaving and obtain

$$\frac{v_1}{R_2} + \frac{v_1 - (-15)}{R_1} + \frac{v_2}{R_4} + \frac{v_2 - (-15)}{R_3} = 0 \tag{37}$$

Each term on the left-hand side of this equation represents a current leaving the supernode through one of the resistors. Thus, by enclosing the 10-V source within the supernode, we have obtained a current equation without introducing a new variable for the current in the source.

Next, we might be tempted to write another current equation for the other supernode. However, we would find that the equation is equivalent to the one already written. *In general, we obtain dependent equations if we use all of the nodes in writing current equations.* Nodes 1 and 2 were part of the first supernode, while node 3 and the reference node are part of the second supernode. Thus, in writing equations for both supernodes, we would have used all four nodes in the network.

If we tried to solve for the node voltages by using substitution, at some point all of the terms would drop out of the equations and we would not be able to solve for those voltages. In MATLAB, you will receive a warning that the G matrix is singular, in other words, its determinant is zero. If this happens, we know that we should return to writing equations and find another equation to use in the solution. This will not happen if we avoid using all of the nodes in writing current equations.

There is a way to obtain an independent equation for the network under consideration. We can use KVL because v_1, the 10-V source, and v_2 form a closed loop. This is illustrated in Figure 26, where we have used arrows to indicate the polarities of v_1 and v_2. Traveling clockwise and summing the voltages around the loop, we obtain

$$-v_1 - 10 + v_2 = 0 \tag{38}$$

Equations 37 and 38 form an independent set that can be used to solve for v_1 and v_2 (assuming that the resistance values are known).

> We obtain dependent equations if we use all of the nodes in a network to write KCL equations.

> When a voltage source is connected between nodes so that current equations cannot be written at the individual nodes, first write a KVL equation, including the voltage source, and then enclose the voltage source in a supernode and write a KCL equation for the supernode.

Exercise 12 Write the current equation for the supernode that encloses the 15-V source in Figure 25. Show that your equation is equivalent to Equation 37. □

Exercise 13 Write a set of independent equations for the node voltages shown in Figure 27.
Answer

KVL:

$$-v_1 + 10 + v_2 = 0$$

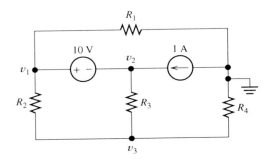

Figure 27 Circuit for Exercise 13.

KCL for the supernode enclosing the 10-V source:

$$\frac{v_1}{R_1} + \frac{v_1 - v_3}{R_2} + \frac{v_2 - v_3}{R_3} = 1$$

KCL for node 3:

$$\frac{v_3 - v_1}{R_2} + \frac{v_3 - v_2}{R_3} + \frac{v_3}{R_4} = 0$$

KCL at the reference node:

$$\frac{v_1}{R_1} + \frac{v_3}{R_4} = 1$$

For independence, the set must include the KVL equation. Any two of the three KCL equations can be used to complete the three-equation set. (The three KCL equations use all of the network nodes and, therefore, do not form an independent set.) □

Circuits with Controlled Sources

Controlled sources present a slight additional complication of the node-voltage technique. (Recall that the value of a controlled source depends on a current or voltage elsewhere in the network.) In applying node-voltage analysis, first we write equations exactly as we have done for networks with independent sources. Then, we express the controlling variable in terms of the node-voltage variables and substitute into the network equations. We illustrate with two examples.

Example 10   Node-Voltage Analysis with a Dependent Source

Write an independent set of equations for the node voltages shown in Figure 28.

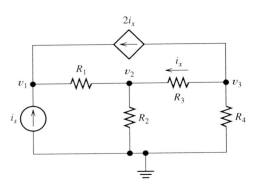

Figure 28 Circuit containing a current-controlled current source. See Example 10.

Solution   First, we write KCL equations at each node, including the current of the controlled source just as if it were an ordinary current source:

$$\frac{v_1 - v_2}{R_1} = i_s + 2i_x \tag{39}$$

$$\frac{v_2 - v_1}{R_1} + \frac{v_2}{R_2} + \frac{v_2 - v_3}{R_3} = 0 \tag{40}$$

$$\frac{v_3 - v_2}{R_3} + \frac{v_3}{R_4} + 2i_x = 0 \tag{41}$$

Next, we find an expression for the controlling variable i_x in terms of the node voltages. Notice that i_x is the current flowing away from node 3 through R_3. Thus, we can write

$$i_x = \frac{v_3 - v_2}{R_3} \tag{42}$$

Finally, we use Equation 42 to substitute into Equations 39, 40, and 41. Thus, we obtain the required equation set:

$$\frac{v_1 - v_2}{R_1} = i_s + 2\frac{v_3 - v_2}{R_3} \tag{43}$$

$$\frac{v_2 - v_1}{R_1} + \frac{v_2}{R_2} + \frac{v_2 - v_3}{R_3} = 0 \tag{44}$$

$$\frac{v_3 - v_2}{R_3} + \frac{v_3}{R_4} + 2\frac{v_3 - v_2}{R_3} = 0 \tag{45}$$

Assuming that the value of i_s and the resistances are known, we could put this set of equations into standard form and solve for v_1, v_2, and v_3.   ■

Example 11   Node-Voltage Analysis with a Dependent Source

Write an independent set of equations for the node voltages shown in Figure 29.

Solution   First, we ignore the fact that the voltage source is a dependent source and write equations just as we would for a circuit with independent sources. We cannot write a current equation at either node 1 or node 2, because of the voltage source connected between them. However, we can write a KVL equation:

$$-v_1 + 0.5v_x + v_2 = 0 \tag{46}$$

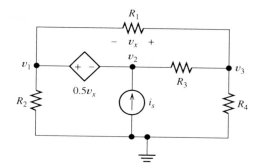

Figure 29 Circuit containing a voltage-controlled voltage source. See Example 11.

Then, we use KCL to write current equations. For a supernode enclosing the controlled voltage source,

$$\frac{v_1}{R_2} + \frac{v_1 - v_3}{R_1} + \frac{v_2 - v_3}{R_3} = i_s$$

For node 3,

$$\frac{v_3}{R_4} + \frac{v_3 - v_2}{R_3} + \frac{v_3 - v_1}{R_1} = 0 \tag{47}$$

For the reference node,

$$\frac{v_1}{R_2} + \frac{v_3}{R_4} = i_s \tag{48}$$

Of course, these current equations are dependent because we have used all four nodes in writing them. We must use Equation 46 and two of the KCL equations to form an independent set. However, Equation 46 contains the controlling variable v_x, which must be eliminated before we have equations in terms of the node voltages.

Thus, our next step is to write an expression for the controlling variable v_x in terms of the node voltages. Notice that v_1, v_x, and v_3 form a closed loop. Traveling clockwise and summing voltages, we have

$$-v_1 - v_x + v_3 = 0$$

Solving for v_x, we obtain

$$v_x = v_3 - v_1$$

Now if we substitute into Equation 46, we get

$$v_1 = 0.5(v_3 - v_1) + v_2 \tag{49}$$

Equation 49 along with any two of the KCL equations forms an independent set that can be solved for the node voltages. ∎

Using the principles we have discussed in this section, we can write node-voltage equations for any network consisting of sources and resistances. Thus, given a computer or calculator to help in solving the equations, we can compute the currents and voltages for any network.

Next, we summarize the steps in analyzing circuits by the node-voltage technique:

Here is a convenient step-by-step guide to node-voltage analysis.

1. Select a reference node and assign variables for the unknown node voltages. If the reference node is chosen at one end of an independent voltage source, one node voltage is known at the start, and fewer need to be computed.

2. Write network equations. First, use KCL to write current equations for nodes and supernodes. Write as many current equations as you can without using all of the nodes. Then if you do not have enough equations because of voltage sources connected between nodes, use KVL to write additional equations.

3. If the circuit contains dependent sources, find expressions for the controlling variables in terms of the node voltages. Substitute into the network equations, and obtain equations having only the node voltages as unknowns.

4. Put the equations into standard form and solve for the node voltages.

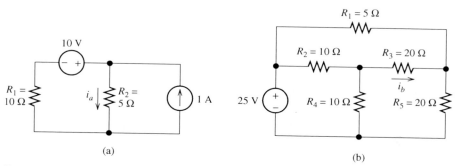

(a)

(b)

Figure 30 Circuits for Exercise 14.

5. Use the values found for the node voltages to calculate any other currents or voltages of interest.

Exercise 14 Use the node-voltage technique to solve for the currents labeled in the circuits shown in Figure 30.
Answer **a.** $i_a = 1.33$ A; **b.** $i_b = -0.259$ A. □

Exercise 15 Use the node-voltage technique to solve for the values of i_x and i_y in Figure 31.
Answer $i_x = 0.5$ A, $i_y = 2.31$ A. □

Using the MATLAB Symbolic Toolbox to Obtain Symbolic Solutions

If the Symbolic Toolbox is included with your version of MATLAB, you can use it to solve node voltage and other equations symbolically. (LabVIEW MathScript does not have symbolic mathematics capabilities.) We illustrate by solving Equations 43, 44, and 45 from Example 10.

For help with a command such as "solve" simply type "help solve" at the command prompt.

```
>> clear
>> % First we clear the workspace, then we enter the equations into
>> % the solve command followed by the variables for which we want
>> % to solve.
>> [V1, V2, V3] = solve('(V1 - V2)/R1 = Is + 2*(V3 - V2)/R3', ...
                '(V2 - V1)/R1 + V2/R2 + (V2 - V3)/R3 = 0', ...
                '(V3 - V2)/R3 + V3/R4 + 2*(V3 - V2)/R3 = 0',...
                'V1','V2','V3')
```

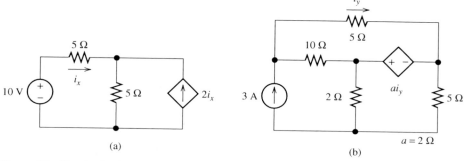

(a)

(b)

Figure 31 Circuits for Exercise 15.

```
V1 =
(Is*R1*R2 + Is*R1*R3 + 3*Is*R1*R4 + Is*R2*R3 + 3*Is*R2*R4)/(3*R2 + R3 +
3*R4)
V2 =
(Is*R2*R3 + 3*Is*R2*R4)/(3*R2 + R3 + 3*R4)
V3 =
(3*Is*R2*R4)/(3*R2 + R3 + 3*R4)
>> % The solve command gives the answers, but in a form that is
>> % somewhat difficult to read.
>> % A more readable version of the answers is obtained using the
>> % pretty command. We combine the three commands on one line
>> % by placing commas between them.
>> pretty(V1), pretty(V2), pretty(V3)
   Is R1 R2 + Is R1 R3 + 3 Is R1 R4 + Is R2 R3 + 3 Is R2 R4
   --------------------------------------------------------
                      3 R2 + R3 + 3 R4

   Is R2 R3 + 3 Is R2 R4
   ---------------------
      3 R2 + R3 + 3 R4

      3 Is R2 R4
   ----------------
   3 R2 + R3 + 3 R4
```

(Here we have shown the results obtained using MATLAB version R2008b; other versions may give results different in appearance but equivalent mathematically.) In more standard mathematical format, the results are:

$$v_1 = \frac{i_s R_1 R_2 + i_s R_1 R_3 + 3i_s R_1 R_4 + i_s R_2 R_3 + 3i_s R_2 R_4}{3R_2 + R_3 + 3R_4}$$

$$v_2 = \frac{i_s R_2 R_3 + 3i_s R_2 R_4}{3R_2 + R_3 + 3R_4}$$

$$\text{and } v_3 = \frac{3i_s R_2 R_4}{3R_2 + R_3 + 3R_4}$$

Checking Answers

As usual, it is a good idea to apply some checks to the answers. First of all, make sure that the answers have proper units, which are volts in this case. If the units don't check, look to see if any of the numerical values entered in the equations have units. Referring to the circuit (Figure 28), we see that the only numerical parameter entered into the equations was the gain of the current-controlled current source, which has no units.

Again referring to the circuit diagram, we can see that we should have $v_2 = v_3$ for $R_3 = 0$, and we check the results to see that this is the case. Another check is obtained by observing that we should have $v_3 = 0$ for $R_4 = 0$. Still another check of the results comes from observing that, in the limit as R_3 approaches infinity, we should have $i_x = 0$, (so the controlled current source becomes an open circuit), $v_3 = 0, v_1 = i_s(R_1 + R_2)$, and $v_2 = i_s R_2$. Various other checks of a similar nature can be applied. This type of checking may not guarantee correct results, but it can find a lot of errors.

Exercise 16 Use the symbolic math features of MATLAB to solve Equations 47, 48, and 49 for the node voltages in symbolic form.

Answer

$$v_1 = \frac{2i_s R_1 R_2 R_3 + 3i_s R_1 R_2 R_4 + 2i_s R_2 R_3 R_4}{3 R_1 R_2 + 2 R_1 R_3 + 3 R_1 R_4 + 2 R_2 R_3 + 2 R_3 R_4}$$

$$v_2 = \frac{3i_s R_1 R_2 R_3 + 3i_s R_1 R_2 R_4 + 2i_s R_2 R_3 R_4}{3 R_1 R_2 + 2 R_1 R_3 + 3 R_1 R_4 + 2 R_2 R_3 + 2 R_3 R_4}$$

$$v_3 = \frac{3i_s R_1 R_2 R_4 + 2i_s R_2 R_3 R_4}{3 R_1 R_2 + 2 R_1 R_3 + 3 R_1 R_4 + 2 R_2 R_3 + 2 R_3 R_4}$$

Depending on the version of MATLAB and the Symbolic Toolbox that you use, your answers may have a different appearance but should be algebraically equivalent to these.

□

5 MESH-CURRENT ANALYSIS

In this section, we show how to analyze networks by using another general technique, known as mesh-current analysis. Networks that can be drawn on a plane without having one element (or conductor) crossing over another are called **planar networks**. On the other hand, circuits that must be drawn with one or more elements crossing others are said to be **nonplanar**. We consider only planar networks.

Let us start by considering the planar network shown in Figure 32(a). Suppose that the source voltages and resistances are known and that we wish to solve for the currents. We first write equations for the currents shown in Figure 32(a), which are called branch currents because a separate current is defined in each branch of the network. However, we will eventually see that using the mesh currents illustrated in Figure 32(b) makes the solution easier.

Three independent equations are needed to solve for the three branch currents shown in Figure 32(a). In general, the number of independent KVL equations that can be written for a planar network is equal to the number of open areas defined by the network layout. For example, the circuit of Figure 32(a) has two open areas: one defined by v_A, R_1, and R_3, while the other is defined by R_3, R_2, and v_B. Thus, for this network, we can write only two independent KVL equations. We must employ KCL to obtain the third equation.

Application of KVL to the loop consisting of v_A, R_1, and R_3 yields

$$R_1 i_1 + R_3 i_3 = v_A \tag{50}$$

Similarly, for the loop consisting of R_3, R_2, and v_B, we get

$$-R_3 i_3 + R_2 i_2 = -v_B \tag{51}$$

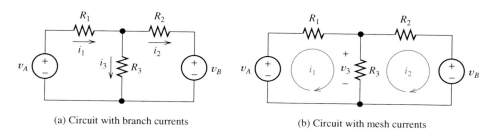

(a) Circuit with branch currents   (b) Circuit with mesh currents

Figure 32 Circuit for illustrating the mesh-current method of circuit analysis.

Applying KCL to the node at the top end of R_3, we have

$$i_1 = i_2 + i_3 \tag{52}$$

Next, we solve Equation 52 for i_3 and substitute into Equations 50 and 51. This yields the following two equations:

$$R_1 i_1 + R_3(i_1 - i_2) = v_A \tag{53}$$

$$-R_3(i_1 - i_2) + R_2 i_2 = -v_B \tag{54}$$

Thus, we have used the KCL equation to reduce the KVL equations to two equations in two unknowns.

Now, consider the mesh currents i_1 and i_2 shown in Figure 32(b). As indicated in the figure, mesh currents are considered to flow around closed paths. Hence, mesh currents automatically satisfy KCL. *When several mesh currents flow through one element, we consider the current in that element to be the algebraic sum of the mesh currents.* Thus, assuming a reference direction pointing downward, the current in R_3 is $(i_1 - i_2)$. Thus, $v_3 = R_3(i_1 - i_2)$. Now if we follow i_1 around its loop and apply KVL, we get Equation 53 directly. Similarly, following i_2, we obtain Equation 54 directly.

Because mesh currents automatically satisfy KCL, some work is saved in writing and solving the network equations. The circuit of Figure 32 is fairly simple, and the advantage of mesh currents is not great. However, for more complex networks, the advantage can be quite significant.

> When several mesh currents flow through one element, we consider the current in that element to be the algebraic sum of the mesh currents.

Choosing the Mesh Currents

For a planar circuit, we can choose the current variables to flow through the elements around the periphery of each of the open areas of the circuit diagram. For consistency, we usually define the mesh currents to flow clockwise.

Two networks and suitable choices for the mesh currents are shown in Figure 33. When a network is drawn with no crossing elements, it resembles a window, with each open area corresponding to a pane of glass. Sometimes it is said that the mesh currents are defined by "soaping the window panes."

Keep in mind that, if two mesh currents flow through a circuit element, we consider the current in that element to be the algebraic sum of the mesh currents. For example, in Figure 33(a), the current in R_2 referenced to the left is $i_3 - i_1$. Furthermore, the current referenced upward in R_3 is $i_2 - i_1$.

> We usually choose the current variables to flow clockwise around the periphery of each of the open areas of the circuit diagram.

Exercise 17 Consider the circuit shown in Figure 33(b). In terms of the mesh currents, find the current in **a.** R_2 referenced upward; **b.** R_4 referenced to the right; **c.** R_8 referenced downward; **d.** R_8 referenced upward.
Answer **a.** $i_4 - i_1$; **b.** $i_2 - i_1$; **c.** $i_3 - i_4$; **d.** $i_4 - i_3$. [Notice that the answer for part (d) is the negative of the answer for part (c).] □

Writing Equations to Solve for Mesh Currents

If a network contains only resistances and independent voltage sources, we can write the required equations by following each current around its mesh and applying KVL. (We do not need to apply KCL because the mesh currents flow out of each node that they flow into.)

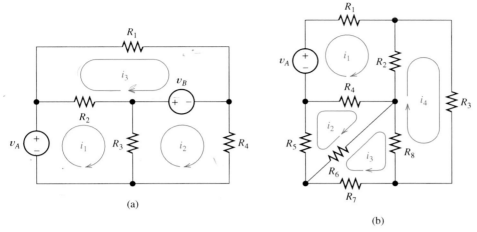

Figure 33 Two circuits and their mesh-current variables.

Example 12 — Mesh-Current Analysis

Write the equations needed to solve for the mesh currents in Figure 33(a).

Solution Using a pattern in solving networks by the mesh-current method helps to avoid errors. Part of the pattern that we use is to select the mesh currents to flow clockwise. Then, we write a KVL equation for each mesh, going around the meshes clockwise. As usual, we add a voltage if its positive reference is encountered first in traveling around the mesh, and we subtract the voltage if the negative reference is encountered first. Our pattern is always to take the first end of each resistor encountered as the positive reference for its voltage. Thus, we are always adding the resistor voltages.

If a network contains only resistances and independent voltage sources, we can write the required equations by following each current around its mesh and applying KVL.

For example, in mesh 1 of Figure 33(a), we first encounter the left-hand end of R_2. The voltage across R_2 referenced positive on its left-hand end is $R_2(i_1 - i_3)$. Similarly, we encounter the top end of R_3 first, and the voltage across R_3 referenced positive at the top end is $R_3(i_1 - i_2)$. By using this pattern, we add a term for each resistor in the KVL equation, consisting of the resistance times the current in the mesh under consideration minus the current in the adjacent mesh (if any). Using this pattern for mesh 1 of Figure 33(a), we have

$$R_2(i_1 - i_3) + R_3(i_1 - i_2) - v_A = 0$$

Similarly, for mesh 2, we obtain

$$R_3(i_2 - i_1) + R_4 i_2 + v_B = 0$$

Finally, for mesh 3, we have

$$R_2(i_3 - i_1) + R_1 i_3 - v_B = 0$$

Notice that we have taken the positive reference for the voltage across R_3 at the top in writing the equation for mesh 1 and at the bottom for mesh 3. This is not an error because the terms for R_3 in the two equations are opposite in sign.

In standard form, the equations become:

$$(R_2 + R_3)i_1 - R_3 i_2 - R_2 i_3 = v_A$$

$$- R_3 i_1 + (R_3 + R_4)i_2 = -v_B$$

$$- R_2 i_1 + (R_1 + R_2)i_3 = v_B$$

In matrix form, we have

$$\begin{bmatrix} (R_2 + R_3) & -R_3 & -R_2 \\ -R_3 & (R_3 + R_4) & 0 \\ -R_2 & 0 & (R_1 + R_2) \end{bmatrix} \begin{bmatrix} i_1 \\ i_2 \\ i_3 \end{bmatrix} = \begin{bmatrix} v_A \\ -v_B \\ v_B \end{bmatrix}$$

Often, we use $\mathbf{R}$ to represent the coefficient matrix, $\mathbf{I}$ to represent the column vector of mesh currents, and $\mathbf{V}$ to represent the column vector of the terms on the right-hand sides of the equations in standard form. Then, the mesh-current equations are represented as:

$$\mathbf{RI} = \mathbf{V}$$

We refer to the element of the ith row and jth column of $\mathbf{R}$ as r_{ij}. ∎

Exercise 18   Write the equations for the mesh currents in Figure 32(b) and put them into matrix form.

Answer   Following each mesh current in turn, we obtain

$$R_1 i_1 + R_2(i_1 - i_4) + R_4(i_1 - i_2) - v_A = 0$$

$$R_5 i_2 + R_4(i_2 - i_1) + R_6(i_2 - i_3) = 0$$

$$R_7 i_3 + R_6(i_3 - i_2) + R_8(i_3 - i_4) = 0$$

$$R_3 i_4 + R_2(i_4 - i_1) + R_8(i_4 - i_3) = 0$$

$$\begin{bmatrix} (R_1 + R_2 + R_4) & -R_4 & 0 & -R_2 \\ -R_4 & (R_4 + R_5 + R_6) & -R_6 & 0 \\ 0 & -R_6 & (R_6 + R_7 + R_8) & -R_8 \\ -R_2 & 0 & -R_8 & (R_2 + R_3 + R_8) \end{bmatrix} \begin{bmatrix} i_1 \\ i_2 \\ i_3 \\ i_4 \end{bmatrix} = \begin{bmatrix} v_A \\ 0 \\ 0 \\ 0 \end{bmatrix}$$

(55)

□

Solving Mesh Equations

After we write the mesh-current equations, we can solve them by using the methods that we discussed in Section 4 for the node-voltage approach. We illustrate with a simple example.

| Example 13 | Mesh-Current Analysis |

Solve for the current in each element of the circuit shown in Figure 34.

Solution   First, we select the mesh currents. Following our standard pattern, we define the mesh currents to flow clockwise around each mesh of the circuit. Then, we write a KVL equation around mesh 1:

$$20(i_1 - i_3) + 10(i_1 - i_2) - 70 = 0 \tag{56}$$

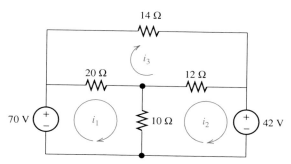

Figure 34 Circuit of Example 13.

For meshes 2 and 3, we have:

$$10(i_2 - i_1) + 12(i_2 - i_3) + 42 = 0 \tag{57}$$

$$20(i_3 - i_1) + 14i_3 + 12(i_3 - i_2) = 0 \tag{58}$$

Putting the equations into standard form, we have:

$$30i_1 - 10i_2 - 20i_3 = 70 \tag{59}$$

$$-10i_1 + 22i_2 - 12i_3 = -42 \tag{60}$$

$$-20i_1 - 12i_2 + 46i_3 = 0 \tag{61}$$

In matrix form, the equations become:

$$
\begin{bmatrix}
30 & -10 & -20 \\
-10 & 22 & -12 \\
-20 & -12 & 46
\end{bmatrix}
\begin{bmatrix}
i_1 \\
i_2 \\
i_3
\end{bmatrix}
=
\begin{bmatrix}
70 \\
-42 \\
0
\end{bmatrix}
$$

These equations can be solved in a variety of ways. We will demonstrate using MATLAB. (The same results can be obtained by using these same commands in LabVIEW MathScript.) We use **R** for the coefficient matrix, because the coefficients often are resistances. Similarly, we use **V** for the column vector for the right-hand side of the equations and **I** for the column vector of the mesh currents. The commands and results are:

```
>> R = [30 -10 -20; -10 22 -12; -20 -12 46];
>> V = [70; -42; 0];
>> I = R\V % Try to avoid using i, which represents the square root of
>> % -1 in MATLAB.
I =
    4.0000
    1.0000
    2.0000
```

Thus, the values of the mesh currents are $i_1 = 4\,\text{A}$, $i_2 = 1\,\text{A}$, and $i_3 = 2\,\text{A}$. Next, we can find the current in any element. For example, the current flowing downward in the 10-Ω resistance is $i_1 - i_2 = 3\,\text{A}$. ∎

Exercise 19 Use mesh currents to solve for the current flowing through the 10-Ω resistance in Figure 35. Check your answer by combining resistances in series and parallel to solve the circuit. Check a second time by using node voltages.

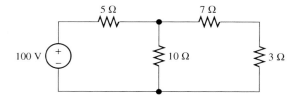

Figure 35 Circuit of Exercise 19.

Answer The current through the 10-Ω resistance is 5 A. □

Exercise 20 Use mesh currents to solve for the current flowing through the 2-Ω resistance in Figure 24.

Answer The current is 1.613 A directed toward the right. □

Writing Mesh Equations Directly in Matrix Form

If a circuit contains only resistances and independent voltage sources, and if we select the mesh currents flowing clockwise, the mesh equations can be obtained directly in matrix form using these steps:

1. Make sure that the circuit contains only resistances and independent voltage sources. Select all of the mesh currents to flow in the clockwise direction.

2. Write the sum of the resistances contained in each mesh as the corresponding element on the main diagonal of **R**. In other words, r_{jj} equals the sum of the resistances encountered in going around mesh j.

3. Insert the negatives of the resistances common to the corresponding meshes as the off diagonal terms of **R**. Thus, for $i \neq j$, the elements r_{ij} and r_{ji} are the same and are equal to negative of the sum of the resistances common to meshes i and j.

4. For each element of the **V** matrix, go around the corresponding mesh clockwise, *subtracting* the values of voltage sources for which we encounter the positive reference first and *adding* the values of voltage sources for which we encounter the negative reference first. (We have reversed the rules for adding or subtracting the voltage source values from what we used when writing KVL equations because the elements of **V** correspond to terms on the opposite side of the KVL equations.)

Keep in mind that this procedure does not apply to circuits having current sources or controlled sources.

Example 14   Writing Mesh Equations Directly in Matrix Form

Write the mesh equations directly in matrix form for the circuit of Figure 36.

Solution The matrix equation is:

$$
\begin{bmatrix}
(R_2 + R_4 + R_5) & -R_2 & -R_5 \\
-R_2 & (R_1 + R_2 + R_3) & -R_3 \\
-R_5 & -R_3 & (R_3 + R_5 + R_6)
\end{bmatrix}
\begin{bmatrix}
i_1 \\
i_2 \\
i_3
\end{bmatrix}
=
\begin{bmatrix}
-v_A + v_B \\
v_A \\
-v_B
\end{bmatrix}
$$

Notice that mesh 1 includes R_2, R_4, and R_5, so the r_{11} element of **R** is the sum of these resistances. Similarly, mesh 2 contains R_1, R_2, and R_3, so r_{22} is the sum of these resistances. Because R_2 is common to meshes 1 and 2, we have $r_{12} = r_{21} = -R_2$. Similar observations can be made for the other elements of **R**.

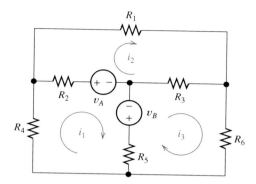

Figure 36 Circuit of Example 14.

As we go around mesh 1 clockwise, we encounter the positive reference for v_A first and the negative reference for v_B first, so we have $v_1 = -v_A + v_B$, and so forth. ∎

Exercise 21 Examine the circuit of Figure 33(a), and write its mesh equations equations directly in matrix form.
Answer

$$
\begin{bmatrix}
(R_2 + R_3) & -R_3 & -R_2 \\
-R_3 & (R_3 + R_4) & 0 \\
-R_2 & 0 & (R_1 + R_2)
\end{bmatrix}
\begin{bmatrix}
i_1 \\
i_2 \\
i_3
\end{bmatrix}
=
\begin{bmatrix}
v_A \\
-v_B \\
v_B
\end{bmatrix}
$$
□

Mesh Currents in Circuits Containing Current Sources

Recall that a current source forces a specified current to flow through its terminals, but the voltage across its terminals is not predetermined. Instead, the voltage across a current source depends on the circuit to which the source is connected. Often, it is not easy to write an expression for the voltage across a current source. *A common mistake made by beginning students is to assume that the voltages across current sources are zero.*

Consequently, when a circuit contains a current source, we must depart from the pattern that we use for circuits consisting of voltage sources and resistances. First, consider the circuit of Figure 37. As usual, we have defined the mesh currents flowing clockwise. If we were to try to write a KVL equation for mesh 1, we would need to include an unknown for the voltage across the current source. Because we do not wish to increase the number of unknowns in our equations, we avoid writing KVL equations for loops that include current sources. In the circuit in Figure 37, we have defined the current in the current source as i_1. However, we know that this

A common mistake made by beginning students is to assume that the voltages across current sources are zero.

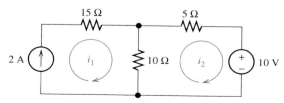

Figure 37 In this circuit, we have $i_1 = 2$ A.

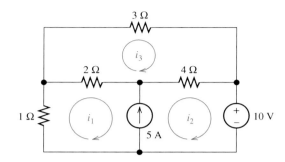

Figure 38 A circuit with a current source common to two meshes.

current is 2 A. Thus, we can write

$$i_1 = 2 \text{ A} \tag{62}$$

The second equation needed can be obtained by applying KVL to mesh 2, which yields

$$10(i_2 - i_1) + 5i_2 + 10 = 0 \tag{63}$$

Equations 62 and 63 can readily be solved for i_2. Notice that in this case the presence of a current source facilitates the solution.

Now let us consider the somewhat more complex situation shown in Figure 38. As usual, we have defined the mesh currents flowing clockwise. We cannot write a KVL equation around mesh 1 because the voltage across the 5-A current source is unknown (and we do not want to increase the number of unknowns in our equations). A solution is to combine meshes 1 and 2 into a **supermesh**. In other words, we write a KVL equation around the periphery of meshes 1 and 2 combined. This yields

$$i_1 + 2(i_1 - i_3) + 4(i_2 - i_3) + 10 = 0 \tag{64}$$

Next, we can write a KVL equation for mesh 3:

$$3i_3 + 4(i_3 - i_2) + 2(i_3 - i_1) = 0 \tag{65}$$

Finally, we recognize that we have defined the current in the current source referenced upward as $i_2 - i_1$. However, we know that the current flowing upward through the current source is 5 A. Thus, we have

$$i_2 - i_1 = 5 \tag{66}$$

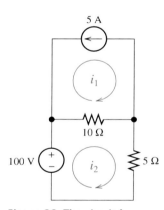

Figure 39 The circuit for Exercise 22.

It is important to realize that Equation 66 is not a KCL equation.

It is important to realize that Equation 66 is not a KCL equation. Instead, it simply states that we have defined the current referenced upward through the current source in terms of the mesh currents as $i_2 - i_1$, but this current is known to be 5 A. Equations 64, 65, and 66 can be solved for the mesh currents.

Exercise 22 Write the equations needed to solve for the mesh currents in Figure 39.
Answer

$$i_1 = -5 \text{ A}$$
$$10(i_2 - i_1) + 5i_2 - 100 = 0 \qquad\qquad \square$$

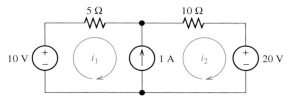

Figure 40 The circuit for Exercise 23.

Exercise 23 Write the equations needed to solve for the mesh currents in Figure 40. Then solve for the currents.
Answer The equations are $i_2 - i_1 = 1$ and $5i_1 + 10i_2 + 20 - 10 = 0$. Solving, we have $i_1 = -4/3$ A and $i_2 = -1/3$ A. □

Circuits with Controlled Sources

Controlled sources present a slight additional complication to the mesh-current technique. First, we write equations exactly as we have done for networks with independent sources. Then, we express the controlling variables in terms of the mesh-current variables and substitute into the network equations. We illustrate with an example.

Example 15   Mesh-Current Analysis with Controlled Sources

Solve for the currents in the circuit of Figure 41(a), which contains a voltage-controlled current source common to the two meshes.

Solution   First, we write equations for the mesh currents as we have done for independent sources. Since there is a current source common to mesh 1 and mesh 2, we start by combining the meshes to form a supermesh and write a voltage equation:

$$-20 + 4i_1 + 6i_2 + 2i_2 = 0 \qquad (67)$$

Then, we write an expression for the source current in terms of the mesh currents:

$$av_x = 0.25v_x = i_2 - i_1 \qquad (68)$$

Next, we see that the controlling voltage is

$$v_x = 2i_2 \qquad (69)$$

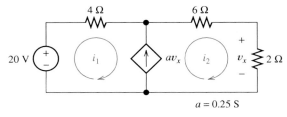

Figure 41 A circuit with a voltage-controlled current source. See Example 15.

Using Equation 58 to substitute for v_x in Equation 57, we have

$$\frac{i_2}{2} = i_2 - i_1 \qquad (70)$$

Finally, we put Equations 67 and 70 into standard form, resulting in

$$4i_1 + 8i_2 = 20 \qquad (71)$$

$$i_1 - \frac{i_2}{2} = 0 \qquad (72)$$

Solving these equations yields $i_1 = 1$ A and $i_2 = 2$ A.   ∎

Using the principles we have discussed in this section, we can write mesh-current equations for any planar network consisting of sources and resistances.

Next, we summarize the steps in analyzing planar circuits by the mesh-current technique:

Here is a convenient step-by-step guide to mesh-current analysis.

1. If necessary, redraw the network without crossing conductors or elements. Then, define the mesh currents flowing around each of the open areas defined by the network. For consistency, we usually select a clockwise direction for each of the mesh currents, but this is not a requirement.

2. Write network equations, stopping after the number of equations is equal to the number of mesh currents. First, use KVL to write voltage equations for meshes that do not contain current sources. Next, if any current sources are present, write expressions for their currents in terms of the mesh currents. Finally, if a current source is common to two meshes, write a KVL equation for the supermesh.

3. If the circuit contains dependent sources, find expressions for the controlling variables in terms of the mesh currents. Substitute into the network equations, and obtain equations having only the mesh currents as unknowns.

4. Put the equations into standard form. Solve for the mesh currents by use of determinants or other means.

5. Use the values found for the mesh currents to calculate any other currents or voltages of interest.

Exercise 24   Use the mesh-current technique to solve for the currents labeled in the circuits shown in Figure 30.
Answer   **a.** $i_a = 1.33$ A; **b.** $i_b = -0.259$ A.   □

Exercise 25   Use the mesh-current technique to solve for the values of i_x and i_y in Figure 31.
Answer $i_x = 0.5$ A, $i_y = 2.31$ A.   □

6 THÉVENIN AND NORTON EQUIVALENT CIRCUITS

In this section, we learn how to replace two-terminal circuits containing resistances and sources by simple equivalent circuits. By a two-terminal circuit, we mean that the original circuit has only two points that can be connected to other circuits. The original circuit can be any complex interconnection of resistances and sources. However, a restriction is that the controlling variables for any controlled sources must appear inside the original circuit.

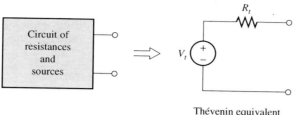

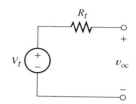

Thévenin equivalent
circuit

Figure 42 A two-terminal circuit consisting of resistances and sources can be replaced by a Thévenin equivalent circuit.

Figure 43 Thévenin equivalent circuit with open-circuited terminals. The open-circuit voltage v_{oc} is equal to the Thévenin voltage V_t.

Thévenin Equivalent Circuits

One type of equivalent circuit is the **Thévenin equivalent**, which consists of an independent voltage source in series with a resistance. This is illustrated in Figure 42.

Consider the Thévenin equivalent with open-circuited terminals as shown in Figure 43. By definition, no current can flow through an open circuit. Therefore, no current flows through the Thévenin resistance, and the voltage across the resistance is zero. Applying KVL, we conclude that

$$V_t = v_{oc}$$

Both the original circuit and the equivalent circuit are required to have the same open-circuit voltage. *Thus, the Thévenin source voltage V_t is equal to the open-circuit voltage of the original network.*

Now, consider the Thévenin equivalent with a short circuit connected across its terminals as shown in Figure 44. The current flowing in this circuit is

$$i_{sc} = \frac{V_t}{R_t}$$

The short-circuit current i_{sc} is the same for the original circuit as for the Thévenin equivalent. Solving for the Thévenin resistance, we have

$$R_t = \frac{V_t}{i_{sc}} \tag{73}$$

Using the fact that the Thévenin voltage is equal to the open-circuit voltage of the network, we have

$$R_t = \frac{v_{oc}}{i_{sc}} \tag{74}$$

The Thévenin equivalent circuit consists of an independent voltage source in series with a resistance.

The Thévenin voltage v_t is equal to the open-circuit voltage of the original network.

Figure 44 Thévenin equivalent circuit with short-circuited terminals. The short-circuit current is $i_{sc} = V_t/R_t$.

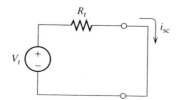

Thus, to determine the Thévenin equivalent circuit, we can start by analyzing the original network for its open-circuit voltage and its short-circuit current. The Thévenin voltage equals the open-circuit voltage, and the Thévenin resistance is given by Equation 74.

Example 16   Determining the Thévenin Equivalent Circuit

Find the Thévenin equivalent for the circuit shown in Figure 45(a).

Solution   First, we analyze the circuit with open-circuited terminals. This is shown in Figure 45(b). The resistances R_1 and R_2 are in series and have an equivalent resistance of $R_1 + R_2$. Therefore, the current circulating is

$$i_1 = \frac{v_s}{R_1 + R_2} = \frac{15}{100 + 50} = 0.10 \text{ A}$$

The open-circuit voltage is the voltage across R_2:

$$v_{oc} = R_2 i_1 = 50 \times 0.10 = 5 \text{ V}$$

Thus, the Thévenin voltage is $V_t = 5$ V.

Now, we consider the circuit with a short circuit connected across its terminals as shown in Figure 45(c). By definition, the voltage across a short circuit is zero. Hence, the voltage across R_2 is zero, and the current through it is zero, as shown in the figure. Therefore, the short-circuit current i_{sc} flows through R_1. The source voltage v_s appears across R_1, so we can write

$$i_{sc} = \frac{v_s}{R_1} = \frac{15}{100} = 0.15 \text{ A}$$

Now, we can use Equation 74 to determine the Thévenin resistance:

$$R_t = \frac{v_{oc}}{i_{sc}} = \frac{5 \text{ V}}{0.15 \text{ A}} = 33.3 \ \Omega$$

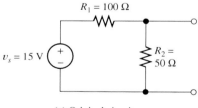

(a) Original circuit

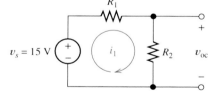

(b) Analysis with an open circuit

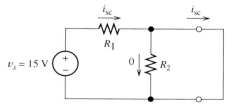

(c) Analysis with a short circuit

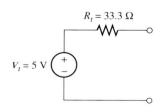

(d) Thévenin equivalent

Figure 45   Circuit for Example 16.

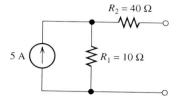

Figure 46 Circuit for Exercise 26.

The Thévenin equivalent circuit is shown in Figure 45(d). ∎

Exercise 26   Find the Thévenin equivalent circuit for the circuit shown in Figure 46.
Answer $V_t = 50$ V, $R_t = 50\ \Omega$. □

Finding the Thévenin Resistance Directly.   If a network contains no dependent sources, there is an alternative way to find the Thévenin resistance. First, we *zero* the sources in the network. In zeroing a voltage source, we reduce its voltage to zero. A voltage source with zero voltage is equivalent to a short circuit.

In zeroing a current source, we reduce its current to zero. By definition, an element that always carries zero current is an open circuit. *Thus, to zero the independent sources, we replace voltage sources with short circuits and replace current sources with open circuits.*

Figure 47 shows a Thévenin equivalent before and after zeroing its voltage source. Looking back into the terminals after the source is zeroed, we see the Thévenin resistance. *Thus, we can find the Thévenin resistance by zeroing the sources in the original network and then computing the resistance between the terminals.*

When zeroing a current source, it becomes an open circuit. When zeroing a voltage source, it becomes a short circuit.

We can find the Thévenin resistance by zeroing the sources in the original network and then computing the resistance between the terminals.

| **Example 17** | **Zeroing Sources to Find Thévenin Resistance** |

Find the Thévenin resistance for the circuit shown in Figure 48(a) by zeroing the sources. Then, find the short-circuit current and the Thévenin equivalent circuit.

Solution   To zero the sources, we replace the voltage source by a short circuit and replace the current source by an open circuit. The resulting circuit is shown in Figure 48(b).

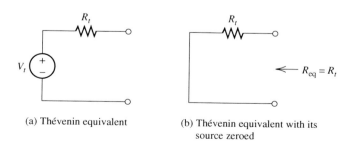

(a) Thévenin equivalent

(b) Thévenin equivalent with its source zeroed

Figure 47 When the source is zeroed, the resistance seen from the circuit terminals is equal to the Thévenin resistance.

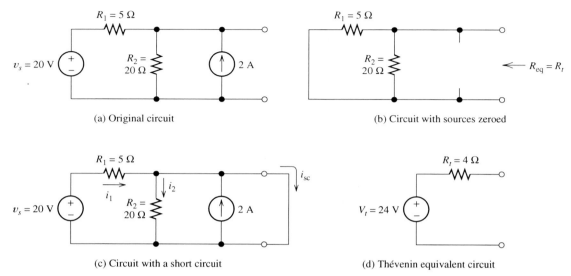

Figure 48 Circuit for Example 17.

The Thévenin resistance is the equivalent resistance between the terminals. This is the parallel combination of R_1 and R_2, which is given by

$$R_t = R_{eq} = \frac{1}{1/R_1 + 1/R_2} = \frac{1}{1/5 + 1/20} = 4\ \Omega$$

Next, we find the short-circuit current for the circuit. The circuit is shown in Figure 48(c). In this circuit, the voltage across R_2 is zero because of the short circuit. Thus, the current through R_2 is zero:

$$i_2 = 0$$

Furthermore, the voltage across R_1 is equal to 20 V. Thus, the current is

$$i_1 = \frac{v_s}{R_1} = \frac{20}{5} = 4\ \text{A}$$

Finally, we write a current equation for the node joining the top ends of R_2 and the 2-A source. Setting the sum of the currents entering equal to the sum of the currents leaving, we have

$$i_1 + 2 = i_2 + i_{sc}$$

This yields $i_{sc} = 6$ A.

Now, the Thévenin voltage can be found. From Equation 74, we get

$$V_t = R_t i_{sc} = 4 \times 6 = 24\ \text{V}$$

The Thévenin equivalent circuit is shown in Figure 48(d). ■

Exercise 27 Use node-voltage analysis of the circuit shown in Figure 48(a) to show that the open-circuit voltage is equal to the Thévenin voltage found in Example 17. □

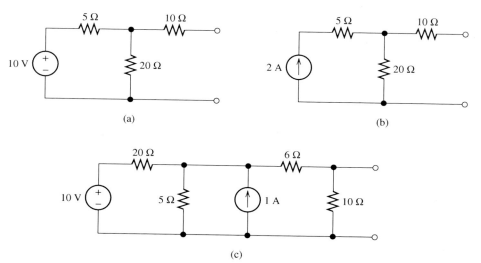

(a)

(b)

(c)

Figure 49 Circuits for Exercise 28.

Exercise 28 Find the Thévenin resistance for each of the circuits shown in Figure 49 by zeroing the sources.
Answer **a.** $R_t = 14\ \Omega$; **b.** $R_t = 30\ \Omega$; **c.** $R_t = 5\ \Omega$. ☐
We complete our discussion of Thévenin equivalent circuits with one more example.

| **Example 18** | Thévenin Equivalent of a Circuit with a Dependent Source |

Find the Thévenin equivalent for the circuit shown in Figure 50(a).

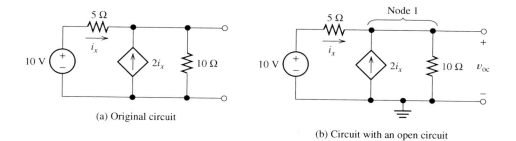

(a) Original circuit

(b) Circuit with an open circuit

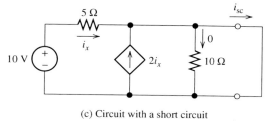

(c) Circuit with a short circuit

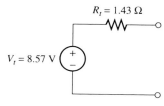

(d) Thévenin equivalent

Figure 50 Circuit for Example 18.

Because this circuit contains a
dependent source, we cannot
find the Thévenin resistance
by zeroing the sources and
combining resistances in
series and parallel.

Solution Because this circuit contains a dependent source, we cannot find the Thévenin resistance by zeroing the sources and combining resistances in series and parallel. Thus, we must analyze the circuit to find the open-circuit voltage and the short-circuit current.

We start with the open-circuit voltage. Consider Figure 50(b). We use node-voltage analysis, picking the reference node at the bottom of the circuit. Then, v_{oc} is the unknown node-voltage variable. First, we write a current equation at node 1.

$$i_x + 2i_x = \frac{v_{oc}}{10} \tag{75}$$

Next, we write an expression for the controlling variable i_x in terms of the node voltage v_{oc}:

$$i_x = \frac{10 - v_{oc}}{5}$$

Substituting this into Equation 75, we have

$$3\frac{10 - v_{oc}}{5} = \frac{v_{oc}}{10}$$

Solving, we find that $v_{oc} = 8.57$ V.

Now, we consider short-circuit conditions as shown in Figure 50(c). In this case, the current through the 10-Ω resistance is zero. Furthermore, we get

$$i_x = \frac{10 \text{ V}}{5 \text{ }\Omega} = 2 \text{ A}$$

and

$$i_{sc} = 3i_x = 6 \text{ A}$$

Next, we use Equation 74 to compute the Thévenin resistance:

$$R_t = \frac{v_{oc}}{i_{sc}} = \frac{8.57 \text{ V}}{6 \text{ A}} = 1.43 \text{ }\Omega$$

Finally, the Thévenin equivalent circuit is shown in Figure 50(d). ∎

Norton Equivalent Circuit

Another type of equivalent, known as the **Norton equivalent circuit**, is shown in Figure 51. It consists of an independent current source I_n in parallel with the Thévenin resistance. Notice that if we zero the Norton current source, replacing it by an open circuit, the Norton equivalent becomes a resistance of R_t. This also happens if we zero the voltage source in the Thévenin equivalent by replacing the

Figure 51 The Norton equivalent circuit consists of an independent current source I_n in parallel with the Thévenin resistance R_t.

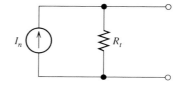

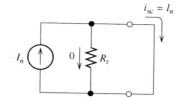

Figure 52 The Norton equivalent circuit with a short circuit across its terminals.

voltage source by a short circuit. Thus, the resistance in the Norton equivalent is the same as the Thévenin resistance.

Consider placing a short circuit across the Norton equivalent as shown in Figure 52. In this case, the current through R_t is zero. *Therefore, the Norton current is equal to the short-circuit current:*

$$I_n = i_{sc}$$

We can find the Norton equivalent by using the same techniques as we used for the Thévenin equivalent.

Step-by-Step Thévenin/Norton-Equivalent-Circuit Analysis

1. Perform two of these:
   a. Determine the open-circuit voltage $V_t = v_{oc}$.
   b. Determine the short-circuit current $I_n = i_{sc}$.
   c. Zero the independent sources and find the Thévenin resistance R_t looking back into the terminals. Do not zero dependent sources.
2. Use the equation $V_t = R_t I_n$ to compute the remaining value.
3. The Thévenin equivalent consists of a voltage source V_t in series with R_t.
4. The Norton equivalent consists of a current source I_n in parallel with R_t.

Norton Equivalent Circuit

Find the Norton equivalent for the circuit shown in Figure 53(a).

Solution Because the circuit contains a controlled source, we cannot zero the sources and combine resistances to find the Thévenin resistance. First, we consider the circuit with an open circuit as shown in Figure 53(a). We treat v_{oc} as a node-voltage variable. Writing a current equation at the top of the circuit, we have

$$\frac{v_x}{4} + \frac{v_{oc} - 15}{R_1} + \frac{v_{oc}}{R_2 + R_3} = 0 \tag{76}$$

Next, we use the voltage-divider principle to write an expression for v_x in terms of resistances and v_{oc}:

$$v_x = \frac{R_3}{R_2 + R_3} v_{oc} = 0.25 v_{oc}$$

Substituting into Equation 76, we find that

$$\frac{0.25 v_{oc}}{4} + \frac{v_{oc} - 15}{R_1} + \frac{v_{oc}}{R_2 + R_3} = 0$$

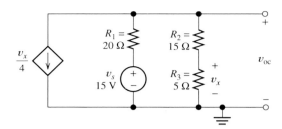

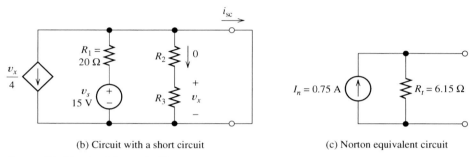

(a) Original circuit under open-circuit conditions

(b) Circuit with a short circuit   (c) Norton equivalent circuit

Figure 53 Circuit of Example 19.

Substituting resistance values and solving, we observe that $v_{oc} = 4.62$ V.

Next, we consider short-circuit conditions as shown in Figure 53(b). In this case, the current through R_2 and R_3 is zero. Thus, $v_x = 0$, and the controlled current source appears as an open circuit. The short-circuit current is given by

$$i_{sc} = \frac{v_s}{R_1} = \frac{15 \text{ V}}{20 \text{ } \Omega} = 0.75 \text{ A}$$

Now, we can find the Thévenin resistance:

$$R_t = \frac{v_{oc}}{i_{sc}} = \frac{4.62}{0.75} = 6.15 \text{ } \Omega$$

The Norton equivalent circuit is shown in Figure 53(c). ∎

Exercise 29 Find the Norton equivalent for each of the circuits shown in Figure 54.

Answer   **a.** $I_n = 1.67$ A, $R_t = 9.375$ Ω; **b.** $I_n = 2$ A, $R_t = 15$ Ω.   □

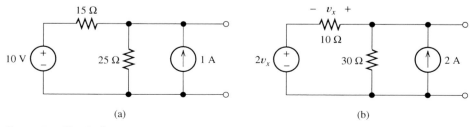

(a)   (b)

Figure 54 Circuits for Exercise 29.

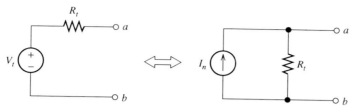

Figure 55 A voltage source in series with a resistance is externally equivalent to a current source in parallel with the resistance, provided that $I_n = V_t / R_t$.

Source Transformations

We can replace a voltage source in series with a resistance by a Norton equivalent circuit, which consists of a current source in parallel with the resistance. This is called a **source transformation** and is illustrated in Figure 55. The two circuits are identical in terms of their external behavior. In other words, the voltages and currents at terminals a and b remain the same after the transformation is made. However, in general, the current flowing through R_t is different for the two circuits. For example, suppose that the two circuits shown in Figure 55 are open circuited. Then no current flows through the resistor in series with the voltage source, but the current I_n flows through the resistance in parallel with the current source.

In making source transformations it is very important to maintain the proper relationship between the reference direction for the current source and the polarity of the voltage source. If the positive polarity is closest to terminal a, the current reference must point toward terminal a, as shown in Figure 55.

Sometimes, we can simplify the solution of a circuit by source transformations. This is similar to solving circuits by combining resistances in series or parallel. We illustrate with an example.

Here is a "trick" question that you might have some fun with: Suppose that the circuits of Figure 55 are placed in identical black boxes with the terminals accessible from outside the box. How could you determine which box contains the Norton equivalent? An answer can be found at the end of the chapter summary.

Example 20	Using Source Transformations

Use source transformations to aid in solving for the currents i_1 and i_2 shown in Figure 56(a).

Solution Several approaches are possible. One is to transform the 1-A current source and R_2 into a voltage source in series with R_2. This is shown in Figure 56(b). Notice that the positive polarity of the 10-V source is at the top, because the 1-A source reference points upward. The single-loop circuit of Figure 56(b) can be solved by writing a KVL equation. Traveling clockwise and summing voltages, we have

$$R_1 i_1 + R_2 i_1 + 10 - 20 = 0$$

Solving and substituting values, we get

$$i_1 = \frac{10}{R_1 + R_2} = 0.667 \text{ A}$$

Then in the original circuit, we can write a current equation at the top node and solve for i_2:

$$i_2 = i_1 + 1 = 1.667 \text{ A}$$

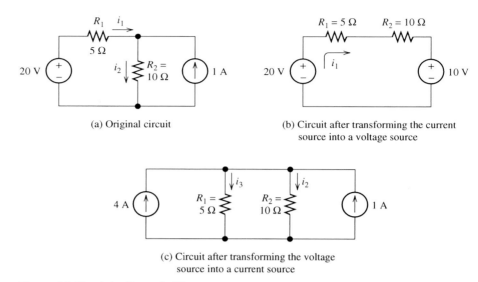

(a) Original circuit

(b) Circuit after transforming the current source into a voltage source

(c) Circuit after transforming the voltage source into a current source

Figure 56 Circuit for Example 20.

Another approach is to transform the voltage source and R_1 into a current source in parallel with R_1. Making this change to the original circuit yields the circuit shown in Figure 56(c). Notice that we have labeled the current through R_1 as i_3 rather than i_1. This is because the current in the resistance of the transformed source is not the same as in the original circuit. Now, in Figure 56(c), we see that a total current of 5 A flows into the parallel combination of R_1 and R_2. Using the current-division principle, we find the current through R_2:

$$i_2 = \frac{R_1}{R_1 + R_2} i_{\text{total}} = \frac{5}{5 + 10}(5) = 1.667 \text{ A}$$

This agrees with our previous result. ∎

Exercise 30 Use source transformations to solve for the values of i_1 and i_2 in Figure 57. First, transform the current source and R_1 into a voltage source in series with R_1. (Make sure in making the transformation that the polarity of the voltage source bears the correct relationship to the current reference direction.) Solve the circuit by a second approach. Starting with the original circuit, transform the 10-V source and R_2 into a current source in parallel with R_2. Of course, the answers should be the same for both approaches.
Answer $i_1 = -0.667 \text{ A}, i_2 = 1.333 \text{ A}$. □

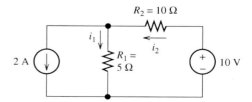

Figure 57 Circuit for Exercise 30.

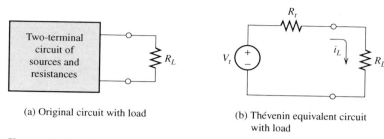

(a) Original circuit with load

(b) Thévenin equivalent circuit with load

Figure 58 Circuits for analysis of maximum power transfer.

Maximum Power Transfer

Suppose that we have a two-terminal circuit and we want to connect a load resistance R_L such that the maximum possible power is delivered to the load. This is illustrated in Figure 58(a). To analyze this problem, we replace the original circuit by its Thévenin equivalent as shown in Figure 58(b). The current flowing through the load resistance is given by

$$i_L = \frac{V_t}{R_t + R_L}$$

The power delivered to the load is

$$p_L = i_L^2 R_L$$

Substituting for the current, we have

$$p_L = \frac{V_t^2 R_L}{(R_t + R_L)^2} \tag{77}$$

To find the value of the load resistance that maximizes the power delivered to the load, we set the derivative of p_L with respect to R_L equal to zero:

$$\frac{dp_L}{dR_L} = \frac{V_t^2 (R_t + R_L)^2 - 2V_t^2 R_L (R_t + R_L)}{(R_t + R_L)^4} = 0$$

Solving for the load resistance, we have

$$R_L = R_t$$

Thus, the load resistance that absorbs the maximum power from a two-terminal circuit is equal to the Thévenin resistance. The maximum power is found by substituting $R_L = R_t$ into Equation 77. The result is

The load resistance that absorbs the maximum power from a two-terminal circuit is equal to the Thévenin resistance.

$$P_{L\,max} = \frac{V_t^2}{4R_t} \tag{78}$$

An All-Too-Common Example. You may have had difficulty in starting your car on a frigid morning. The battery in your car can be represented by a Thévenin equivalent circuit. It turns out that the Thévenin voltage of the battery does not change greatly with temperature. However, when the battery is very cold, the chemical reactions

Example 21 Determining Maximum Power Transfer

Find the load resistance for maximum power transfer from the circuit shown in Figure 59. Also, find the maximum power.

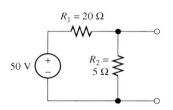

$R_1 = 20 \, \Omega$

$R_2 = 5 \, \Omega$

50 V

Figure 59 Circuit for Example 21.

Solution First, we must find the Thévenin equivalent circuit. Zeroing the voltage source, we find that the resistances R_1 and R_2 are in parallel. Thus, the Thévenin resistance is

$$R_t = \frac{1}{1/R_1 + 1/R_2} = \frac{1}{1/20 + 1/5} = 4 \, \Omega$$

The Thévenin voltage is equal to the open-circuit voltage. Using the voltage-division principle, we find that

$$V_t = v_{oc} = \frac{R_2}{R_1 + R_2}(50) = \frac{5}{5 + 20}(50) = 10 \, \text{V}$$

Hence, the load resistance that receives maximum power is

$$R_L = R_t = 4 \, \Omega$$

and the maximum power is given by Equation 78:

$$P_{L\max} = \frac{V_t^2}{4R_t} = \frac{10^2}{4 \times 4} = 6.25 \, \text{W}$$

■

Using Resistance to Measure Strain

Imagine pollution-free electric vehicles with exciting performance and 500-mile range. They do not exist, but they are the target of an ongoing large-scale engineering effort to which you may contribute. Such electric vehicles (EVs) are a worthwhile goal because they can be very efficient in their use of energy, particularly in stop-and-go traffic. Kinetic energy can be recovered during braking and saved for later use during acceleration. Furthermore, EVs emit little pollution into crowded urban environments.

So far, EV range and performance remains dismal. The availability of suitable energy-storage devices is the key stumbling block in achieving practical EVs (and a multitude of other highly desirable devices, such as laptop computers that do not need recharging for a week).

Capacitors and inductors are capabel of storing electrical energy. How-ever, it turns out that their energy content per unit volume is too small to make them a practical solution for EVs. The energy content of modern rechargeable batteries is better but still not on a par with the energy content of gasoline, which is approximately 10,000 watt-hours/liter (Wh/L). In contrast, the energy content of nickel-metal hydride batteries used in current EVs is about 175 Wh/L. Lithium-ion batteries under current development are expected to increase this to about 300 Wh/L. Thus, even allowing for the relative inefficiency of the internal combustion engine in converting chemical energy to mechanical energy, much more usable energy can be obtained from gasoline than from current batteries of comparable volume.

Although EVs do not emit pollutants at the point of use, the mining, refining, and disposal of metals pose grave environmental dangers. We must always consider the entire environmental (as well as economic) impact of the systems we design. As an engineer, you can do a great service to humanity by accepting the challenge to develop safe, clean systems for storing energy in forms that are readily converted to and from electrical form.

Naturally, one possibility currently under intense development is improved electrochemical batteries based on nontoxic chemicals. Another option is a mechanical flywheel system that would be coupled through an electrical generator to electric drive motors. Still another solution is a hybrid vehicle that uses a small internal combustion engine, an electrical generator, an energy-storage system, and electrical drive motors. The engine achieves low pollution levels by being optimized to run at a constant load while charging a relatively small energy-storage system. When the storage capacity becomes full, the engine shuts down automatically and the vehicle runs on stored energy. The engine is just large enough to keep up with energy demands under high-speed highway conditions.

Whatever form the ultimate solution to vehicle pollution may take, we can anticipate that it will include elements from mechanical, chemical, manufacturing, and civil engineering in close combination with electrical-engineering principles.

Application of Maximum Power Transfer. When a load resistance equals the internal Thévenin resistance of the source, half of the power is dissipated in the source resistance and half is delivered to the load. In higher power applications for which efficiency is important, we do not usually design for maximum power transfer. For example, in designing an electric vehicle, we would want to deliver the energy stored in the batteries mainly to the drive motors and minimize the power loss in the resistance of the battery and wiring. This system would approach maximum power transfer rarely when maximum acceleration is needed.

On the other hand, when small amounts of power are involved, we would design for maximum power transfer. For example, we would design a radio receiver to extract the maximum signal power from the receiving antenna. In this application, the power is very small, typically much less than one microwatt, and efficiency is not a consideration.

7 SUPERPOSITION PRINCIPLE

Suppose that we have a circuit composed of resistances, linear dependent sources, and n independent sources. (We will explain the term *linear* dependent source shortly.) The current flowing through a given element (or the voltage across it) is called a **response**, because the currents and voltages appear in response to the independent sources.

Recall that we zeroed the independent sources as a method for finding the Thévenin resistance of a two-terminal circuit. To zero a source, we reduce its value to zero. Then, current sources become open circuits, and voltage sources become short circuits.

Now, consider zeroing all of the independent sources except the first, observe a particular response (a current or voltage), and denote the value of that response as r_1. (We use the symbol r rather than i or v because the response could be either a current or a voltage.) Similarly, with only source 2 activated, the response is denoted as r_2, and so on. The response with all the sources activated is called the total response, denoted as r_T. The **superposition principle** states that the total response is the sum of the responses to each of the independent sources acting individually. In equation

The superposition principle states that any response in a linear circuit is the sum of the responses for each independent source acting alone with the other independent sources zeroed. When zeroed, current sources become open circuits and voltage sources become short circuits.

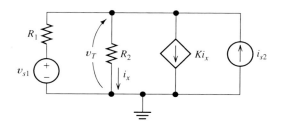

Figure 60 Circuit used to illustrate the superposition principle.

form, this is

$$r_T = r_1 + r_2 + \cdots + r_n \tag{79}$$

Next, we illustrate the validity of superposition for the example circuit shown in Figure 60. In this circuit, there are two independent sources: the first, the voltage source v_{s1}, and the second, the current source i_{s2}. Suppose that the response of interest is the voltage across the resistance R_2.

First, we solve for the total response v_T by solving the circuit with both sources in place. Writing a current equation at the top node, we obtain

$$\frac{v_T - v_{s1}}{R_1} + \frac{v_T}{R_2} + Ki_x = i_{s2} \tag{80}$$

The control variable i_x is given by

$$i_x = \frac{v_T}{R_2} \tag{81}$$

Substituting Equation 81 into Equation 80 and solving for the total response, we get

$$v_T = \frac{R_2}{R_1 + R_2 + KR_1}v_{s1} + \frac{R_1 R_2}{R_1 + R_2 + KR_1}i_{s2} \tag{82}$$

If we set i_{s2} to zero, we obtain the response to v_{s1} acting alone:

$$v_1 = \frac{R_2}{R_1 + R_2 + KR_1}v_{s1} \tag{83}$$

Similarly, if we set v_{s1} equal to zero in Equation 82, the response due to i_{s2} is given by

$$v_2 = \frac{R_1 R_2}{R_1 + R_2 + KR_1}i_{s2} \tag{84}$$

Comparing Equations 82, 83, and 84, we see that

$$v_T = v_1 + v_2$$

Thus, as expected from the superposition principle, the total response is equal to the sum of the responses for each of the independent sources acting individually.

Notice that if we zero both of the independent sources ($v_{s1} = 0$ and $i_{s2} = 0$), the response becomes zero. Hence, the dependent source does not contribute to the total response. However, the dependent source affects the contributions of the two independent sources. This is evident because the gain parameter K of the dependent source appears in the expressions for both v_1 and v_2. *In general, dependent sources do not contribute a separate term to the total response, and we must not zero dependent sources in applying superposition.*

Dependent sources do not contribute a separate term to the total response, and we must not zero dependent sources in applying superposition.

Linearity

If we plot voltage versus current for a resistance, we have a straight line. This is illustrated in Figure 61. Thus, we say that Ohm's law is a **linear equation**. Similarly, the current in the controlled source shown in Figure 60 is given by $i_{cs} = Ki_x$, which is also a linear equation. In this text, the term **linear controlled source** means a source whose value is a constant times a control variable that is a current or a voltage appearing in the network.

Some examples of nonlinear equations are

$$v = 10i^2$$

$$i_{cs} = K \cos(i_x)$$

and

$$i = e^v$$

The superposition principle does not apply to any circuit that has element(s) described by nonlinear equation(s). We will encounter nonlinear elements later in our study of electronic circuits.

Furthermore, superposition does not apply for power in resistances, because $P = v^2/R$ and $P = i^2R$ are nonlinear equations.

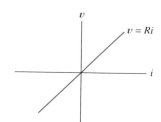

Figure 61 A resistance that obeys Ohm's law is linear.

The superposition principle does not apply to any circuit that has element(s) described by nonlinear equation(s).

Using Superposition to Solve Circuits

We can apply superposition in circuit analysis by analyzing the circuit for each source separately. Then, we add the individual responses to find the total response. Sometimes, the analysis of a circuit is simplified by considering each independent source separately. We illustrate with an example.

Example 22	Circuit Analysis Using Superposition

Use superposition in solving the circuit shown in Figure 62(a) for the voltage v_T.

Solution We analyze the circuit with only one source activated at a time and add the responses. Figure 62(b) shows the circuit with only the voltage source active. The response can be found by applying the voltage-division principle:

$$v_1 = \frac{R_2}{R_1 + R_2} v_s = \frac{5}{5 + 10}(15) = 5 \text{ V}$$

Next, we analyze the circuit with only the current source active. The circuit is shown in Figure 62(c). In this case, the resistances R_1 and R_2 are in parallel, and the equivalent resistance is

$$R_{eq} = \frac{1}{1/R_1 + 1/R_2} = \frac{1}{1/10 + 1/5} = 3.33 \ \Omega$$

The voltage due to the current source is given by

$$v_2 = i_s R_{eq} = 2 \times 3.33 = 6.66 \text{ V}$$

Finally, we obtain the total response by adding the individual responses:

$$v_T = v_1 + v_2 = 5 + 6.66 = 11.66$$

■

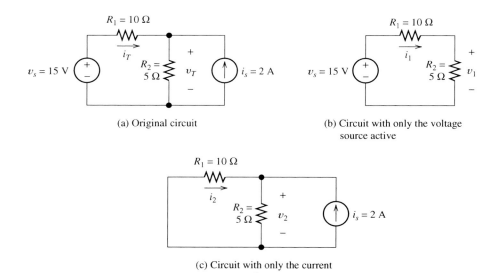

(a) Original circuit

(b) Circuit with only the voltage source active

(c) Circuit with only the current source active

Figure 62   Circuit for Example 22 and Exercise 31.

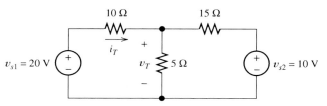

Figure 63   Circuit for Exercise 32.

Exercise 31   Find the responses i_1, i_2, and i_T for the circuit of Figure 62.
Answer $i_1 = 1$ A, $i_2 = -0.667$ A, $i_T = 0.333$ A.   □

Exercise 32   Use superposition to find the responses v_T and i_T for the circuit shown in Figure 63.
Answer $v_1 = 5.45$ V, $v_2 = 1.82$ V, $v_T = 7.27$ V, $i_1 = 1.45$ A, $i_2 = -0.181$ A, $i_T = 1.27$ A.   □

8 WHEATSTONE BRIDGE

The **Wheatstone bridge** is a circuit used to measure unknown resistances. For example, it is used by mechanical and civil engineers to measure the resistances of strain gauges in experimental stress studies of machines and buildings. The circuit is shown in Figure 64. The circuit consists of a dc voltage source v_s, a detector, the unknown resistance to be measured R_x, and three precision resistors, R_1, R_2, and R_3. Usually, R_2 and R_3 are adjustable resistances, which is indicated in the figure by the arrow drawn through the resistance symbols.

The detector is capable of responding to very small currents (less than one microampere). However, it is not necessary for the detector to be calibrated. It is only necessary for the detector to indicate whether or not current is flowing through

The Wheatstone bridge is used by mechanical and civil engineers to measure the resistances of strain gauges in experimental stress studies of machines and buildings.

106

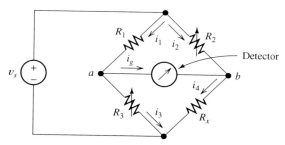

Figure 64 The Wheatstone bridge. When the Wheatstone bridge is balanced, $i_g = 0$ and $v_{ab} = 0$.

it. Often, the detector is a d'Arsonval galvanometer, which has a pointer that deflects one way or the other, depending on the direction of the current through it.

In operation, the resistors R_2 and R_3 are adjusted in value until the detector indicates zero current. In this condition, we say that the bridge is **balanced**. Then, the current i_g and the voltage across the detector v_{ab} are zero.

Applying KCL at node a (Figure 64) and using the fact that $i_g = 0$, we have

$$i_1 = i_3 \qquad (85)$$

Similarly, at node b, we get

$$i_2 = i_4 \qquad (86)$$

Writing a KVL equation around the loop formed by R_1, R_2, and the detector, we obtain

$$R_1 i_1 + v_{ab} = R_2 i_2 \qquad (87)$$

However, when the bridge is balanced, $v_{ab} = 0$, so that

$$R_1 i_1 = R_2 i_2 \qquad (88)$$

Similarly, for the loop consisting of R_3, R_4, and the detector, we have

$$R_3 i_3 = R_x i_4 \qquad (89)$$

Using Equations 85 and 86 to substitute into Equation 89, we obtain

$$R_3 i_1 = R_x i_2 \qquad (90)$$

Dividing each side of Equation 90 by the respective sides of Equation 88, we find that

$$\frac{R_3}{R_1} = \frac{R_x}{R_2}$$

Finally, solving for the unknown resistance, we have

$$R_x = \frac{R_2}{R_1} R_3 \qquad (91)$$

Often, in commercial bridges, a multiposition switch selects an order-of-magnitude scale factor R_2/R_1 by changing the value of R_2. Then, R_3 is adjusted by means of calibrated switches until balance is achieved. Finally, the unknown resistance R_x is the scale factor times the value of R_3.

Example 23   Using a Wheatstone Bridge to Measure Resistance

In a certain commercial Wheatstone bridge, R_1 is a fixed 1-kΩ resistor, R_3 can be adjusted in 1-Ω steps from 0 to 1100 Ω, and R_2 can be selected to be 1 kΩ, 10 kΩ, 100 kΩ, or 1 MΩ. **a.** Suppose that the bridge is balanced with $R_3 = 732$ Ω and $R_2 = 10$ kΩ. What is the value of R_x? **b.** What is the largest value of R_x for which the bridge can be balanced? **c.** Suppose that $R_2 = 1$ MΩ. What is the increment between values of R_x for which the bridge can be precisely balanced?

Solution

1. From Equation 91, we have

$$R_x = \frac{R_2}{R_1}R_3 = \frac{10 \text{ k}\Omega}{1 \text{ k}\Omega} \times 732 \ \Omega = 7320 \ \Omega$$

Notice that R_2/R_1 is a scale factor that can be set at 1, 10, 100, or 1000, depending on the value selected for R_2. The unknown resistance is the scale factor times the value of R_3 needed to balance the bridge.

2. The maximum resistance for which the bridge can be balanced is determined by the largest values available for R_2 and R_3. Thus,

$$R_{x\,\text{max}} = \frac{R_{2\,\text{max}}}{R_1}R_{3\,\text{max}} = \frac{1 \text{ M}\Omega}{1 \text{ k}\Omega} \times 1100 \ \Omega = 1.1 \text{ M}\Omega$$

3. The increment between values of R_x for which the bridge can be precisely balanced is the scale factor times the increment in R_3:

$$R_{x\text{inc}} = \frac{R_2}{R_1}R_{3\text{inc}} = \frac{1 \text{ M}\Omega}{1 \text{ k}\Omega} \times 1 \ \Omega = 1 \text{ k}\Omega \qquad \blacksquare$$

Summary

1. Series resistances have an equivalent resistance equal to their sum. For n resistances in series, we have

$$R_{\text{eq}} = R_1 + R_2 + \cdots + R_n$$

2. Parallel resistances have an equivalent resistance equal to the reciprocal of the sum of their reciprocals. For n resistances in parallel, we get

$$R_{\text{eq}} = \frac{1}{1/R_1 + 1/R_2 + \cdots + 1/R_n}$$

3. Some resistive networks can be solved by repeatedly combining resistances in series or parallel. The simplified network is solved, and results are transferred back through the chain of equivalent circuits. Eventually, the currents and voltages of interest in the original circuit are found.

4. The voltage-division principle applies when a voltage is applied to several resistances in series. A fraction of the total voltage appears across each resistance. The fraction that appears across a given resistance is the ratio of the given resistance to the total series resistance.

5. The current-division principle applies when current flows through two resistances in parallel. A fraction of the total current flows through each resistance. The fraction of the total current flowing through R_1 is equal to $R_2/(R_1 + R_2)$.

6. The node-voltage method can be used to solve for the voltages in any resistive network. A step-by-step summary of the method is given in this chapter.

7. A step-by-step procedure to write the node-voltage equations directly in matrix form for circuits consisting of resistances and independent current sources appears in this chapter.

8. The mesh-current method can be used to solve for the currents in any planar resistive network. A step-by-step summary of the method is given in this chapter.

9. A step-by-step procedure to write the mesh-current equations directly in matrix form for circuits consisting of resistances and independent voltage sources appears in this chapter. For this method to apply, all of the mesh currents must flow in the clockwise direction.

10. A two-terminal network of resistances and sources has a Thévenin equivalent that consists of a voltage source in series with a resistance. The Thévenin voltage is equal to the open-circuit voltage of the original network. The Thévenin resistance is the open-circuit voltage divided by the short-circuit current of the original network. Sometimes, the Thévenin resistance can be found by zeroing the independent sources in the original network and combining resistances in series

and parallel. When independent voltage sources are zeroed, they are replaced by short circuits. Independent current sources are replaced by open circuits. Dependent sources must not be zeroed.

11. A two-terminal network of resistances and sources has a Norton equivalent that consists of a current source in parallel with a resistance. The Norton current is equal to the short-circuit current of the original network. The Norton resistance is the same as the Thévenin resistance. A step-by-step procedure for determining Thévenin and Norton equivalent circuits is given in this chapter.

12. Sometimes source transformations (i.e., replacing a Thévenin equivalent with a Norton equivalent or vice versa) are useful in solving networks.

13. For maximum power from a two-terminal network, the load resistance should equal the Thévenin resistance.

14. The superposition principle states that the total response in a resistive circuit is the sum of the responses to each of the independent sources acting individually. The superposition principle does not apply to any circuit that has element(s) described by nonlinear equation(s).

15. The Wheatstone bridge is a circuit used to measure unknown resistances. The circuit consists of a voltage source, a detector, three precision calibrated resistors, of which two are adjustable, and the unknown resistance. The resistors are adjusted until the bridge is balanced, and then the unknown resistance is given in terms of the three known resistances.

Here's the answer to the trick question using Figure 55: Suppose that we open circuit the terminals. Then, no current flows through the Thévenin equivalent, but a current I_n circulates in the Norton equivalent. Thus, the box containing the Norton equivalent will become warm because of power dissipation in the resistance. The point of this question is that the circuits are equivalent in terms of their terminal voltage and current, not in terms of their internal behavior.

Note: **You can check the answers to many of the problems in this chapter by using a computer-aided circuit-analysis program such as Multisim from National Instruments or OrCAD Capture from Cadence Inc.**

Problems

Section 1: Resistances in Series and Parallel

*P1.   Reduce each of the networks shown in Figure P1 to a single equivalent resistance by combining resistances in series and parallel.

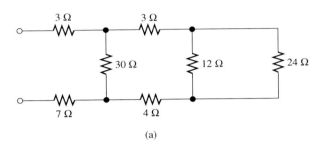

(a)

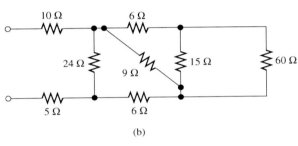

(b)

Figure P1

*P2.   A 4-Ω resistance is in series with the parallel combination of a 20-Ω resistance and an unknown resistance R_x. The equivalent resistance for the network is 8 Ω. Determine the value of R_x.

*P3.   Find the equivalent resistance looking into terminals a and b in Figure P3.

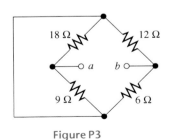

Figure P3

*P4.   Suppose that we need a resistance of 1.5 kΩ and you have a box of 1-kΩ resistors. Devise a network of 1-kΩ resistors so the equivalent resistance is 1.5 kΩ. Repeat for an equivalent resistance of 2.2 kΩ.

*P5.   Find the equivalent resistance between terminals a and b in Figure P5.

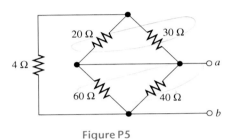

Figure P5

P6.   Find the equivalent resistance between terminals a and b for each of the networks shown in Figure P6.

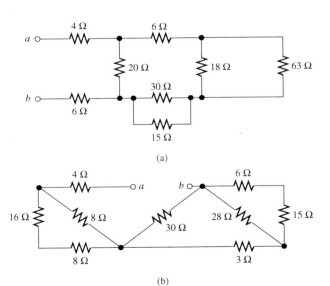

Figure P6

---

*   Denotes that answers are contained in the Student Solutions files.

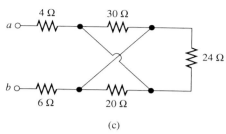

4 Ω   30 Ω
a o—WW——•——WW——•
                        24 Ω
b o—WW——•——WW——•
6 Ω   20 Ω

(c)

Figure P6 (*Cont.*)

P7. What resistance in parallel with 120 Ω results in an equivalent resistance of 48 Ω?

P8. **a.** Determine the resistance between terminals a and b for the network shown in Figure P8. **b.** Repeat after connecting c and d with a short circuit.

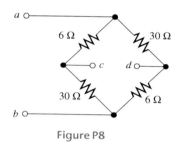

a o

6 Ω   30 Ω

o c   d o

30 Ω   6 Ω

b o

Figure P8

P9. Two resistances having values of R and $2R$ are in parallel. R and the equivalent resistance are both integers. What are the possible values for R?

P10. A network connected between terminals a and b consists of two parallel combinations that are in series. The first parallel combination is composed of a 16-Ω resistor and a 48-Ω resistor. The second parallel combination is composed of a 12-Ω resistor and a 24-Ω resistor. Draw the network and determine its equivalent resistance.

P11. Two resistances R_1 and R_2 are connected in parallel. We know that $R_1 = 90\,\Omega$ and that the current through R_2 is three times the value of the current through R_1. Determine the value of R_2.

P12. Find the equivalent resistance for the infinite network shown in Figure P12(a). Because of its form, this network is called a semi-infinite ladder. (*Hint:* If another

section is added to the ladder as shown in Figure P12(b), the equivalent resistance is the same. Thus, working from Figure P12(b), we can write an expression for R_{eq} in terms of R_{eq}. Then, we can solve for R_{eq}.)

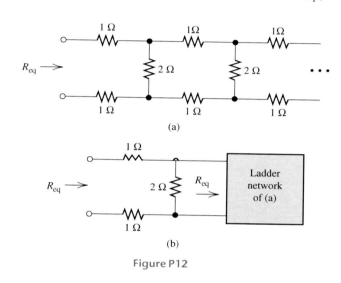

(a)

(b)

Figure P12

P13. If we connect n 1000-Ω resistances in parallel, what value is the equivalent resistance?

P14. The heating element of an electric cook top has two resistive elements, $R_1 = 57.6\,\Omega$ and $R_2 = 115.2\,\Omega$, that can be operated separately, in series, or in parallel from voltages of either 120 V or 240 V. For the lowest power, R_1 is in series with R_2, and the combination is operated from 120 V. What is the lowest power? For the highest power, how should the elements be operated? What power results? List three more modes of operation and the resulting power for each.

P15. We are designing an electric space heater to operate from 120 V. Two heating elements with resistances R_1 and R_2 are to be used that can be operated in parallel, separately, or in series. The highest power is to be 1280 W, and the lowest power is to be 240 W. What values are needed for R_1 and R_2? What intermediate power settings are available?

P16. Sometimes, we can use symmetry considerations to find the resistance of a circuit that cannot be reduced by series or parallel combinations. A classic problem of this type is illustrated in Figure P16. Twelve

1-Ω resistors are arranged on the edges of a cube, and terminals *a* and *b* are connected to diagonally opposite corners of the cube. The problem is to find the resistance between the terminals. Approach the problem this way: Assume that 1 A of current enters terminal *a* and exits through terminal *b*. Then, the voltage between terminals *a* and *b* is equal to the unknown resistance. By symmetry considerations, we can find the current in each resistor. Then, using KVL, we can find the voltage between *a* and *b*.

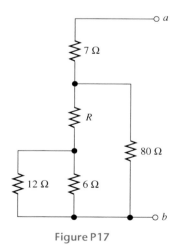

Figure P16 Each resistor has a value of 1 Ω.

P17. The equivalent resistance between terminals *a* and *b* in Figure P17 is $R_{ab} = 23$ Ω. Determine the value of *R*.

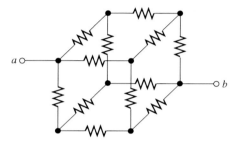

Figure P17

P18. **a.** Three conductances $G_1, G_2,$ and G_3 are in series. Write an expression for the equivalent conductance $G_{eq} = 1/R_{eq}$ in terms of $G_1, G_2,$ and G_3. **b.** Repeat part (a) with the conductances in parallel.

P19. Most sources of electrical power behave as (approximately) ideal voltage sources. In this case, if we have several loads that we want to operate independently, we place the loads in parallel with a switch in series with each load. Thereupon, we can switch each load on or off without affecting the power delivered to the other loads.

How would we connect the loads and switches if the source is an ideal independent current source? Draw the diagram of the current source and three loads with on–off switches such that each load can be switched on or off without affecting the power supplied to the other loads. To turn a load off, should the corresponding switch be opened or closed? Explain.

P20. The resistance for the network shown in Figure P20 between terminals *a* and *b* with *c* open circuited is $R_{ab} = 50$ Ω. Similarly, the resistance between terminals *b* and *c* with *a* open is $R_{bc} = 100$ Ω, and between *c* and *a* with *b* open is $R_{ca} = 70$ Ω. Now, suppose that a short circuit is connected from terminal *b* to terminal *c*, and determine the resistance between terminal *a* and the shorted terminals *b–c*.

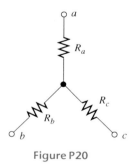

Figure P20

P21. Often, we encounter delta-connected loads, such as that illustrated in Figure P21, in three-phase power distribution system. If we only have access to the three terminals, a method for determining the resistances is to repeatedly short two terminals together and measure the resistance between the shorted terminals and the third terminal. Then, the resistances can be calculated from the three measurements. Suppose that the measurements are $R_{as} = 12\ \Omega$, $R_{bs} = 20\ \Omega$, and $R_{cs} = 15\ \Omega$. Where R_{as} is the resistance between terminal a and the short between b and c, etc. Determine the values of R_a, R_b, and R_c. (*Hint:* You may find the equations easier to deal with if you work in terms of conductances rather than resistances. Once the conductances are known, you can easily invert their values to find the resistances.)

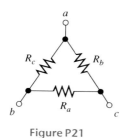

Figure P21

Section 2: Network Analysis by Using Series and Parallel Equivalents

P22. What are the steps in solving a circuit by network reduction (series/parallel combinations)? Does this method always provide the solution? Explain.

*P23. Find the values of i_1 and i_2 in Figure P23.

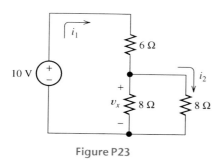

Figure P23

*P24. Find the voltages v_1 and v_2 for the circuit shown in Figure P24 by combining resistances in series and parallel.

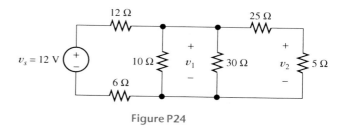

Figure P24

*P25. Find the values of v and i in Figure P25.

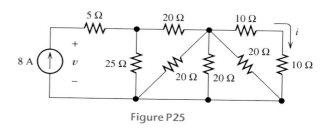

Figure P25

P26. Consider the circuit shown in Figure P24. Suppose that the value of v_s is adjusted until $v_2 = 5\,\text{V}$. Determine the new value of v_s. (*Hint:* Start at the right-hand side of the circuit and compute currents and voltages, moving to the left until you reach the source.)

P27. Find the voltage v and the currents i_1 and i_2 for the circuit shown in Figure P27.

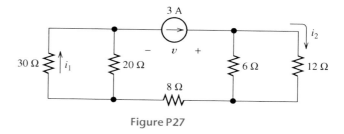

Figure P27

P28. Find the values of v_s, v_1, and i_2 in Figure P28.

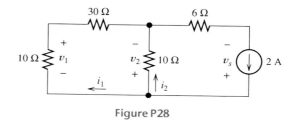

Figure P28

P29. Find the values of i_1 and i_2 in Figure P29.

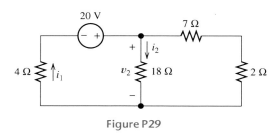

Figure P29

P30. Consider the circuit shown in Figure P30. Find the values of v_1, v_2, and v_{ab}.

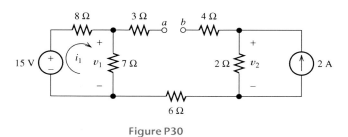

Figure P30

P31. Solve for the values of i_1, i_2, and the powers for the sources in Figure P31. Is the current source absorbing energy or delivering energy? Is the voltage source absorbing energy or delivering it?

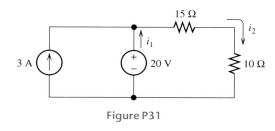

Figure P31

P32. The 12-V source in Figure P32 is delivering 36 mW of power. All four resistors have the same value R. Find the value of R.

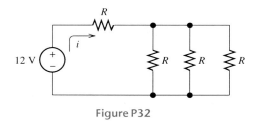

Figure P32

P33. Refer to the circuit shown in Figure P33. With the switch open, we have $v_2 = 8\,\text{V}$. On the other hand, with the switch closed, we have $v_2 = 6\,\text{V}$. Determine the values of R_2 and R_L.

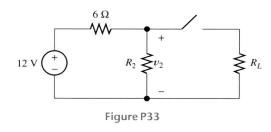

Figure P33

*P34. Find the values of i_1 and i_2 in Figure P34. Find the power for each element in the circuit, and state whether each is absorbing or delivering energy. Verify that the total power absorbed equals the total power delivered.

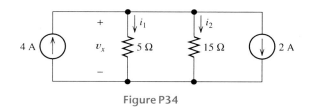

Figure P34

*P35. Find the values of i_1 and i_2 in Figure P35.

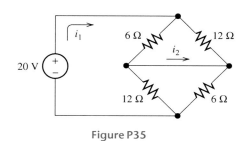

Figure P35

Section 3: Voltage-Divider and Current-Divider Circuits

*P36. Use the voltage-division principle to calculate v_1, v_2, and v_3 in Figure P36.

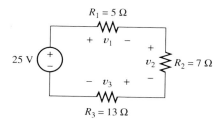

Figure P36

*P37. Use the current-division principle to calculate i_1 and i_2 in Figure P37.

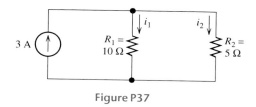

Figure P37

*P38. Use the voltage-division principle to calculate v in Figure P38.

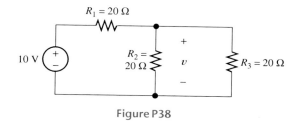

Figure P38

P39. Use the current-division principle to calculate the value of i_3 in Figure P39.

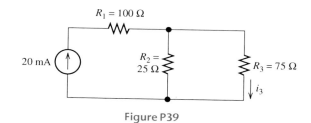

Figure P39

P40. Suppose we need to design a voltage-divider circuit to provide an output voltage $v_o = 5\,\text{V}$ from a 15-V source as shown in Figure P40. The current taken from the 15-V source is to be 200 mA. **a.** Find the values of R_1 and R_2. **b.** Now suppose that a load resistance of 200 Ω is connected across the output terminals (i.e., in parallel with R_2). Find the value of v_o.

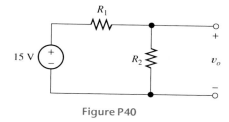

Figure P40

P41. A source supplies 120 V to the series combination of a 10-Ω resistance, a 5-Ω resistance, and an unknown resistance R_x. The voltage across the 5-Ω resistance is 20 V. Determine the value of the unknown resistance.

P42. We have a 60-Ω resistance, a 20-Ω resistance, and an unknown resistance R_x in parallel with a 15 mA current source. The current through the unknown resistance is 10 mA. Determine the value of R_x.

*P43. A worker is standing on a wet concrete floor, holding an electric drill having a metallic case. The metallic case is connected through the ground wire of a three-terminal power outlet to power-system ground. The resistance of the ground wire is R_g. The resistance of the worker's body is $R_w = 500\,\Omega$. Due to faulty insulation in the drill, a current of 2 A flows into its metallic case. The circuit diagram for this situation is shown in Figure P43. Find the maximum value of R_g so that the current through the worker does not exceed 0.1 mA.

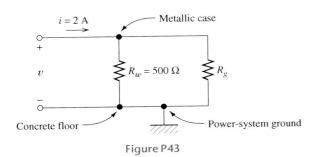

Figure P43

P44. Suppose we have a load that absorbs power and requires a current varying between 0 and 50 mA. The voltage across the load must remain between 4.7 and 5.0 V. A 15-V source is available. Design a voltage-divider network to supply the load. You may assume that resistors of any value desired are available. Also, give the minimum power rating for each resistor.

P45. We have a load resistance of $50\,\Omega$ that we wish to supply with 5 V. A 12.6-V voltage source and resistors of any value needed are available. Draw a suitable circuit consisting of the voltage source, the load, and one additional resistor. Specify the value of the resistor.

P46. We have a load resistance of $1\,\text{k}\Omega$ that we wish to supply with 25 mW. A 20-mA current source and resistors of any value needed are available. Draw a suitable circuit consisting of the current source, the load, and one additional resistor. Specify the value of the resistor.

P47. The circuit of Figure P47 is similar to networks used in digital-to-analog converters. For this problem, assume that the circuit continues indefinitely to the right. Find the values of i_1, i_2, i_3, and i_4. How is i_{n+2} related to i_n? What is the value of i_{18}? (*Hint:* See Problem P12.)

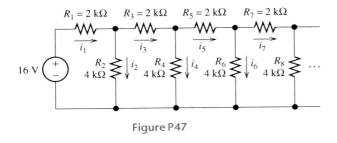

Figure P47

Section 4: Node-Voltage Analysis

*P48. Write equations and solve for the node voltages shown in Figure P48. Then, find the value of i_1.

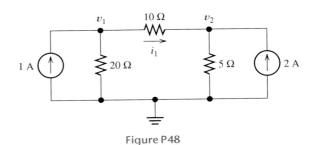

Figure P48

*P49. Solve for the node voltages shown in Figure P49. Then, find the value of i_s.

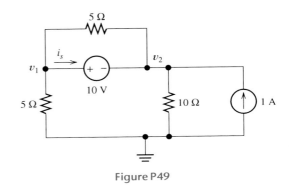

Figure P49

P50. Solve for the node voltages shown in Figure P50. What are the new values of the node voltages after the direction of the current source is reversed? How are the values related?

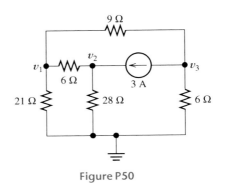

Figure P50

P51. Given $R_1 = 4\,\Omega$, $R_2 = 5\,\Omega$, $R_3 = 8\,\Omega$, $R_4 = 10\,\Omega$, $R_5 = 2\,\Omega$, and $I_s = 2\,\text{A}$, solve for the node voltages shown in Figure P51.

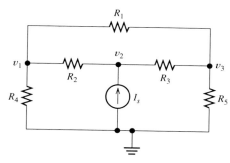

Figure P51

P52. Determine the value of i_1 in Figure P52 using node voltages to solve the circuit. Select the location of the reference node to minimize the number of unknown node voltages. What effect does the 20-Ω resistance have on the answer? Explain.

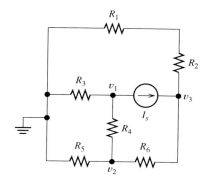

Figure P52

P53. Given $R_1 = 15\,\Omega$, $R_2 = 5\,\Omega$, $R_3 = 20\,\Omega$, $R_4 = 10\,\Omega$, $R_5 = 8\,\Omega$, $R_6 = 4\,\Omega$, and $I_s = 5\,\text{A}$, solve for the node voltages shown in Figure P53.

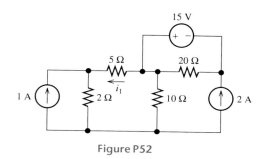

Figure P53

P54. In solving a network, what rule must you observe when writing KCL equations? Why?

P55. Use the symbolic features of MATLAB to find an expression for the equivalent resistance for the network shown in Figure P55. (*Hint:* First, connect a 1-A current source across terminals a and b. Then, solve the network by the node-voltage technique. The voltage across the current source is equal in value to the equivalent resistance.) Finally, use the subs command to evaluate for $R_1 = 15\,\Omega$, $R_2 = 5\,\Omega$, $R_3 = 20\,\Omega$, $R_4 = 10\,\Omega$, and $R_5 = 8\,\Omega$.

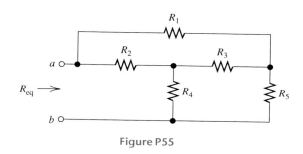

Figure P55

*P56. Solve for the values of the node voltages shown in Figure P56. Then, find the value of i_x.

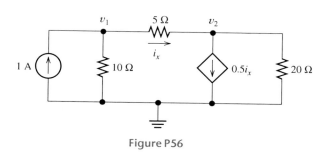

Figure P56

*P57. Solve for the node voltages shown in Figure P57.

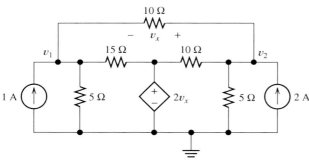

Figure P57

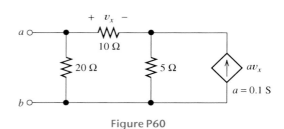

solve the network by the node-voltage technique. The voltage across the current source is equal in value to the equivalent resistance.)

Figure P60

P58. Solve for the power delivered to the 16-Ω resistance and for the node voltages shown in Figure P58.

P61. Find the equivalent resistance looking into terminals *a–b* for the network shown in Figure P61. (*Hint:* First, connect a 1-A current source across terminals *a* and *b*. Then, solve the network by the node-voltage technique. The voltage across the current source is equal in value to the equivalent resistance.)

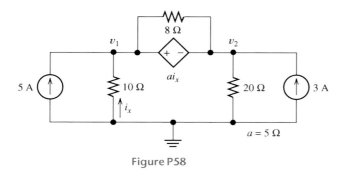

Figure P58

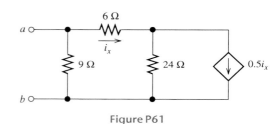

Figure P61

P59. Solve for the node voltages shown in Figure P59.

P62. Figure P62 shows an unusual voltage-divider circuit. Use node-voltage analysis and the symbolic math commands in MATLAB to solve for the voltage division ratio V_{out}/V_{in} in terms of the resistances. Notice that the node-voltage variables are V_1, V_2, and V_{out}.

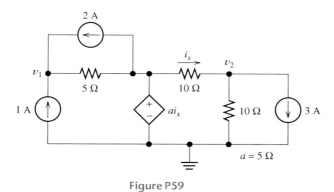

Figure P59

P60. Find the equivalent resistance looking into terminals *a–b* for the network shown in Figure P60. (*Hint:* First, connect a 1-A current source across terminals *a* and *b*. Then,

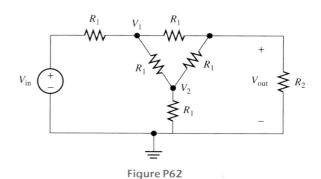

Figure P62

P63. Solve for the node voltages in the circuit of Figure P63. Disregard the mesh currents, i_1, i_2, i_3, and i_4 when working with the node voltages.

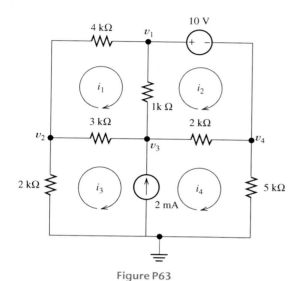

Figure P63

the currents and voltages. With the shorts in place, the resistances can be combined in series and parallel to obtain the answers. Of course, if the resistors have arbitrary values, the MATLAB approach will still work, but considerations of symmetry will not.)

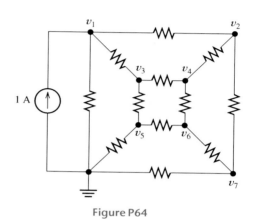

Figure P64

P64. We have a cube with 1-Ω resistances along each edge as illustrated in Figure P64 in which we are looking into the front face which has corners at nodes 1, 2, 7, and the reference node. Nodes 3, 4, 5, and 6 are the corners on the rear face of the cube. (Alternatively, you can consider it to be a planar network.) We want to find the resistance between adjacent nodes, such as node 1 and the reference node. We do this by connecting a 1-A current source as shown and solving for v_1, which is equal in value to the resistance between any two adjacent nodes. **a.** Use MATLAB to solve the matrix equation $\mathbf{GV} = \mathbf{I}$ for the node voltages and determine the resistance. **b.** Modify your work to determine the resistance between nodes at the ends of a diagonal across a face, such as node 2 and the reference node. **c.** Finally, find the resistance between opposite corners of the cube. (*Comment:* Part (c) is the same as Problem 16 in which we suggested using symmetry to solve for the resistance. Parts (a) and (b) can also be solved by use of symmetry and the fact that nodes having the same value of voltage can be connected by short circuits without changing

Section 5: Mesh-Current Analysis

*P65.** Solve for the power delivered to the 15-Ω resistor and for the mesh currents shown in Figure P65.

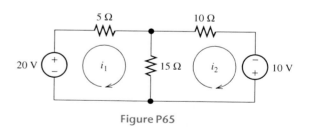

Figure P65

*P66.** Determine the value of v_2 and the power delivered by the source in the circuit of Figure P24 by using mesh-current analysis.

*P67.** Use mesh-current analysis to find the value of i_1 in the circuit of Figure P48.

P68. Solve for the power delivered by the voltage source in Figure P68, using the mesh-current method.

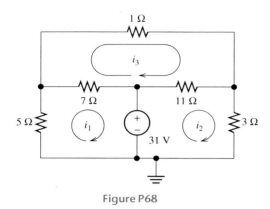

Figure P68

analysis to determine the voltage magnitude
for each load and the current in the neutral
wire. **b.** Now suppose that due to a fault in the
wiring at the distribution panel, the neutral
wire becomes an open circuit. Again compute
the voltages across the loads and comment on
the probable outcome for a sensitive device
such as a computer or plasma television that
is part of the 15-Ω load

P69. Use mesh-current analysis to find the value of v in the circuit of Figure P38.

P70. Use mesh-current analysis to find the value of i_3 in the circuit of Figure P39.

P71. Use mesh-current analysis to find the values of i_1 and i_2 in Figure P27. Select i_1 clockwise around the left-hand mesh, i_2 clockwise around the right-hand mesh, and i_3 clockwise around the center mesh.

P72. Find the power delivered by the source and the values of i_1 and i_2 in the circuit of Figure P23, using mesh-current analysis.

P73. Use mesh-current analysis to find the values of i_1 and i_2 in Figure P29. First, select i_A clockwise around the left-hand mesh and i_B clockwise around the right-hand mesh. After solving for the mesh currents, i_A and i_B, determine the values of i_1 and i_2.

P74. Use mesh-current analysis to find the values of i_1 and i_2 in Figure P28. First, select i_A clockwise around the left-hand mesh and i_B clockwise around the right-hand mesh. After solving for the mesh currents, i_A and i_B, determine the values of i_1 and i_2.

P75. The circuit shown in Figure P75 is the dc equivalent of a simple residential power distribution system. Each of the resistances labeled R_1 and R_2 represent various parallel-connected loads, such as lights or devices plugged into outlets that nominally operate at 120 V, while R_3 represents a load, such as the heating element in an oven that nominally operates at 240 V. The resistances labeled R_w represent the resistances of wires. R_n represents the "neutral" wire. **a.** Use mesh-current

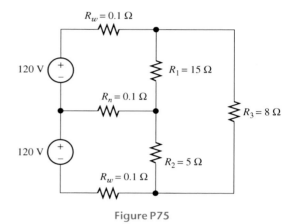

Figure P75

P76. Use MATLAB and mesh-current analysis to determine the value of v_3 in the circuit of Figure P51. The component values are $R_1 = 4\,\Omega$, $R_2 = 5\,\Omega$, $R_3 = 8\,\Omega$, $R_4 = 10\,\Omega$, $R_5 = 2\,\Omega$, and $I_s = 2\,A$.

P77. Connect a 1-V voltage source across terminals a and b of the network shown in Figure P55. Then, solve the network by the mesh-current technique to find the current through the source. Finally, divide the source voltage by the current to determine the equivalent resistance looking into terminals a and b. The resistance values are $R_1 = 6\,\Omega$, $R_2 = 5\,\Omega$, $R_3 = 4\,\Omega$, $R_4 = 8\,\Omega$, and $R_5 = 2\,\Omega$.

P78. Connect a 1-V voltage source across the terminals of the network shown in Figure P1(a). Then, solve the network by the mesh-current technique to find the current through the source. Finally, divide the source voltage by the current to determine the equivalent resistance looking into the terminals. Check your answer by combining resistances in series and parallel.

P79. Use MATLAB to solve for the mesh currents in Figure P63.

Section 6: Thévenin and Norton Equivalent Circuits

*P80. Find the Thévenin and Norton equivalent circuits for the two-terminal circuit shown in Figure P80.

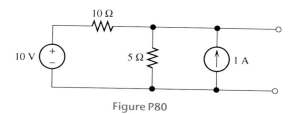

Figure P80

*P81. We can model a certain battery as a voltage source in series with a resistance. The open-circuit voltage of the battery is 9 V. When a 100-Ω resistor is placed across the terminals of the battery, the voltage drops to 6 V. Determine the internal resistance (Thévenin resistance) of the battery.

P82. Find the Thévenin and Norton equivalent circuits for the circuit shown in Figure P82.

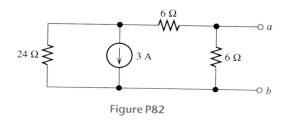

Figure P82

P83. Find the Thévenin and Norton equivalent circuits for the two-terminal circuit shown in Figure P83.

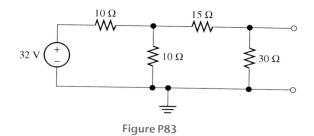

Figure P83

P84. Find the Thévenin and Norton equivalent circuits for the circuit shown in Figure P84. Take care that you orient the polarity of the voltage source and the direction of the current source correctly relative to terminals a and b. What effect does the 7-Ω resistor have on the equivalent circuits? Explain your answer.

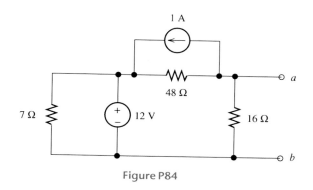

Figure P84

P85. An automotive battery has an open-circuit voltage of 12.6 V and supplies 100 A when a 0.1-Ω resistance is connected across the battery terminals. Draw the Thévenin and Norton equivalent circuits, including values for the circuit parameters. What current can this battery deliver to a short circuit? Considering that the energy stored in the battery remains constant under open-circuit conditions, which of these equivalent circuits seems more realistic? Explain.

P86. A certain two-terminal circuit has an open-circuit voltage of 15 V. When a 2-kΩ load is attached, the voltage across the load is 10 V. Determine the Thévenin resistance for the circuit.

P87. If we measure the voltage at the terminals of a two-terminal network with two known (and different) resistive loads attached, we can determine the Thévenin and Norton equivalent circuits. When a 2.2-kΩ load is attached to a two-terminal circuit, the load voltage is 4.4 V. When the load is increased to 10 kΩ, the load voltage becomes 5 V. Find the Thévenin voltage and resistance for the circuit.

P88. Find the Thévenin and Norton equivalent circuits for the circuit shown in Figure P88.

121

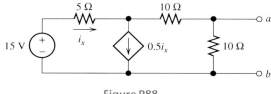

Figure P88

P89. Find the maximum power that can be delivered to a resistive load by the circuit shown in Figure P80. For what value of load resistance is the power maximum?

P90. Find the maximum power that can be delivered to a resistive load by the circuit shown in Figure P82. For what value of load resistance is the power maximum?

*P91. Figure P91 shows a resistive load R_L connected to a Thévenin equivalent circuit. For what value of Thévenin resistance is the power delivered to the load maximized? Find the maximum power delivered to the load. (*Hint:* Be careful; this is a trick question if you don't stop to think about it.)

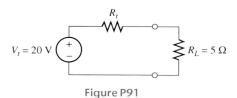

Figure P91

P92. Starting from the Norton equivalent circuit with a resistive load R_L attached, find an expression for the power delivered to the load in terms of I_n, R_t, and R_L. Assuming that I_n and R_t are fixed values and that R_L is variable, show that maximum power is delivered for $R_L = R_t$. Find an expression for maximum power delivered to the load in terms of I_n and R_t.

P93. A battery can be modeled by a voltage source V_t in series with a resistance R_t. Assuming that the load resistance is selected to maximize the power delivered, what percentage of the power taken from the voltage source V_t is actually delivered to the load? Suppose that $R_L = 9R_t$; what percentage of the power taken from V_t is delivered to the load?

Usually, we want to design battery-operated systems so that nearly all of the energy stored in the battery is delivered to the load. Should we design for maximum power transfer?

Section 7: Superposition Principle

*P94. Use superposition to find the current i in Figure P94. First, zero the current source and find the value i_v caused by the voltage source alone. Then, zero the voltage source and find the value i_c caused by the current source alone. Finally, add the results algebraically.

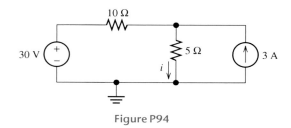

Figure P94

*P95. Solve for i_s in Figure P49 by using superposition.

P96. Solve the circuit shown in Figure P48 by using superposition. First, zero the 1-A source and find the value of i_1 with only the 2-A source activated. Then, zero the 2-A source and find the value of i_1 with only the 1-A source activated. Finally, find the total value of i_1 with both sources activated by algebraically adding the previous results.

P97. Solve for i_1 in Figure P34 by using superposition.

P98. Another method of solving the circuit of Figure P24 is to start by assuming that $v_2 = 1$ V. Accordingly, we work backward toward the source, using Ohm's law, KCL, and KVL to find the value of v_s. Since we know that v_2 is proportional to the value of v_s, and since we have found the value of v_s that produces $v_2 = 1$ V, we can calculate the value of v_2 that results when $v_s = 12$ V. Solve for v_2 by using this method.

P99. Use the method of Problem P98 for the circuit of Figure P23, starting with the assumption that $i_2 = 1$ A.

P100. Solve for the actual value of i_6 for the circuit of Figure P100, starting with the assumption that $i_6 = 1\,$A. Work back through the circuit to find the value of I_s that results in $i_6 = 1\,$A. Then, use proportionality to determine the value of i_6 that results for $I_s = 10\,$A.

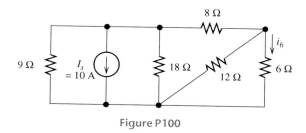

Figure P100

P101. Device A shown in Figure P101 has $v = 3i^2$ for $i \geq 0$ and $v = 0$ for $i < 0$.

a. Solve for v with the 2-A source active and the 1-A source zeroed.

b. Solve for v with the 1-A source active and the 2-A source zeroed.

c. Solve for v with both sources active. Why doesn't superposition apply?

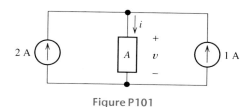

Figure P101

Section 8: Wheatstone Bridge

P102. **a.** The Wheatstone bridge shown in Figure 64 is balanced with $R_1 = 10\,$kΩ, $R_3 = 3419\,\Omega$, and $R_2 = 1\,$kΩ. Find R_x. **b.** Repeat if R_2 is $100\,$kΩ and the other values are unchanged.

*P103. The Wheatstone bridge shown in Figure 64 has $v_s = 10\,$V, $R_1 = 10\,$kΩ, $R_2 = 10\,$kΩ, and $R_x = 5932\,\Omega$. The detector can be modeled as a 5-kΩ resistance. **a.** What value of R_3 is required to balance the bridge? **b.** Suppose that R_3 is 1 Ω higher than the value found in part (a). Find the current through the detector. (*Hint:* Find the Thévenin equivalent for the circuit with the detector removed. Then, place the detector across the Thévenin equivalent and solve for the current.) Comment.

P104. In theory, any values can be used for R_1 and R_3 in the Wheatstone bridge of Figure 64. For the bridge to balance, it is only the *ratio* R_3/R_1 that is important. What practical problems might occur if the values are very small? What practical problems might occur if the values are very large?

P105. Derive expressions for the Thévenin voltage and resistance "seen" by the detector in the Wheatstone bridge in Figure 64. (In other words, remove the detector from the circuit and determine the Thévenin resistance for the remaining two-terminal circuit.) What is the value of the Thévenin voltage when the bridge is balanced?

Practice Test

Here is a practice test you can use to check your comprehension of the most important concepts in this chapter. Answers can be found at the end of this chapter and complete solutions are included in the Student Solutions files.

T1. Match each entry in Table T1(a) with the best choice from the list given in Table T1(b)

for circuits composed of sources and resistances. [Items in Table T1(b) may be used more than once or not at all.]

T2. Consider the circuit of Figure T2 with $v_s = 96\,$V, $R_1 = 6\,\Omega$, $R_2 = 48\,\Omega$, $R_3 = 16\,\Omega$, and $R_4 = 60\,\Omega$. Determine the values of i_s and i_4.

Table T1

Item	Best Match

(a)

a. The equivalent resistance of parallel-connected resistances...
b. Resistances in parallel combine as do...
c. Loads in power distribution systems are most often connected...
d. Solving a circuit by series/parallel combinations applies to...
e. The voltage-division principle applies to...
f. The current-division principle applies to...
g. The superposition principle applies to...
h. Node-voltage analysis can be applied to...
i. In this book, mesh-current analysis is applied to...
j. The Thévenin resistance of a two-terminal circuit equals...
k. The Norton current source value of a two-terminal circuit equals...
l. A voltage source in parallel with a resistance is equivalent to...

(b)

1. conductances in parallel
2. in parallel
3. all circuits
4. resistances or conductances in parallel
5. is obtained by summing the resistances
6. is the reciprocal of the sum of the reciprocals of the resistances
7. some circuits
8. planar circuits
9. a current source in series with a resistance
10. conductances in series
11. circuits composed of linear elements
12. in series
13. resistances or conductances in series
14. a voltage source
15. the open-circuit voltage divided by the short-circuit current
16. a current source
17. the short-circuit current

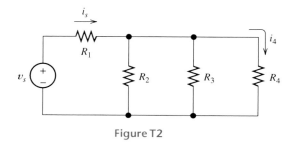

Figure T2

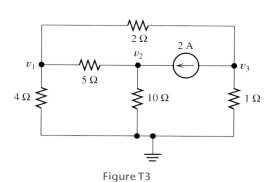

Figure T3

T3. Write MATLAB code to solve for the node voltages for the circuit of Figure T3.

124

T4. Write a set of equations that can be used to solve for the mesh currents of Figure T4. Be sure to indicate which of the equations you write form the set.

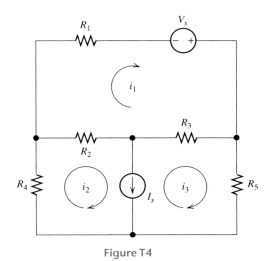

Figure T4

T5. Determine the Thévenin and Norton equivalent circuits for the circuit of Figure T5. Draw the equivalent circuits labeling the terminals to correspond with the original circuit.

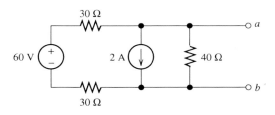

Figure T5

T6. According to the superposition principle, what percentage of the total current flowing through the 5-Ω resistance in the circuit of Figure T6 results from the 5-V source? What percentage of the power supplied to the 5-Ω resistance is supplied by the 5-V source? Assume that both sources are active when answering both questions.

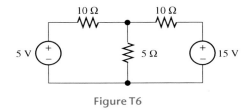

Figure T6

Answers for the Practice Test

T1. **a.** 6; **b.** 10; **c.** 2; **d.** 7; **e.** 10 or 13; **f.** 1 or 4; **g.** 11; **h.** 3; **i.** 8; **j.** 15; **k.** 17; **l.** 14.

T2. $i_s = 6\,\text{A}; i_4 = 1\,\text{A}$.

T3. ```
G = [0.95 -0.20 -0.50; -0.20 0.30 0; -0.50 0 1.50]
I = [0; 2; -2]
V = G\ I % As an alternative, we could use V = inv(G)*I
```

**T4.** A proper set of equations consists of any two of the following three

**1.** KVL mesh 1:

$$R_1 i_1 - V_s + R_3(i_1 - i_3) + R_2(i_1 - i_2) = 0$$

**2.** KVL for the supermesh obtained by combining meshes 2 and 3:

$$R_4 i_2 + R_2 (i_2 - i_1) + R_3 (i_3 - i_1) + R_5 i_3 = 0$$

**3.** KVL around the periphery of the circuit:

$$R_1 i_1 - V_s + R_4 i_2 + R_5 i_3 = 0$$

in combination with this equation for the current source:

$$i_2 - i_3 = I_s$$
```

T5. $V_t = 24\,\text{V}$, $R_t = 24\,\Omega$, and $I_n = 1\,\text{A}$. The reference direction for I_n should point toward terminal b. The positive reference for V_t should be on the side of the b terminal.

T6. By superposition, 25 percent of the current through the 5-Ω resistance is due to the 5-V source. Superposition does not apply for power, but we can see from analysis of the complete circuit that all of the power is supplied by the 15-V source. Thus, 0 percent of the power in the 5-Ω resistance is due to the 5-V source.

Inductance and Capacitance

From Chapter 3 of *Electrical Engineering: Principles and Applications*, Fifth Edition, Allan R. Hambley. Copyright © 2011 by Pearson Education, Inc. Published by Pearson Prentice Hall. All rights reserved.

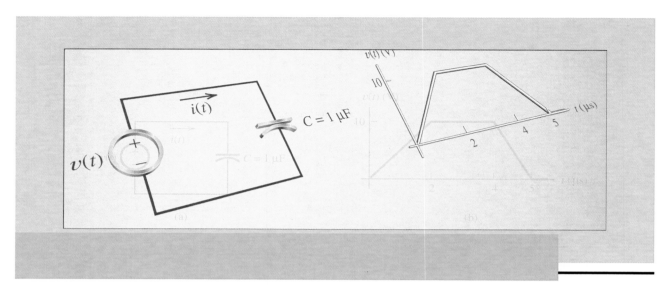

Inductance and Capacitance

Study of this chapter will enable you to:

■ Find the current (voltage) for a capacitance or inductance given the voltage (current) as a function of time.

■ Compute the capacitances of parallel-plate capacitors.

■ Compute the energies stored in capacitances or inductances.

■ Describe typical physical construction of capacitors and inductors and identify parasitic effects.

■ Find the voltages across mutually coupled inductances in terms of the currents.

■ Apply the MATLAB Symbolic Toolbox to the current–voltage relationships for capacitances and inductances.

Introduction to this chapter:

In this chapter, we discuss two circuit elements: inductors and capacitors. Whereas resistors convert electrical energy into heat, inductors and capacitors are **energy-storage elements**. They can store energy and later return it to the circuit.

Capacitors and inductors do not generate energy —only the energy that has been put into these elements can be extracted. Thus, like resistors, they are said to be **passive** elements.

Electromagnetic field theory is the basic approach to the study of the effects of electrical charge. However, circuit theory is a simplification of field theory that is much easier to apply. Capacitance is the circuit property that accounts for energy stored in electric fields. Inductance accounts for energy stored in magnetic fields.

We will learn that the voltage across an ideal inductor is proportional to the time derivative of the current. On the other hand, the voltage across an ideal capacitor is proportional to the time integral of the current.

We will also study mutual inductance, a circuit property that accounts for magnetic fields that are mutual to several inductors. Mutual inductance forms the basis for transformers, which are critical to the transmission of electrical power over long distances.

Several types of transducers are based on inductance and capacitance. For example, one type of microphone is basically a capacitor in which the capacitance changes with sound pressure. An application of mutual inductance is the linear variable differential transformer in which position of a moving iron core is converted into a voltage.

Sometimes an electrical signal that represents a physical variable such as displacement is noisy. For example, in an active (electronically controlled) suspension for an automobile, the position sensors are affected by road roughness as well as by the loading of the vehicle. To obtain an electrical signal representing the displacement of each wheel, the rapid fluctuations due to road roughness must be eliminated. Later, we will see that this can be accomplished using inductance and capacitance in circuits known as filters.

After studying this chapter, we will be ready to extend basic circuit-analysis techniques to circuits having inductance and capacitance.

1 CAPACITANCE

Capacitors are constructed by separating two sheets of conductor, which is usually metallic, by a thin layer of insulating material. In a parallel-plate capacitor, the sheets are flat and parallel as shown in Figure 1. The insulating material between the plates, called a **dielectric**, can be air, Mylar®, polyester, polypropylene, mica, or a variety of other materials.

Let us consider what happens as current flows through a capacitor. Suppose that current flows downward, as shown in Figure 2(a). In most metals, current consists of electrons moving, and conventional current flowing downward represents electrons actually moving upward. As electrons move upward, they collect on the lower plate of the capacitor. Thus, the lower plate accumulates a net negative charge that produces an electric field in the dielectric. This electric field forces electrons to leave the upper plate at the same rate that they accumulate on the lower plate. Therefore, current appears to flow through the capacitor. As the charge builds up, voltage appears across the capacitor.

Capacitors are constructed by separating two conducting plates, which are usually metallic, by a thin layer of insulating material.

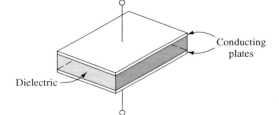

Figure 1 A parallel-plate capacitor consists of two conductive plates separated by a dielectric layer.

Conducting plates

Dielectric

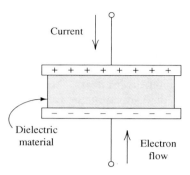

Current

+ + + + + + + +

Dielectric
material

Electron
flow

(a) As current flows through a capacitor, charges
of opposite signs collect on the respective plates

Elastic
membrane

(b) Fluid-flow analogy for capacitance

Figure 2 A capacitor and its fluid-flow analogy.

Positive charge on one plate is balanced by negative charge of equal magnitude on the other plate.

We say that the charge accumulated on one plate is stored in the capacitor. However, the total charge on both plates is always zero, because positive charge on one plate is balanced by negative charge of equal magnitude on the other plate.

Fluid-Flow Analogy

In terms of the fluid-flow analogy, a capacitor represents a reservoir with an elastic membrane separating the inlet and outlet.

In terms of the fluid-flow analogy, a capacitor represents a reservoir with an elastic membrane separating the inlet and outlet as shown in Figure 2(b). As the fluid flows into the inlet, the membrane is stretched, creating a force (analogous to capacitor voltage) that opposes further flow. The displaced fluid volume starting from the unstretched membrane position is analogous to the charge stored on one plate of the capacitor.

Stored Charge in Terms of Voltage

In an ideal capacitor, the stored charge q is proportional to the voltage between the plates.

In an ideal capacitor, the stored charge q is proportional to the voltage between the plates:

$$q = Cv \qquad (1)$$

The constant of proportionality is the capacitance C, which has units of farads (F). Farads are equivalent to coulombs per volt.

To be more precise, the charge q is the net charge on the plate corresponding to the positive reference for v. Thus, if v is positive, there is positive charge on the plate corresponding to the positive reference for v. On the other hand, if v is negative, there is negative charge on the plate corresponding to the positive reference.

In most applications, we deal with capacitances in the range from a few picofarads up to perhaps 0.01 F.

A farad is a very large amount of capacitance. In most applications, we deal with capacitances in the range from a few picofarads (1 pF $= 10^{-12}$ F) up to perhaps 0.01 F. Capacitances in the femtofarad (1 fF $= 10^{-15}$ F) range are responsible for limiting the performance of computer chips.

Current in Terms of Voltage

Recall that current is the time rate of flow of charge. Taking the derivative of each side of Equation 1 with respect to time, we have

$$i = \frac{dq}{dt} = \frac{d}{dt}(Cv) \qquad (2)$$

Ordinarily, capacitance is not a function of time. (An exception is the capacitor microphone mentioned earlier.) Thus, the relationship between current and voltage becomes

$$i = C\frac{dv}{dt} \tag{3}$$

Equations 1 and 3 show that as voltage increases, current flows through the capacitance and charge accumulates on each plate. If the voltage remains constant, the charge is constant and the current is zero. Thus, a capacitor appears to be an open circuit for a steady dc voltage.

The circuit symbol for capacitance and the references for v and i are shown in Figure 3. Notice that the references for the voltage and current have the passive configuration. In other words, the current reference direction points into the positive reference polarity. If the references were opposite to the passive configuration, Equation 3 would have a minus sign:

$$i = -C\frac{dv}{dt} \tag{4}$$

Sometimes, we emphasize the fact that in general the voltage and current are functions of time by denoting them as $v(t)$ and $i(t)$.

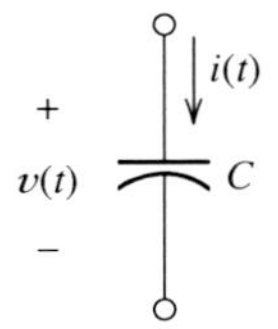

Capacitors act as open circuits for steady dc voltages.

Figure 3 The circuit symbol for capacitance, including references for the current $i(t)$ and voltage $v(t)$.

Determining Current for a Capacitance Given Voltage

Suppose that the voltage $v(t)$ shown in Figure 4(b) is applied to a 1-μF capacitance. Plot the stored charge and the current through the capacitance versus time.

Solution   The charge stored on the top plate of the capacitor is given by Equation 1. [We know that $q(t)$ represents the charge on the top plate because that is the plate corresponding to the positive reference for $v(t)$.] Thus,

$$q(t) = Cv(t) = 10^{-6}v(t)$$

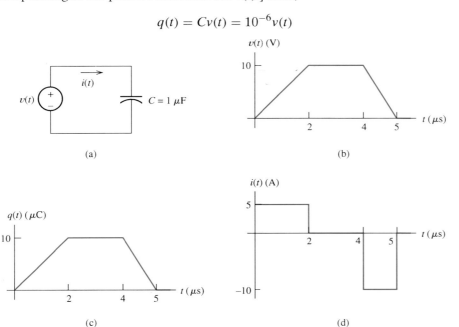

Figure 4 Circuit and waveforms for Example 1.

This is shown in Figure 4(c).

The current flowing through the capacitor is given by Equation 3:

$$i(t) = C\frac{dv(t)}{dt} = 10^{-6}\frac{dv(t)}{dt}$$

Of course, the derivative of the voltage is the slope of the voltage versus time plot. Hence, for t between 0 and 2 μs, we have

$$\frac{dv(t)}{dt} = \frac{10 \text{ V}}{2 \times 10^{-6} \text{ s}} = 5 \times 10^6 \text{ V/s}$$

and

$$i(t) = C\frac{dv(t)}{dt} = 10^{-6} \times 5 \times 10^6 = 5 \text{ A}$$

Between $t = 2$ and 4 μs, the voltage is constant ($dv/dt = 0$) and the current is zero. Finally, between $t = 4$ and 5 μs, we get

$$\frac{dv(t)}{dt} = \frac{-10 \text{ V}}{10^{-6} \text{ s}} = -10^7 \text{ V/s}$$

and

$$i(t) = C\frac{dv(t)}{dt} = 10^{-6} \times (-10^7) = -10 \text{ A}$$

A plot of $i(t)$ is shown in Figure 4(d).

Notice that as the voltage increases, current flows through the capacitor and charges accumulate on the plates. For constant voltage, the current is zero and the charge is constant. When the voltage decreases, the direction of the current reverses, and the stored charge is removed from the capacitor. ■

Exercise 1 The charge on a 2-μF capacitor is given by

$$q(t) = 10^{-6}\sin(10^5 t) \text{ C}$$

Find expressions for the voltage and for the current. (The angle is in radians.)
Answer $v(t) = 0.5\sin(10^5 t) \text{ V}, i(t) = 0.1\cos(10^5 t) \text{ A}$. □

Voltage in Terms of Current

Suppose that we know the current $i(t)$ flowing through a capacitance C and we want to compute the charge and voltage. Since current is the time rate of charge flow, we must integrate the current to compute charge. Often in circuit analysis problems, action starts at some initial time t_0, and the initial charge $q(t_0)$ is known. Then, charge as a function of time is given by

$$q(t) = \int_{t_0}^{t} i(t)\,dt + q(t_0) \tag{5}$$

Setting the right-hand sides of Equations 1 and 5 equal to each other and solving for the voltage $v(t)$, we have

$$v(t) = \frac{1}{C}\int_{t_0}^{t} i(t)\,dt + \frac{q(t_0)}{C} \tag{6}$$

However, the initial voltage across the capacitance is given by

$$v(t_0) = \frac{q(t_0)}{C} \tag{7}$$

Substituting this into Equation 6, we have

$$v(t) = \frac{1}{C} \int_{t_0}^{t} i(t)\, dt + v(t_0) \tag{8}$$

Usually, we take the initial time to be $t_0 = 0$.

Determining Voltage for a Capacitance Given Current

After $t_0 = 0$, the current in a 0.1-μF capacitor is given by

$$i(t) = 0.5 \sin(10^4 t)$$

(The argument of the sin function is in radians.) The initial charge on the capacitor is $q(0) = 0$. Plot $i(t)$, $q(t)$, and $v(t)$ to scale versus time.

Solution First, we use Equation 5 to find an expression for the charge:

$$\begin{aligned}
q(t) &= \int_0^t i(t)\, dt + q(0) \\
&= \int_0^t 0.5 \sin(10^4 t)\, dt \\
&= -0.5 \times 10^{-4} \cos(10^4 t)\Big|_0^t \\
&= 0.5 \times 10^{-4}[1 - \cos(10^4 t)]
\end{aligned}$$

Solving Equation 1 for voltage, we have

$$\begin{aligned}
v(t) &= \frac{q(t)}{C} = \frac{q(t)}{10^{-7}} \\
&= 500[1 - \cos(10^4 t)]
\end{aligned}$$

Plots of $i(t)$, $q(t)$, and $v(t)$ are shown in Figure 5. Immediately after $t = 0$, the current is positive and $q(t)$ increases. After the first half-cycle, $i(t)$ becomes negative and $q(t)$ decreases. At the completion of one cycle, the charge and voltage have returned to zero. ■

Stored Energy

The power delivered to a circuit element is the product of the current and the voltage (provided that the references have the passive configuration):

$$p(t) = v(t)i(t) \tag{9}$$

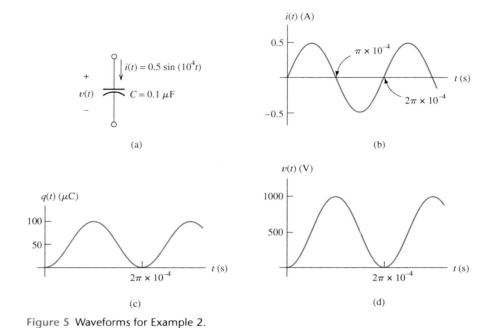

Figure 5 Waveforms for Example 2.

Using Equation 3 to substitute for the current, we have

$$p(t) = Cv\frac{dv}{dt} \tag{10}$$

Suppose we have a capacitor that initially has $v(t_0) = 0$. Then the initial stored electrical energy is zero, and we say that the capacitor is uncharged. Furthermore, suppose that between time t_0 and some later time t the voltage changes from 0 to $v(t)$ volts. As the voltage magnitude increases, energy is delivered to the capacitor, where it is stored in the electric field between the plates.

If we integrate the power delivered from t_0 to t, we find the energy delivered:

$$w(t) = \int_{t_0}^{t} p(t)\, dt \tag{11}$$

Using Equation 10 to substitute for power, we find that

$$w(t) = \int_{t_0}^{t} Cv\frac{dv}{dt}\, dt \tag{12}$$

Canceling differential time and changing the limits to the corresponding voltages, we have

$$w(t) = \int_{0}^{v(t)} Cv\, dv \tag{13}$$

Integrating and evaluating, we get

$$w(t) = \frac{1}{2}Cv^2(t) \tag{14}$$

This represents energy stored in the capacitance that can be returned to the circuit.

Solving Equation 1 for $v(t)$ and substituting into Equation 14, we can obtain two alternative expressions for the stored energy:

$$w(t) = \frac{1}{2}v(t)q(t) \tag{15}$$

$$w(t) = \frac{q^2(t)}{2C} \tag{16}$$

Current, Power, and Energy for a Capacitance

Suppose that the voltage waveform shown in Figure 6(a) is applied to a $10\mu F$ capacitance. Find and plot the current, the power delivered, and the energy stored for time between 0 and 5 s.

Solution First, we write expressions for the voltage as a function of time:

$$v(t) = \begin{cases} 1000t \text{ V} & \text{for } 0 < t < 1 \\ 1000 \text{ V} & \text{for } 1 < t < 3 \\ 500(5-t) \text{ V} & \text{for } 3 < t < 5 \end{cases}$$

Using Equation 3, we obtain expressions for the current:

$$i(t) = C\frac{dv(t)}{dt}$$

$$i(t) = \begin{cases} 10 \times 10^{-3} \text{ A} & \text{for } 0 < t < 1 \\ 0 \text{ A} & \text{for } 1 < t < 3 \\ -5 \times 10^{-3} \text{ A} & \text{for } 3 < t < 5 \end{cases}$$

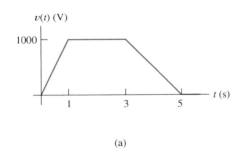

(a)

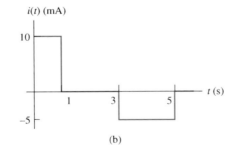

(b)

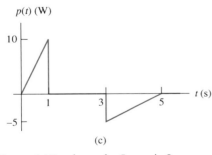

(c)

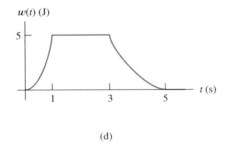

(d)

Figure 6 Waveforms for Example 3.

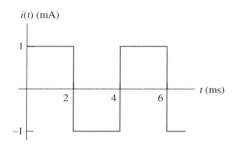

Figure 7 Square-wave current for Exercise 2.

The plot of $i(t)$ is shown in Figure 6(b).

Next, we find expressions for power by multiplying the voltage by the current:

$$p(t) = v(t)i(t)$$

$$p(t) = \begin{cases} 10t \text{ W} & \text{for } 0 < t < 1 \\ 0 \text{ W} & \text{for } 1 < t < 3 \\ 2.5(t-5) \text{ W} & \text{for } 3 < t < 5 \end{cases}$$

The plot of $p(t)$ is shown in Figure 6(c). Notice that between $t = 0$ and $t = 1$ power is positive, showing that energy is being delivered to the capacitance. Between $t = 3$ and $t = 5$, energy flows out of the capacitance back into the rest of the circuit.

Next, we use Equation 14 to find expressions for the stored energy:

$$w(t) = \frac{1}{2}Cv^2(t)$$

$$w(t) = \begin{cases} 5t^2 \text{ J} & \text{for } 0 < t < 1 \\ 5 \text{ J} & \text{for } 1 < t < 3 \\ 1.25(5-t)^2 \text{ J} & \text{for } 3 < t < 5 \end{cases}$$

The plot of $w(t)$ is shown in Figure 6(d). ∎

Exercise 2 The current through a $0.1\text{-}\mu\text{F}$ capacitor is shown in Figure 7. At $t_0 = 0$, the voltage across the capacitor is zero. Find the charge, voltage, power, and stored energy as functions of time and plot them to scale versus time.
Answer The plots are shown in Figure 8. □

2 CAPACITANCES IN SERIES AND PARALLEL

Capacitances in Parallel

Suppose that we have three capacitances in parallel as shown in Figure 9. Of course, the same voltage appears across each of the elements in a parallel circuit. The currents are related to the voltage by Equation 3. Thus, we can write

$$i_1 = C_1 \frac{dv}{dt} \tag{17}$$

$$i_2 = C_2 \frac{dv}{dt} \tag{18}$$

$$i_3 = C_3 \frac{dv}{dt} \tag{19}$$

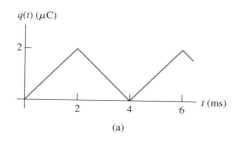

(a)

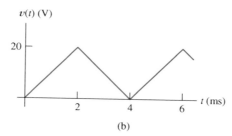

(b)

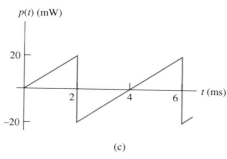

(c)

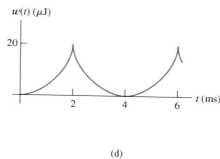

(d)

Figure 8 Answers for Exercise 2.

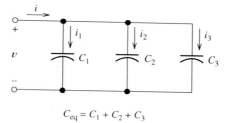

Figure 9 Three capacitances in parallel.

$$C_{eq} = C_1 + C_2 + C_3$$

Applying KCL at the top node of the circuit, we have

$$i = i_1 + i_2 + i_3 \qquad (20)$$

Using Equations 17, 18, and 19 to substitute into Equation 20, we obtain

$$i = C_1 \frac{dv}{dt} + C_2 \frac{dv}{dt} + C_3 \frac{dv}{dt} \qquad (21)$$

This can be written as

$$i = (C_1 + C_2 + C_3) \frac{dv}{dt} \qquad (22)$$

Now, we define the equivalent capacitance as the sum of the capacitances in parallel:

$$C_{eq} = C_1 + C_2 + C_3 \qquad (23)$$

We add parallel capacitances to find the equivalent capacitance.

Using this definition in Equation 22, we find that

$$i = C_{eq} \frac{dv}{dt} \qquad (24)$$

137

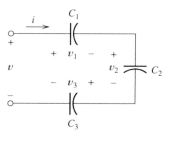

Figure 10 Three capacitances in series.

$$C_{eq} = \frac{1}{1/C_1 + 1/C_2 + 1/C_3}$$

Thus, the current in the equivalent capacitance is the same as the total current flowing through the parallel circuit.

In sum, we add parallel capacitances to find the equivalent capacitance. Recall that for resistances, the resistances are added if they are in *series* rather than parallel. Thus, we say that capacitances in parallel are combined like resistances in series.

Capacitances in parallel are combined like resistances in series.

Capacitances in Series

By a similar development, it can be shown that the equivalent capacitance for three series capacitances is

Capacitances in series are combined like resistances in parallel.

$$C_{eq} = \frac{1}{1/C_1 + 1/C_2 + 1/C_3} \qquad (25)$$

We conclude that capacitances in series are combined like resistances in parallel.

A technique for obtaining high voltages from low-voltage sources is to charge n capacitors in parallel with the source, and then to switch them to a series combination. The resulting voltage across the series combination is n times the source voltage. For example, in some cardiac pacemakers, a 2.5-V battery is used, but 5 V need to be applied to the heart muscle to initiate a beat. This is accomplished by charging two capacitors from the 2.5-V battery. The capacitors are then connected in series to deliver a brief 5-V pulse to the heart.

Exercise 3   Derive Equation 25 for the three capacitances shown in Figure 10. □

Exercise 4   **a.** Two capacitances of 2 μF and 1 μF are in series. Find the equivalent capacitance. **b.** Repeat if the capacitances are in parallel.
Answer   **a.** 2/3 μF; **b.** 3 μF. □

3 PHYSICAL CHARACTERISTICS OF CAPACITORS

Capacitance of the Parallel-Plate Capacitor

A parallel-plate capacitor is shown in Figure 11, including dimensions. The area of each plate is denoted as A. (Actually, A is the area of one side of the plate.) The rectangular plate shown has a width W, length L, and area $A = W \times L$. The plates are parallel, and the distance between them is denoted as d.

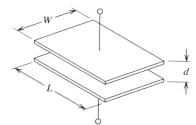

Figure 11 A parallel-plate capacitor, including dimensions.

Table 1. Relative Dielectric Constants for Selected Materials

Air	1.0
Diamond	5.5
Mica	7.0
Polyester	3.4
Quartz	4.3
Silicon dioxide	3.9
Water	78.5

If the distance d between the plates is much smaller than both the width and the length of the plates, the capacitance is approximately given by

$$C = \frac{\epsilon A}{d} \tag{26}$$

in which ϵ is the **dielectric constant** of the material between the plates. For vacuum, the dielectric constant is

$$\epsilon = \epsilon_0 \cong 8.85 \times 10^{-12} \text{ F/m}$$

Dielectric constant of vacuum.

For other materials, the dielectric constant is

$$\epsilon = \epsilon_r \epsilon_0 \tag{27}$$

where ϵ_r is the **relative dielectric constant**. Values of the relative dielectric constant for selected materials are given in Table 1.

Calculating Capacitance Given Physical Parameters

Compute the capacitance of a parallel-plate capacitor having rectangular plates 10 cm by 20 cm separated by a distance of 0.1 mm. The dielectric is air. Repeat if the dielectric is mica.

Solution First, we compute the area of a plate:

$$A = L \times W = (10 \times 10^{-2}) \times (20 \times 10^{-2}) = 0.02 \text{ m}^2$$

From Table 1, we see that the relative dielectric constant of air is 1.00. Thus, the dielectric constant is

$$\epsilon = \epsilon_r \epsilon_0 = 1.00 \times 8.85 \times 10^{-12} \text{ F/m}$$

Then, the capacitance is

$$C = \frac{\epsilon A}{d} = \frac{8.85 \times 10^{-12} \times 0.02}{10^{-4}} = 1770 \times 10^{-12} \text{ F}$$

For a mica dielectric, the relative dielectric constant is 7.0. Thus, the capacitance is seven times larger than for air or vacuum:

$$C = 12{,}390 \times 10^{-12} \text{ F} \qquad \blacksquare$$

Exercise 5 We want to design a 1-μF capacitor. Compute the length required for rectangular plates of 2-cm width if the dielectric is polyester of 15-μm thickness.
Answer $L = 24.93$ m. □

Practical Capacitors

To achieve capacitances on the order of a microfarad, the dimensions of parallel-plate capacitors are too large for compact electronic circuits such as portable computers or cellular telephones. Frequently, capacitors are constructed by alternating the plates with two layers of dielectric, which are then rolled to fit in a smaller area. By staggering the plates before rolling, electrical contact can be made with the plates from the ends of the roll. This type of construction is illustrated in Figure 12.

To achieve small-volume capacitors, a very thin dielectric having a high dielectric constant is desirable. However, dielectric materials break down and become conductors when the electric field intensity (volts per meter) is too high. Thus, real capacitors have maximum voltage ratings. For a given voltage, the electric field intensity becomes higher as the dielectric layer becomes thinner. Clearly, an engineering trade-off exists between compact size and voltage rating.

Real capacitors have maximum voltage ratings.

An engineering trade-off exists between compact size and high voltage rating.

Only voltages of the proper polarity should be applied to electrolytic capacitors.

Electrolytic Capacitors

In **electrolytic capacitors**, one of the plates is metallic aluminum or tantalum, the dielectric is an oxide layer on the surface of the metal, and the other "plate" is an electrolytic solution. The oxide-coated metallic plate is immersed in the electrolytic solution.

This type of construction results in high capacitance per unit volume. However, only one polarity of voltage should be applied to electrolytic capacitors. For the opposite polarity, the dielectric layer is chemically attacked, and a conductive path appears between the plates. (Usually, the allowed polarity is marked on the outer case.) On the other hand, capacitors constructed with polyethylene, Mylar®, and so on can be used in applications where the voltage polarity reverses. When the application results in voltages of only one polarity and a large-value capacitance is required, designers frequently use electrolytic capacitors.

Figure 12 Practical capacitors can be constructed by interleaving the plates with two dielectric layers and rolling them up. By staggering the plates, connection can be made to one plate at each end of the roll.

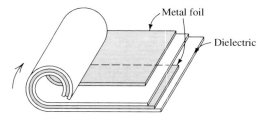

Parasitic Effects

Real capacitors are not always well modeled simply as a capacitance. A more complete circuit model for a capacitor is shown in Figure 13. In addition to the capacitance C, series resistance R_s appears because of the resistivity of the material composing the plates. A series inductance L_s (we discuss inductance later in this chapter) occurs because the current flowing through the capacitor creates a magnetic field. Finally, no practical material is a perfect insulator, and the resistance R_p represents conduction through the dielectric.

We call R_s, L_s, and R_p **parasitic elements**. We design capacitors to minimize the effects of parasitic circuit elements consistent with other requirements such as physical size and voltage rating. However, parasitics are always present to some degree. In designing circuits, care must be used to select components for which the parasitic effects do not prevent proper operation of the circuit.

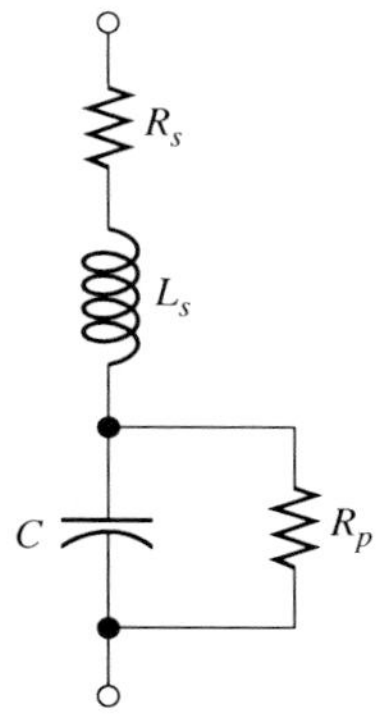

Figure 13 The circuit model for a capacitor, including the parasitic elements R_s, L_s, and R_p.

Example 5	What Happened to the Missing Energy?

Consider the situation shown in Figure 14. Prior to $t = 0$, the capacitor C_1 is charged to a voltage of $v_1 = 100$ V and the other capacitor has no charge (i.e., $v_2 = 0$). At $t = 0$, the switch closes. Compute the total energy stored by both capacitors before and after the switch closes.

Solution The initial stored energy for each capacitor is

$$w_1 = \frac{1}{2}C_1 v_1^2 = \frac{1}{2}(10^{-6})(100)^2 = 5 \text{ mJ}$$
$$w_2 = 0$$

and the total energy is
$$w_\text{total} = w_1 + w_2 = 5 \text{ mJ}$$

To find the voltage and stored energy after the switch closes, we make use of the fact that the total charge on the top plates cannot change when the switch closes. This is true because there is no path for charge to leave the upper part of the circuit.

The charge stored on the top plate of C_1 prior to $t = 0$ is given by

$$q_1 = C_1 v_1 = 1 \times 10^{-6} \times 100 = 100 \ \mu\text{C}$$

Furthermore, the initial charge on C_2 is zero:

$$q_2 = 0$$

Thus, after the switch closes, the charge on the equivalent capacitance is

$$q_\text{eq} = q_1 + q_2 = 100 \ \mu\text{C}$$

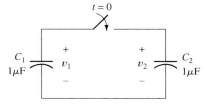

Figure 14 See Example 5.

Also, notice that after the switch is closed, the capacitors are in parallel and have an equivalent capacitance of

$$C_{eq} = C_1 + C_2 = 2 \; \mu F$$

The voltage across the equivalent capacitance is

$$v_{eq} = \frac{q_{eq}}{C_{eq}} = \frac{100 \; \mu C}{2 \; \mu F} = 50 \; V$$

Of course, after the switch is closed, $v_1 = v_2 = v_{eq}$.

Now, we compute the stored energy with the switch closed:

$$w_1 = \frac{1}{2} C_1 v_{eq}^2 = \frac{1}{2} (10^{-6})(50)^2 = 1.25 \; mJ$$

$$w_2 = \frac{1}{2} C_2 v_{eq}^2 = \frac{1}{2} (10^{-6})(50)^2 = 1.25 \; mJ$$

The total stored energy with the switch closed is

$$w_{total} = w_1 + w_2 = 2.5 \; mJ$$

Thus, we see that the stored energy after the switch is closed is half of the value before the switch is closed. What happened to the missing energy?

Usually, the answer to this question is that it is absorbed in the parasitic resistances. It is impossible to construct capacitors that do not have some parasitic effects. Even if we use superconductors for the wires and capacitor plates, there would be parasitic inductance. If we included the parasitic inductance in the circuit model, we would not have missing energy.

To put it another way, a physical circuit that is modeled exactly by Figure 14 does not exist. Invariably, if we use a realistic model for an actual circuit, we can account for all of the energy. ∎

Usually, the missing energy is absorbed in the parasitic resistances.

A physical circuit that is modeled exactly by Figure 14 does not exist.

4 INDUCTANCE

Inductors are usually constructed by coiling wire around a form.

An inductor is usually constructed by coiling a wire around some type of form. Several examples of practical construction are illustrated in Figure 15. Current flowing through the coil creates a magnetic field or flux that links the coil. Frequently, the coil form is composed of a magnetic material such as iron or iron oxides that increases the magnetic flux for a given current.

When the current changes in value, the resulting magnetic flux changes. According to Faraday's law of electromagnetic induction, time-varying magnetic flux linking a coil induces voltage across the coil. For an ideal inductor, the voltage is proportional to the time rate of change of the current. Furthermore, the polarity of the voltage is such as to oppose the change in current. The constant of proportionality is called inductance, usually denoted by the letter L.

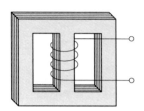

(a) Toroidal inductor

(b) Coil with an iron-oxide slug that can be screwed in or out to adjust the inductance

(c) Inductor with a laminated iron core

Figure 15 An inductor is constructed by coiling a wire around some type of form.

The circuit symbol for inductance is shown in Figure 16. In equation form, the voltage and current are related by

$$v(t) = L\frac{di}{dt} \qquad (28)$$

As usual, we have assumed the passive reference configuration. In case the references are opposite to the passive configuration, Equation 28 becomes

$$v(t) = -L\frac{di}{dt} \qquad (29)$$

Inductance has units of henries (H), which are equivalent to volt seconds per ampere. Typically, we deal with inductances ranging from a fraction of a microhenry (μH) to several tens of henries.

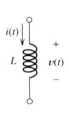

$$v(t) = L\frac{di}{dt}$$

Figure 16 Circuit symbol and the $v - i$ relationship for inductance.

Inductance has units of henries (H), which are equivalent to volt seconds per ampere.

Fluid-Flow Analogy

The fluid-flow analogy for inductance is the inertia of the fluid flowing through a *frictionless* pipe of constant diameter. The pressure differential between the ends of the pipe is analogous to voltage, and the flow rate or velocity is analogous to current. Thus, the acceleration of the fluid is analogous to rate of change of current. A pressure differential exists between the ends of the pipe only when the flow rate is increasing or decreasing.

One place where the inertia of flowing fluid is encountered is when a valve (typically operated by an electrical solenoid) closes suddenly, cutting off the flow. For example, in a washing machine, the sudden change in velocity of the water flow can cause high pressure, resulting in a bang and vibration of the plumbing. This is similar to electrical effects that occur when current in an inductor is suddenly interrupted. An application for the high voltage that appears when current is suddenly interrupted is in the ignition system for a gasoline-powered internal combustion engine.

The fluid-flow analogy for inductance is the inertia of the fluid flowing through a frictionless pipe of constant diameter.

Current in Terms of Voltage

Suppose that we know the initial current $i(t_0)$ and the voltage $v(t)$ across an inductance. Furthermore, suppose that we need to compute the current for $t > t_0$. Rearranging Equation 28, we have

$$di = \frac{1}{L}v(t)\,dt \qquad (30)$$

143

Integrating both sides, we find that

$$\int_{i(t_0)}^{i(t)} di = \frac{1}{L} \int_{t_0}^{t} v(t)\, dt \tag{31}$$

Notice that the integral on the right-hand side of Equation 31 is with respect to time. Furthermore, the limits are the initial time t_0 and the time variable t. The integral on the left-hand side is with respect to current with limits that correspond to the time limits on the right-hand side. Integrating, evaluating, and rearranging, we have

$$i(t) = \frac{1}{L} \int_{t_0}^{t} v(t)\, dt + i(t_0) \tag{32}$$

Notice that as long as $v(t)$ is finite, $i(t)$ can change only by an incremental amount in a time increment. Thus, $i(t)$ must be continuous with no instantaneous jumps in value (i.e., discontinuities). (Later, we encounter idealized circuits in which infinite voltages appear briefly, and then the current in an inductance can change instantaneously.)

Stored Energy

Assuming that the references have the passive configuration, we compute the power delivered to a circuit element by taking the product of the current and the voltage:

$$p(t) = v(t)i(t) \tag{33}$$

Using Equation 28 to substitute for the voltage, we obtain

$$p(t) = Li(t)\frac{di}{dt} \tag{34}$$

Consider an inductor having an initial current $i(t_0) = 0$. Then, the initial electrical energy stored is zero. Furthermore, assume that between time t_0 and some later time t, the current changes from 0 to $i(t)$. As the current magnitude increases, energy is delivered to the inductor, where it is stored in the magnetic field.

Integrating the power from t_0 to t, we find the energy delivered:

$$w(t) = \int_{t_0}^{t} p(t)\, dt \tag{35}$$

Using Equation 34 to substitute for power, we have

$$w(t) = \int_{t_0}^{t} Li\frac{di}{dt}\, dt \tag{36}$$

Canceling differential time and changing the limits to the corresponding currents, we get

$$w(t) = \int_{0}^{i(t)} Li\, di \tag{37}$$

Integrating and evaluating, we obtain

$$w(t) = \frac{1}{2}Li^2(t) \tag{38}$$

This represents energy stored in the inductance that is returned to the circuit if the current changes back to zero.

Example 6   Voltage, Power, and Energy for an Inductance

The current through a 5-H inductance is shown in Figure 17(a). Plot the voltage, power, and stored energy to scale versus time for t between 0 and 5 s.

Solution   We use Equation 28 to compute voltages:

$$v(t) = L\frac{di}{dt}$$

The time derivative of the current is the slope (rise over run) of the current versus time plot. For t between 0 and 2 s, we have $di/dt = 1.5$ A/s and thus $v = 7.5$ V. For t between 2 and 4 s, $di/dt = 0$, and therefore, $v = 0$. Finally, between 4 and 5 s, $di/dt = -3$ A/s, and $v = -15$ V. A plot of the voltage versus time is shown in Figure 17(b).

Next, we obtain power by taking the product of current and voltage at each point in time. The resulting plot is shown in Figure 17(c).

Finally, we use Equation 38 to compute the stored energy as a function of time:

$$w(t) = \frac{1}{2}Li^2(t)$$

The resulting plot is shown in Figure 17(d).

Notice in Figure 17 that as current magnitude increases, power is positive and stored energy accumulates. When the current is constant, the voltage is zero, the

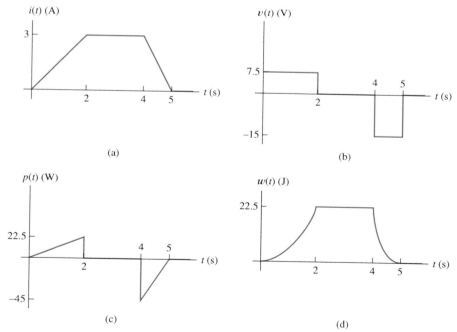

Figure 17 Waveforms for Example 6.

power is zero, and the stored energy is constant. When the current magnitude falls toward zero, the power is negative, showing that energy is being returned to the other parts of the circuit. ∎

Example 7   Inductor Current with Constant Applied Voltage

Consider the circuit shown in Figure 18(a). In this circuit, we have a switch that closes at $t = 0$, connecting a 10-V source to a 2-H inductance. Find the current as a function of time.

Solution   Notice that because the voltage applied to the inductance is finite, the current must be continuous. Prior to $t = 0$, the current must be zero. (Current cannot flow through an open switch.) Thus, the current must also be zero immediately after $t = 0$.

The voltage across the inductance is shown in Figure 18(b). To find the current, we employ Equation 32:

$$i(t) = \frac{1}{L} \int_{t_0}^{t} v(t)\, dt + i(t_0)$$

In this case, we take $t_0 = 0$, and we have $i(t_0) = i(0) = 0$. Substituting values, we get

$$i(t) = \frac{1}{2} \int_{0}^{t} 10\, dt$$

where we have assumed that t is greater than zero. Integrating and evaluating, we obtain

$$i(t) = 5t \ \mathbf{A} \qquad \text{for } t > 0$$

A plot of the current is shown in Figure 18(c).

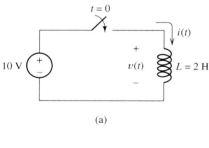

(a)

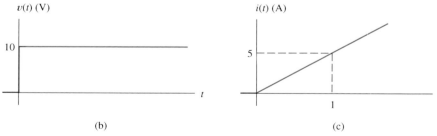

(b)   (c)

Figure 18 Circuit and waveforms for Example 7.

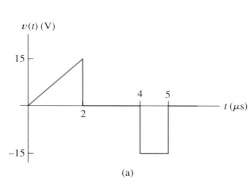

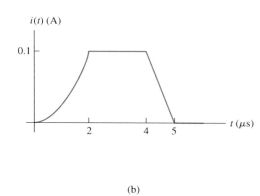

(a)

(b)

Figure 19 See Exercise 7.

Notice that the current in the inductor gradually increases after the switch is closed. Because a constant voltage is applied after $t = 0$, the current increases at a steady rate as predicted by Equation 28, which is repeated here for convenience:

$$v(t) = L\frac{di}{dt}$$

If $v(t)$ is constant, the rate of change of the current di/dt is constant. ∎

Suppose that at $t = 1$ s, we open the switch in the circuit of Figure 18. Ideally, current cannot flow through an open switch. Hence, we expect the current to fall abruptly to zero at $t = 1$ s. However, the voltage across the inductor is proportional to the time rate of change of the current. For an abrupt change in current, this principle predicts infinite voltage across the inductor. This infinite voltage would last for only the instant at which the current falls. Later, we introduce the concept of an impulse function to describe this situation (and similar ones). For now, we simply point out that very large voltages can appear when we switch circuits that contain inductances.

If we set up a real circuit corresponding to Figure 18(a) and open the switch at $t = 1$ s, we will probably find that the high voltage causes an arc across the switch contacts. The arc persists until the energy in the inductor is used up. If this is repeated, the switch will soon be destroyed.

Exercise 6   The current through a 10-mH inductance is $i(t) = 0.1 \cos(10^4 t)$ A. Find the voltage and stored energy as functions of time. Assume that the references for $v(t)$ and $i(t)$ have the passive configuration. (The angle is in radians.)
Answer $v(t) = -10 \sin(10^4 t)$ V, $w(t) = 50 \cos^2(10^4 t)$ μJ. □

Exercise 7   The voltage across a 150-μH inductance is shown in Figure 19(a). The initial current is $i(0) = 0$. Find and plot the current $i(t)$ to scale versus time. Assume that the references for $v(t)$ and $i(t)$ have the passive configuration.
Answer   The current is shown in Figure 19(b). □

5 INDUCTANCES IN SERIES AND PARALLEL

It can be shown that the equivalent inductance for a series circuit is equal to the sum of the inductances connected in series. On the other hand, for inductances in parallel, we find the equivalent inductance by taking the reciprocal of the sum of the

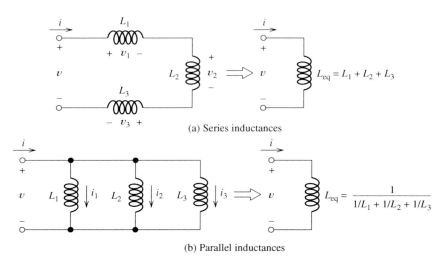

(a) Series inductances

(b) Parallel inductances

Figure 20 Inductances in series and parallel are combined in the same manner as resistances.

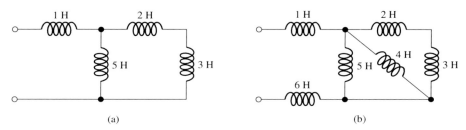

(a)   (b)

Figure 21 See Exercise 10.

Inductances in series and parallel are combined by using the same rules as for resistances: series inductances are added; parallel inductances are combined by taking the reciprocal of the sum of the reciprocals of the individual inductances.

reciprocals of the parallel inductances. Series and parallel equivalents for inductances are illustrated in Figure 20. Notice that inductances are combined in exactly the same way as are resistances. These facts can be proven by following the pattern used earlier in this chapter to derive the equivalents for series capacitances.

Exercise 8 Prove that inductances in series are added to find the equivalent inductance. ☐

Exercise 9 Prove that inductances in parallel are combined according to the formula given in Figure 20(b). ☐

Exercise 10 Find the equivalent inductance for each of the circuits shown in Figure 21.
Answer **a.** 3.5 H; **b.** 8.54 H. ☐

6 PRACTICAL INDUCTORS

Real inductors take a variety of appearances, depending on their inductance and the application. (Some examples were shown earlier in Figure 15.) For example, a $1\text{-}\mu\text{H}$ inductor could consist of 25 turns of fine (say, number 28) wire wound on an iron oxide toroidal (doughnut-shaped) core having an outside diameter of 1/2 cm.

On the other hand, a typical 5-H inductor consists of several hundred turns of number 18 wire on an iron form having a mass of 1 kg.

Usually, metallic iron forms, also called *cores*, are made of thin sheets called *laminations*. [See Figure 15(c) for an example.] This is necessary because voltages are induced in the core by the changing magnetic field. These voltages cause **eddy currents** to flow in the core, dissipating energy. Usually, this **core loss** is undesirable. Using laminations that are insulated from one another helps to reduce eddy-current loss. The laminations are arranged perpendicular to the expected current direction.

Another way to defeat eddy currents is to use a core composed of **ferrites**, which are oxides of iron that are electrical insulators. Still another approach is to combine powdered iron with an insulating binder.

Parasitic Effects

Real inductors have parasitic effects in addition to the desired inductance. A circuit model for a real inductor is shown in Figure 22. The series resistance R_s is caused by the resistivity of the material composing the wire. (This parasitic effect can be avoided by using wire composed of a superconducting material, which has zero resistivity.) The parallel capacitance is associated with the electric field in the dielectric (insulation) between the coils of wire. It is called **interwinding capacitance**. The parallel resistance R_p represents core loss due, in part, to eddy currents in the core.

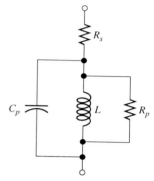

Figure 22 Circuit model for real inductors including several parasitic elements.

PRACTICAL APPLICATION 1

Electronic Photo Flash

Figure PA1 shows the electrical circuit of an electronic photo flash such as you may have seen on a camera. The objective of the unit is to produce a bright flash of light by passing a high current through the flash tube while the camera shutter is open. As much as 1000 W is supplied to the flash tube during the flash, which lasts for less than a millisecond. Although the power level is quite high, the total energy delivered is not great because of the short duration of the flash. (The energy is on the order of a joule.)

It is not possible to deliver the power directly from the battery to the flash tube for several reasons. First, practical batteries supply a few tens of volts at most, while several hundred volts are needed to operate the flash tube. Second, applying

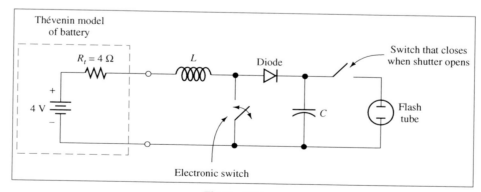

Figure PA1

the principle of maximum power transfer, the maximum power available from the battery is limited to 1 W by its internal Thévenin resistance. This does not nearly meet the needs of the flash tube. Instead, energy is delivered by the battery over a period of several seconds and stored in the capacitor. The stored energy can be quickly extracted from the capacitor because the parasitic resistance in series with the capacitor is very low.

The electronic switch alternates between open and closed approximately 10,000 times per second. (In some units, you can hear a high-pitched whistle resulting from incidental conversion of some of the energy to acoustic form.) While the electronic switch is closed, the battery causes the current in the inductor to build up. Then when the switch opens, the inductor forces current to flow through the diode, charging the capacitor. (Recall that the current in an inductor cannot change instantaneously.) Current can flow through the diode only in the direction of the arrow. Thus, the diode allows charge to flow into the capacitor when the electronic switch is open and prevents charge from flowing off the capacitor

when the electronic switch is closed. Thus, the charge stored on the capacitor increases each time the electronic switch opens. Eventually, the voltage on the capacitor reaches several hundred volts. When the camera shutter is opened, another switch is closed, allowing the capacitor to discharge through the flash tube.

A friend of the author has a remote cabin on the north shore of Lake Superior that has an unusual water system (illustrated in Figure PA2) analogous to the electronic flash circuit. Water flows through a large pipe immersed in the river. Periodically, a valve on the bottom end of the pipe suddenly closes, stopping the flow. The inertia of the flowing water creates a pulse of high pressure when the valve closes. This high pressure forces water through a one-way ball valve into a storage tank. Air trapped in the storage tank is compressed and forces water to flow to the cabin as needed.

Can you identify the features in Figure PA2 that are analogous to each of the circuit elements in Figure PA1?

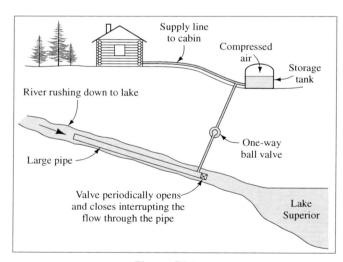

Figure PA2

Actually, the circuit model for a real inductor shown in Figure 22 is an approximation. The series resistance is distributed along the length of the wire, as is the interwinding capacitance. A more accurate model for a real inductor would break each of the parasitic effects into many segments (possibly, an infinite number). Ultimately, we could abandon circuit models altogether and use field theory directly.

Rarely is this degree of detail necessary. Usually, modeling a real inductor as an inductance, including at most a few parasitic effects, is sufficiently accurate. Of course, computer-aided circuit analysis allows us to use more complex models and achieve more accurate results than traditional mathematical analysis.

7 MUTUAL INDUCTANCE

Sometimes, several coils are wound on the same form so that magnetic flux produced by one coil links the others. Then a time-varying current flowing through one coil induces voltages in the other coils. The circuit symbols for two mutually coupled inductances are shown in Figure 23. The **self inductances** of the two coils are denoted as L_1 and L_2, respectively. The **mutual inductance** is denoted as M, which also has units of henries. Notice that we have selected the passive reference configuration for each coil in Figure 23.

The equations relating the voltages to the currents are also shown in Figure 23. The mutual terms, $M \, di_1/dt$ and $M \, di_2/dt$, appear because of the mutual coupling of the coils. The self terms, $L_1 \, di_1/dt$ and $L_2 \, di_2/dt$, are the voltages induced in each coil due to its own current.

The magnetic flux produced by one coil can either aid or oppose the flux produced by the other coil. The dots on the ends of the coils indicate whether the fields are aiding or opposing. If one current enters a dotted terminal and the other leaves, the fields oppose one another. For example, if both i_1 and i_2 have positive values in Figure 23(b), the fields are opposing. If both currents enter the respective dots (or if both leave), the fields aid. Thus, if both i_1 and i_2 have positive values in Figure 23(a), the fields are aiding.

> The magnetic flux produced by one coil can either aid or oppose the flux produced by the other coil.

The signs of the mutual terms in the equations for the voltages depend on how the currents are referenced with respect to the dots. If both currents are referenced into (or if both are referenced out of) the dotted terminals, as in Figure 23(a), the mutual term is positive. If one current is referenced into a dot and the other out, as in Figure 23(b), the mutual term carries a negative sign.

Linear Variable Differential Transformer

An application of mutual inductance can be found in a position transducer known as the linear variable differential transformer (LVDT), illustrated in Figure 24. An ac source connected to the center coil sets up a magnetic field that links both halves of

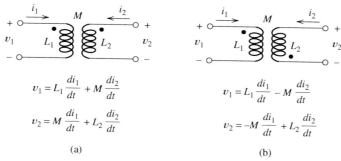

$$v_1 = L_1 \frac{di_1}{dt} + M \frac{di_2}{dt}$$

$$v_2 = M \frac{di_1}{dt} + L_2 \frac{di_2}{dt}$$

(a)

$$v_1 = L_1 \frac{di_1}{dt} - M \frac{di_2}{dt}$$

$$v_2 = -M \frac{di_1}{dt} + L_2 \frac{di_2}{dt}$$

(b)

Figure 23 Circuit symbols and $v - i$ relationships for mutually coupled inductances.

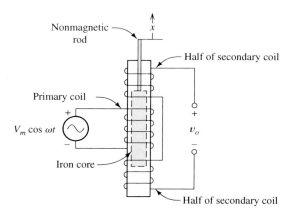

Figure 24 A linear variable differential transformer used as a position transducer.

the secondary coil. When the iron core is centered in the coils, the voltages induced in the two halves of the secondary cancel so that $v_o(t) = 0$. (Notice that the two halves of the secondary winding are wound in opposite directions.) As the core moves up or down, the couplings between the primary and the halves of the secondary change. The voltage across one half of the coil becomes smaller, and the voltage across the other half becomes greater. Ideally, the output voltage is given by

$$v_o(t) = Kx \cos(\omega t)$$

where x is the displacement of the core. LVDTs are used in applications such as automated manufacturing operations to measure displacements.

8 SYMBOLIC INTEGRATION AND DIFFERENTIATION USING MATLAB

This section contains several examples that apply the symbolic math features of MATLAB to the current–voltage relationships for inductance and capacitance, including plotting the results.

One note of caution: We have developed the examples, exercises, and problems using MATLAB version R2008a, which uses the Maple kernel from Maplesoft for symbolic math. Starting with version R2008b of MATLAB, the Symbolic Toolbox is based on the use of MuPAD. As of mid-2009, not all of the examples and problems in this book can be run successfully with these new versions. Mathworks, the maker of MATLAB, is aware of the bugs and is working to correct them. Keep in mind that if you use versions other than R2008a, you may not be able to reproduce our results. Try running our example m-files before sinking a lot of time into solving the problems. Hopefully, your instructor can give you some guidance on what to expect with the MATLAB versions available to you.

In the following, we assume that you have some familiarity with MATLAB. A variety of online interactive tutorials are available at http://www.mathworks. com/academia/student_center/tutorials/register.html. However, you should find it easy to write MATLAB instructions for the exercises and problems in this chapter by modeling your solutions after the code in our examples.

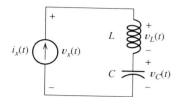

Figure 25 Circuit of Example 8.

Example 8 | Integration and Differentiation Using the MATLAB Symbolic Toolbox

Use MATLAB to find expressions for the three voltages shown in Figure 25 given $v_C(0) = 0$ and

$$i_x(t) = kt^2 \exp(-at) \sin(\omega t) \text{ for } t \geq 0$$
$$= 0 \text{ for } t < 0 \tag{39}$$

Also, plot the current and the voltages for $k = 3, a = 2, \omega = 1, L = 0.5 \text{ H}, C = 1 \text{ F}$, and $t \geq 0$. (These values have been chosen mainly to facilitate the demonstration of MATLAB capabilities.) The currents are in amperes, voltages are in volts, ωt is in radians, and time t is in seconds. *Note:* We have successfully executed this example with MATLAB versions R2008a, R2008b, and R2009a.

Solution At first, we use symbols to represent the various parameters (k, a, ω, L, and C), denoting the current and the voltages as ix, vx, vL, and vC. Then, we substitute the numerical values for the symbols and denote the results as ixn, vxn, vLn, and vCn. (The letter "n" is selected to suggest that the "numerical" values of the parameters have been substituted into the expressions.) ∎

We show the commands in **boldface**, comments in regular font, and MATLAB responses in color. Comments (starting with the % sign) are ignored by MATLAB. We present the work as if we were entering the commands and comments one at a time in the MATLAB command window, however, it is usually more convenient to place all of the commands in an m-file and execute them as a group.

To start, we define the various symbols as symbolic objects in MATLAB, define the current ix, and substitute the numerical values of the parameters to obtain ixn.

```
>> clear % Clear work area of previous work.
>> syms vx ix vC vL vxn ixn vCn vLn k a w t L C
>> % Names for symbolic objects must start with a letter and
>> % contain only alpha-numeric characters.
>> % Next, we define ix.
>> ix=k*t^2*exp(-a*t)*sin(w*t)
     ix =
     k*t^2*exp(-a*t)*sin(w*t)
>> % Next, we substitute k=3, a=2, and w=1
>> % into ix and denote the result as ixn.
>> ixn = subs(ix,[k a w],[3 2 1])
     ixn =
     3*t^2*exp(-2*t)*sin(t)
```

Next, we want to plot the current versus time. We need to consider what range of t should be used for the plot. In standard mathematical typesetting, the expression we need to plot is

$$i_x(t) = 3t^2 \exp(-2t) \sin(t) \text{ for } t \geq 0$$
$$= 0 \text{ for } t < 0$$

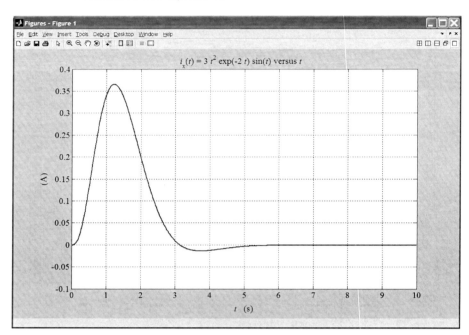

Figure 26 Plot of $i_x(t)$ produced by MATLAB.

Thoughtful examination of this expression (perhaps supplemented with a little work with a calculator) reveals that the current is zero at $t = 0$, builds up quickly after $t = 0$ because of the t^2 term, and decays to relatively small values after about $t = 10$ s because of the exponential term. Thus, we select the range from $t = 0$ to $t = 10$ s for the plot. Continuing in MATLAB, we have

```
>> % Next, we plot ixn for t ranging from 0 to 10s.
>> ezplot(ixn,[0,10])
```

This opens a window with a plot of the current versus time as shown in Figure 26. As expected, the current increases rapidly after $t = 0$ and decays to insignificant values by $t = 10$ s. (We have used various Edit menu commands to improve the appearance of the plot for inclusion in this book.)

Next, we determine the inductance voltage, which is given by

$$v_L(t) = L\frac{di_x(t)}{dt}$$

in which the parameters, a, k, and ω are treated as constants. The corresponding MATLAB command and the result are:

```
>> vL=L*diff(ix,t) % L times the derivative of ix with respect to t.
    vL =
    L*(2*k*t*exp(-a*t)*sin(w*t)-k*t^2*a*exp(-a*t)*sin(w*t)
    +k*t^2*exp(-a*t)*cos(w*t)*w)
>> % A nicer display for vL is produced with the commands:
>> vL = simple(vL);
>> pretty(vL)
    (2sin(w t) - t a sin(w t) + t cos(w t) w) L k t exp(-a t)
```

In more standard mathematical typesetting, this becomes

$$v_L(t) = Lkt\exp(-at)[2\sin(\omega t) - at\sin(\omega t) + \omega t\cos(\omega t)]$$

which we can verify by manually differentiating the right-hand side of Equation 39 and multiplying by L. Next, we determine the voltage across the capacitance.

$$v_C(t) = \frac{1}{C} \int_0^t i_x(t)dt + v_C(0) \text{ for } t \geq 0$$

Substituting the expressions for the current and initial voltage we obtain,

$$v_C(t) = \frac{1}{C} \int_0^t kt^2 \exp(-at) \sin(\omega t)dt \text{ for } t \geq 0$$

This is not a simple integration to perform by hand, but we can accomplish it easily with MATLAB:

```
>> % Integrate ix with respect to t with limits from 0 to t.
>> vC=(1/C)*int(ix,t,0,t);
>> % We included the semicolon to suppress the output, which is
>> % much too complex for easy interpretation.
>> % Next, we find the total voltage vx.
>> vx = vC + vL;
>> % Now we substitute numerical values for the parameters.
>> vLn=subs(vL,[k a w L C],[3 2 1 0.5 1]);
>> vCn=subs(vC,[k a w L C],[3 2 1 0.5 1]);
>> vxn=subs(vx,[k a w L C],[3 2 1 0.5 1]);
>> % Finally, we plot all three voltages in the same window.
>> figure % Open a new figure for this plot.
>> ezplot(vLn,[0,10])
>> hold on % Hold so the following two plots are on the same axes.
>> ezplot(vCn,[0,10])
>> ezplot(vxn,[0,10])
```

The resulting plot is shown in Figure 27. (Here again, we have used various items on the Edit menu to change the scale of the vertical axis and dress up the plot for inclusion in this book.)

The commands for this example are included as an m-file named Example_3_8 in the MATLAB files. If you copy the file and place it in a folder in the MATLAB path for your computer, you can run the file and experiment with it. For example, after running the m-file, if you enter the command

```
>> simple(vC)
```

you will see the rather complicated symbolic mathematical expression for the voltage across the capacitance. ∎

Piecewise Functions in MATLAB

Earlier in this chapter, we often worked with currents or voltages that were described in a piecewise manner with different mathematical expressions over various time intervals. Example 6 is a typical example. We will see that MATLAB can handle functions that are defined in piecewise fashion by use of the unit step function

$$
\begin{aligned}
u(t) &= 0 \quad t < 0 \\
&= 1 \quad t > 0
\end{aligned}
\tag{40}
$$

155

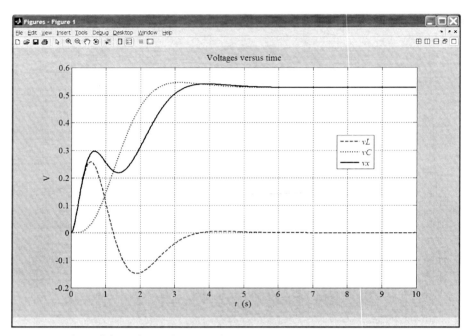

Figure 27 Plots of the voltages for Example 8.

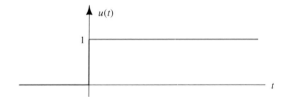

Figure 28 The unit step function.

The unit step function is plotted in Figure 28. In mathematics and in MATLAB, $u(t)$ is known as the Heaviside step function after Oliver Heaviside, an early electrical engineer who pioneered the analysis of electrical circuits and coined many of the terms we use today, such as inductance, conductance, and impedance, among others. [For $t = 0, u(t)$ is not defined, because it is not physically significant.]

Suppose we have two points in time t_a and t_b in which $t_a < t_b$. In other words, t_a is earlier in time than t_b. Then, as shown in Figure 29, we have

$$u(t - t_a) - u(t - t_b) = 1 \quad \text{for } t_a < t < t_b$$
$$= 0 \quad \text{otherwise}$$

If we multiply any function by $[u(t - t_a) - u(t - t_b)]$, we will be left with only the portion of the function between t_a and t_b. By adding a number of such terms, we can write a single equation for any function that is defined in a piecewise manner. Furthermore, we can integrate, differentiate, and otherwise manipulate these equations using the Symbolic Toolbox in MATLAB. We illustrate with an example.

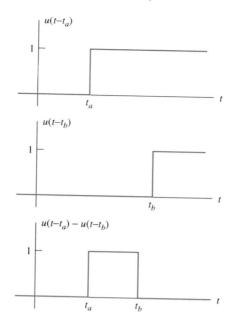

Figure 29 $u(t - t_a) - u(t - t_b)$ is unity only for $t_a < t < t_b$.

Example 9   Integration and Differentiation of Piecewise Continuous Functions

The current flowing through a 0.5-μF capacitance is defined in piecewise fashion as

$$i_C(t) = 2.5t \qquad\qquad\qquad\quad 0 < t < 2 \text{ ms}$$
$$= 5 \times 10^{-3} \qquad\qquad\quad\;\; 2 \text{ ms} < t < 4 \text{ ms}$$
$$= -10 \times 10^{-3} \sin(500\pi t) \quad 4 \text{ ms} < t < 6 \text{ ms}$$
$$= 0 \qquad\qquad\qquad\qquad\;\; \text{otherwise}$$

Write a single equation for $i_C(t)$ using the unit step function. Then, use MATLAB to plot the current for $-2 \text{ ms} < t < 8 \text{ ms}$, determine the voltage across the capacitance as a function of time, and plot the voltage. Assume that the passive reference configuration applies to the current and voltage. (That is, the current reference enters the capacitance at the positive reference for the voltage.) (*Note:* We have executed this example successfully with MATLAB version R2008a but not with later versions.)

Solution   We have three intervals with nonzero descriptions. We use a pair of step functions to write the term for each of these intervals. Thus, the equation for the current is

$$i_C(t) = 2.5t \left[u(t) - u\left(t - 2 \times 10^{-3}\right) \right]$$
$$+ 5 \times 10^{-3} \left[u\left(t - 2 \times 10^{-3}\right) - u\left(t - 4 \times 10^{-3}\right) \right]$$
$$- 10 \times 10^{-3} \sin(500\pi t) \left[u\left(t - 4 \times 10^{-3}\right) - u\left(t - 6 \times 10^{-3}\right) \right]$$

Notice that $\left[u(t) - u\left(t - 2 \times 10^{-3}\right) \right]$ is unity only for t between 0 and 2 ms, $\left[u\left(t - 2 \times 10^{-3}\right) - u\left(t - 4 \times 10^{-3}\right) \right]$ is unity only for t between 2 and 4 ms, and

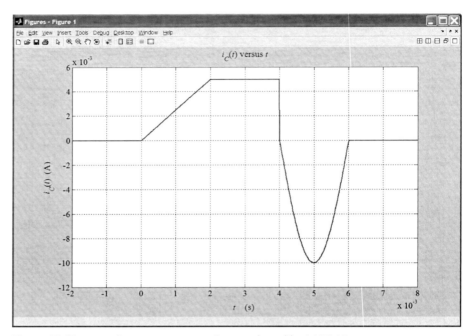

Figure 30 The capacitor current versus time as plotted by MATLAB.

so forth. Thus, each bracketed set of step functions picks out one segment of the piecewise definition.

The equation appears almost identical in MATLAB, except that $u(t)$ is expressed as heaviside(t). The commands to define and plot the current are:

```
>> clear
>> syms t iC vC % Define t, iC and vC as symbolic objects.
>> iC = 2.5*t*(heaviside(t) - heaviside(t-2e-3)) + ...
    5e-3*(heaviside(t-2e-3) - heaviside(t-4e-3)) + ...
    ((-10e-3)*sin(500*pi*t))*(heaviside(t-4e-3) - heaviside(t-6e-3));
>> ezplot(iC, [-2e-3 8e-3])
```

The resulting plot (after a little editing to clean it up) is shown in Figure 30. The voltage is given by,

$$v_C(t) = \frac{1}{C} \int_0^t i_C(t)dt + v_C(0)$$

Continuing in MATLAB:

```
>> figure % Plot the voltage in a new window.
>> vC=2e6*int(iC,t,0,t); % vC equals 1/C times the integral of iC.
>> ezplot(vC, [-2e-3 8e-3])
```

The resulting plot is shown in Figure 31. An m-file (named Example_3_9) containing the commands of this example can be found in the MATLAB folder.

■

Exercise 11 Use MATLAB to work Example 2 resulting in plots like those in Figure 5.

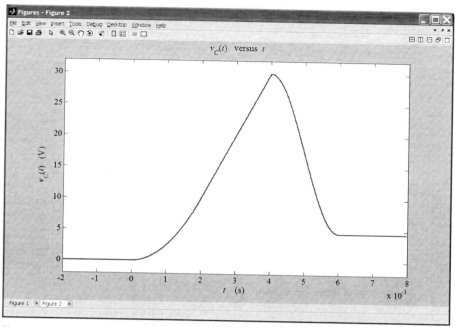

Figure 31 The capacitor voltage versus time as plotted by MATLAB.

Answer The MATLAB commands including some explanatory comments are:

```
clear % Clear the work area.
% We avoid using i alone as a symbol for current because
% we reserve i for the square root of -1 in MATLAB. Thus, we
% will use iC for the capacitor current.
syms t iC qC vC % Define t, iC, qC and vC as symbolic objects.
iC = 0.5*sin((1e4)*t);
ezplot(iC, [0 3*pi*1e-4])
qC=int(iC,t,0,t); % qC equals the integral of iC.
figure % Plot the charge in a new window.
ezplot(qC, [0 3*pi*1e-4])
vC = 1e7*qC;
figure % Plot the voltage in a new window.
ezplot(vC, [0 3*pi*1e-4])
```

The plots are very similar to those of Figure 5. An m-file (named Exercise_3_11) can be found in the MATLAB folder. □

Exercise 12 Use MATLAB to work Example 3 generating plots like those in Figure 6. Use the Heaviside step function to write the expression for $v(t)$.

Answer The MATLAB commands including some explanatory comments are:

```
clear % Clear the work area.
% We avoid using i by itself as a symbol for current because
% we reserve i for the square root of -1 in MATLAB. Thus, we
% will use iC for the capacitor current.
syms t vC iC pC wC % Define t, vC, iC, pC and wC as symbolic objects.
vC = 1000*t*(heaviside(t) - heaviside(t-1)) + ...
     1000*(heaviside(t-1) - heaviside(t-3)) + ...
     500*(5-t)*(heaviside(t-3) - heaviside(t-5));
ezplot(vC, [0 6])
iC = (10e-6)*diff(vC, 't'); % iC equals C times the derivative of vC.
```

159

```
figure % Plot the current in a new window.
ezplot(iC, [0 6])
pC = vC*iC;
figure % Plot the power in a new window.
ezplot(pC, [0 6])
wC = (1/2)*(10e-6)*vC^2;
figure % Plot the energy in a new window.
ezplot(wC, [0 6])
```

The plots are very similar to those of Figure 6. An m-file (named Exercise_3_12) can be found in the MATLAB folder. We have run this code successfully with versions R2008a, R2008b, and R2009a.

$\square$

Summary

1. Capacitance is the circuit property that accounts for electric-field effects. The units of capacitance are farads (F), which are equivalent to coulombs per volt.

2. The charge stored by a capacitance is given by $q = Cv$.

3. The relationships between current and voltage for a capacitance are

$$i = C\frac{dv}{dt}$$

and

$$v(t) = \frac{1}{C}\int_{t_0}^{t} i(t)\,dt + v(t_0)$$

4. The energy stored by a capacitance is given by

$$w(t) = \frac{1}{2}Cv^2(t)$$

5. Capacitances in series are combined in the same manner as resistances in parallel.

6. Capacitances in parallel are combined in the same manner as resistances in series.

7. The capacitance of a parallel-plate capacitor is given by

$$C = \frac{\epsilon A}{d}$$

For vacuum, the dielectric constant is $\epsilon = \epsilon_0 \cong 8.85 \times 10^{-12}$ F/m. For other materials, the dielectric constant is $\epsilon = \epsilon_r\epsilon_0$, where ϵ_r is the relative dielectric constant.

8. Real capacitors have several parasitic effects.

9. Inductance accounts for magnetic-field effects. The units of inductance are henries (H).

10. The relationships between current and voltage for an inductance are

$$v(t) = L\frac{di}{dt}$$

and

$$i(t) = \frac{1}{L}\int_{t_0}^{t} v(t)\,dt + i(t_0)$$

11. The energy stored in an inductance is given by

$$w(t) = \frac{1}{2}Li^2(t)$$

12. Inductances in series or parallel are combined in the same manner as resistances.

13. Real inductors have several parasitic effects.

14. Mutual inductance accounts for mutual coupling of magnetic fields between coils.

15. MATLAB is a powerful tool for symbolic integration, differentiation, and plotting of functions. The Heaviside step function, also known as the unit step function, allows us to readily define functions in piecewise fashion.

Problems

Section 1: Capacitance

P1. What is a dielectric material? Give two examples.

P2. Briefly discuss how current can flow "through" a capacitor even though a non-conducting layer separates the metallic parts.

P3. Describe the internal construction of capacitors.

P4. What current flows through an ideal capacitor if the voltage across the capacitor is constant with time? To what circuit element is an ideal capacitor equivalent in circuits for which the currents and voltages are constant with time?

*P5. A 2000-μF capacitor, initially charged to 100 V, is discharged by a steady current of $100 \, \mu$A. How long does it take to discharge the capacitor to 0 V?

*P6. The voltage across a 10-μF capacitor is given by $v(t) = 100 \sin(1000t)$. Find expressions for the current, power, and stored energy. Sketch the waveforms to scale versus time.

*P7. A constant (dc) current $i(t) = 3$ mA flows into a 50-μF capacitor. The voltage at $t = 0$ is $v(0) = -20$ V. The references for $v(t)$ and $i(t)$ have the passive configuration. Find the power at $t = 0$ and state whether the power flow is into or out of the capacitor. Repeat for $t = 1$ s.

*P8. We want to store sufficient energy in a 0.01-F capacitor to supply 5 horsepower (hp) for one hour. To what voltage must the capacitor be charged? (*Note:* 1 hp is equivalent to 745.7 W.) Does this seem to be a practical method for storing this amount of energy? Do you think that an electric automobile design based on capacitive energy storage is feasible?

P9. We have a 1-μF capacitor with 200 V between its terminals. Determine the magnitude of the net charge stored on each plate and the total net charge on both plates.

P10. Suppose we have a 10-μF capacitor and the voltage across it is given by $v_C(t) = 10e^{-500t}$.

Find expressions for the current, power, and stored energy. Sketch the waveforms to scale versus time.

P11. Suppose we have a 15-μF capacitor that is charged to 500 V. Determine the initial stored charge and energy. If this capacitor is discharged to 0 V in a time interval of 4μs, find the average power delivered by the capacitor during the discharge interval.

P12. Starting at $t = 0$, the voltage across a 100-μF capacitor is increased linearly with time to 200 V in 5 ms. Then, the voltage remains constant at 200 V. Sketch the voltage, current, power, and stored energy to scale versus time.

P13. The current through a 2-μF capacitor is shown in Figure P13. At $t = 0$, the voltage is zero. Sketch the voltage, power, and stored energy to scale versus time.

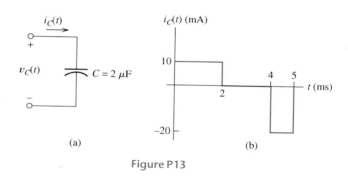

(a)   (b)

Figure P13

P14. Find the voltage, power, and stored energy at $t = 20$ ms for the capacitance in the circuit of Figure P14.

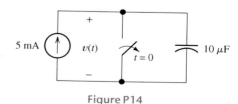

Figure P14

---

*   Denotes that answers are contained in the Student Solutions files.

P15. A current given by $i(t) = I_m \cos(\omega t)$ flows through a capacitance C. The voltage is zero at $t = 0$. Suppose that ω is very large, ideally approaching infinity. For this current, does the capacitance approximate either an open or a short circuit? Explain.

P16. The current through a 5-μF capacitor is shown in Figure P16. At $t = 0$, the voltage is $v_C(0) = 0$ V. Sketch the voltage, power, and stored energy to scale versus time.

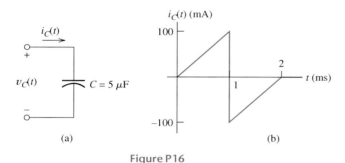

(a)   (b)

Figure P16

P17. The energy stored in a 40-μF capacitor is 80 J and is decreasing at 200 J/s at $t = 3$ s. Determine the voltage magnitude and current magnitude at $t = 3$ s. Does the current enter or leave the positive terminal of the capacitor?

P18. A certain parallel-plate capacitor, which has one plate rotating so the overlap of the plates is a function of time, has a capacitance given by

$$C = 200 + 50 \sin(5000t) \text{ pF}$$

in which the argument of the cosine function is in radians. A constant voltage of 50 V is applied to this capacitor. Determine the current as a function of time.

P19. Suppose we have a very large capacitance (ideally, infinite) charged to 10 V. What other circuit element has the same current–voltage relationship? Explain your answer.

P20. At $t = t_0$, the voltage across a certain capacitance C is zero. A pulse of current flows through the capacitance between t_0 and $t_0 + \Delta t$, and the voltage across the capacitance increases to V_f. What can you say about the peak amplitude I_m and area under the pulse

waveform (i.e., current versus time)? What are the units and physical significance of the area under the pulse? What must happen to the peak amplitude and area under the pulse as Δt approaches zero, assuming that V_f remains the same?

P21. For a resistor, what resistance corresponds to a short circuit? For an uncharged capacitor, what value of capacitance corresponds to a short circuit? Explain your answers. Repeat for an open circuit.

P22. A 20-μF capacitor has a voltage given by $v(t) = 10 - 10 \exp(-2000t)$ V. Find the power at $t = 0$ and state whether the power flow is into or out of the capacitor. Repeat for $t_2 = 0.5$ ms.

Section 2: Capacitances in Series and Parallel

P23. Describe how are capacitances combined in series and in parallel. Compare with how resistances are combined.

*P24. Find the equivalent capacitance for each of the circuits shown in Figure P24.

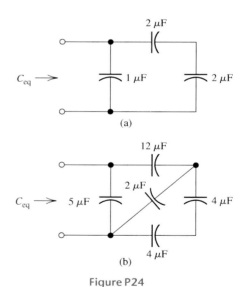

Figure P24

*P25. Suppose that we are designing a cardiac pacemaker circuit. The circuit is required to deliver pulses of 1-ms duration to the heart, which can be modeled as a 500-Ω resistance. The peak amplitude of the pulses is required to be 5 V. However, the battery delivers only

2.5 V. Therefore, we decide to charge two equal-value capacitors in parallel from the 2.5-V battery and then switch the capacitors in series with the heart during the 1-ms pulse. What is the minimum value of the capacitances required so the output pulse amplitude remains between 4.9 V and 5.0 V throughout its 1-ms duration? If the pulses occur once every second, what is the average current drain from the battery? Use approximate calculations, assuming constant current during the output pulse. Find the ampere-hour rating of the battery so it lasts for five years.

P26. Find the equivalent capacitance between terminals x and y for each of the circuits shown in Figure P26.

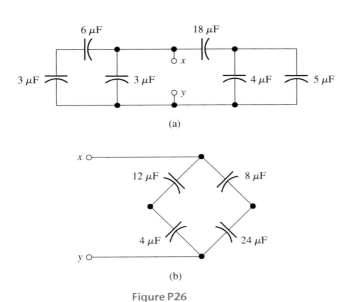

(a)

(b)

Figure P26

P27. We start with two initially uncharged capacitors $C_1 = 5\mu F$ and $C_2 = 20\mu F$ connected in series. Then, a 20-V source is connected to the series combination, as shown in Figure P27. Find the voltages v_1 and v_2 after the source is applied. (*Hint:* The charges stored on the two capacitors must be equal, because the current is the same for both capacitors.)

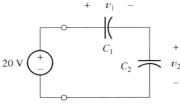

Figure P27

P28. Capacitor $C_1 = 200\ \mu F$ is charged to an initial voltage of 50 V, and capacitor $C_2 = 200\ \mu F$ is charged to 100 V. If they are placed in series with the positive terminal of the first connected to the positive terminal of the second, determine the equivalent capacitance and its initial voltage. Now, compute the total energy stored in the two capacitors. Compute the energy stored in the equivalent capacitance. Why is it less than the total energy stored in the original capacitors?

P29. A 1-μF capacitance is in parallel with the series combination of a 6-μF capacitance and a 3-μF capacitance. Sketch the circuit diagram and determine the equivalent capacitance of the combination.

P30. Find the minimum and maximum values of capacitance that can be obtained by connecting three 1-μF capacitors in series and/or parallel. How should the capacitors be connected in each case?

Section 3: Physical Characteristics of Capacitors

*P31. Determine the capacitance of a parallel-plate capacitor having plates 10 cm by 30 cm separated by 0.01 mm. The dielectric has $\epsilon_r = 15$.

*P32. Suppose that we have a 1000-pF parallel-plate capacitor with air dielectric charged to 1000 V. The capacitor terminals are open circuited. Find the stored energy. If the plates are moved farther apart so that d is doubled, determine the new voltage on the capacitor and the new stored energy. Where did the extra energy come from?

P33. A 200-pF capacitor is constructed of parallel plates of metal, each having a width W and a length L. The plates are separated by air with a distance d. Assume that L and W are both much larger than d. What is the new capacitance if: **a.** both L and W are halved and the other parameters are unchanged? **b.** the separation d is halved and the other parameters are unchanged from their initial values? **c.** the air dielectric is replaced with oil having a relative dielectric constant of 35 and the other parameters are unchanged from their initial values?

P34. Consider a parallel-plate capacitor with plates of metal each having a width W and a length L. The plates are separated by the distance d. Assume that L and W are both much larger than d. The maximum voltage that can be applied is limited to $V_{max} = Kd$, in which K is called the breakdown strength of the dielectric. Derive an expression for the maximum energy that can be stored in the capacitor in terms of K and the volume of the dielectric. If we want to store the maximum energy per unit volume, does it matter what values are chosen for $L, W,$ and d? What parameters are important?

P35. A microphone can be formed from a parallel-plate capacitor arranged so the acoustic pressure of the sound wave affects the distance between the plates. Suppose we have such a microphone in which the plates have an area of 10 cm^2, the dielectric is air, and the distance between the plates is a function of time given by

$$d(t) = 100 + 0.5 \, \cos(5000t) \mu m$$

A constant voltage of 200 V is applied to the plates. Determine the current through the capacitance as a function of time by using the approximation $1/(1 + x) \cong 1 - x$ for $x << 1$. (The argument of the sinusoid is in radians.)

P36. Consider a liquid-level transducer, which consists of two parallel plates of conductor immersed in an insulating liquid, as illustrated in Figure P36. When the tank is empty (i.e., $x = 0$), the capacitance of the plates is 100 pF. The relative dielectric constant of the liquid is 35. Determine an expression for the capacitance C as a function of the height x of the liquid.

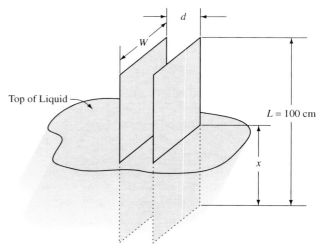

Figure P3.36

P37. A parallel-plate capacitor like that shown in Figure P36 has a capacitance of 2500 pF when the tank is full so the plates are totally immersed in the insulating liquid. (The dielectric constant of the fluid and plate dimensions are different for this problem than for Problem P36.) The capacitance is 100 pF when the tank is empty and the space between the plates is filled with air. Suppose that the tank is full and the capacitance is charged to 1000 V. Then, the capacitance is open circuited so the charge on the plates cannot change, and the tank is drained. Compute the voltage after the tank is drained and the electrical energy stored in the capacitor before and after the tank is drained. With the plates open circuited, there is no electrical source for the extra energy. Where could it have come from?

P38. A 1-μF capacitor has a parasitic series resistance of 2 Ω, as shown in Figure P38. Suppose that the voltage across the capacitance is $v_C(t) = 10 \, \cos(100t)$; find the voltage across the resistance. In this situation, to find the total voltage $v(t) = v_r(t) + v_C(t)$ to within 1 percent accuracy, is it necessary to include the parasitic resistance? Repeat if $v_C(t) = 0.1 \, \cos(10^7t)$.

164

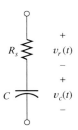

Figure P38

P39. Suppose that a parallel-plate capacitor has a dielectric that breaks down if the electric field exceeds K V/m. Thus, the maximum voltage rating of the capacitor is $V_{max} = Kd$, where d is the thickness of the dielectric. In working Problem P33, we find that the maximum energy that can be stored before breakdown is $w_{max} = 1/2\epsilon_r\epsilon_0 K^2(\text{Vol})$ in which Vol is the volume of the dielectric. Air has approximately $K = 32 \times 10^5$ V/m and $\epsilon_r = 1$. Find the minimum volume of air (as a dielectric in a parallel plate capacitor) needed to store the energy content of one U.S. gallon of gasoline, which is approximately 132 MJ. What thickness should the air dielectric have if we want the voltage for maximum energy storage to be 10 kV?

P40. As shown in Figure P40, two 10-μF capacitors have an initial voltage of 50 V before the switch is closed. Find the total stored energy before the switch is closed. Find the voltage across each capacitor and the total stored energy after the switch is closed. What could have happened to the energy?

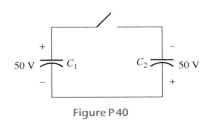

Figure P40

Section 4: Inductance

P41. Briefly discuss how inductors are constructed.

P42. Briefly discuss the fluid-flow analogy for an inductor.

*P43. The current flowing through a 2-H inductance is shown in Figure P43. Sketch the voltage, power, and stored energy versus time.

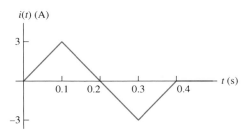

Figure P43

*P44. A constant voltage of 10 V is applied to a 50-μH inductance, as shown in Figure P44. The current in the inductance at $t = 0$ is -100 mA. At what time t_x does the current reach $+100$ mA?

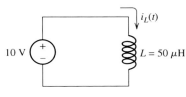

Figure P44

*P45. At $t = 0$, the current flowing in a 0.5-H inductance is 4 A. What constant voltage must be applied to reduce the current to 0 at $t = 0.2$ s?

P46. Starting at $t = 0$, a constant 12-V voltage source is applied to a 2-H inductor. Assume an initial current of zero for the inductor. Determine the current, power, and stored energy at $t_1 = 1$ s.

P47. If the current through an ideal inductor is constant with time, what is the value of the voltage across the inductor? To what circuit element is an ideal inductor equivalent for circuits with constant currents and voltages?

P48. The current flowing through an inductor is increasing in magnitude. Is energy flowing into or out of the inductor?

P49. The current flowing through a 200-mH inductance is given by $2 \cos(2000\pi t)$ A, in which the angle is in radians. Find expressions and sketch the waveforms to scale for the voltage, power, and stored energy, allowing t to range from 0 to 2 ms.

P50. The current flowing through a 300-mH inductance is given by $5\exp(-200t)$ A. Find expressions for the voltage, power, and stored energy. Sketch the waveforms to scale for $0 < t < 20$ ms.

P51. The voltage across a 0.5-H inductance is shown in Figure P51. The initial current in the inductance is $i_L(0) = 0$. Sketch the current, power, and stored energy to scale versus time.

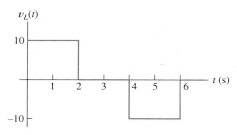

Figure P51

P52. Suppose we have a very large (ideally, infinite) inductance having an initial current of 10 A. What is an equivalent circuit element? Explain your answer.

P53. The voltage across a 50-μH inductance is given by $v_L(t) = 5\cos(2\pi 10^6 t)$ V. The initial current is $i_L(0) = 0$. Find expressions for the current, power, and stored energy for $t > 0$. Sketch the waveforms to scale versus time from 0 to 2 μs.

P54. Before $t = 0$, the current in a 5-H inductance is zero. Starting at $t = 0$, the current is increased linearly with time to 15 A in 3 s. Then, the current remains constant at 15 A. Sketch the voltage, current, power, and stored energy to scale versus time.

P55. We have an inductance L with an initial current of zero and the voltage across the inductance is given by $v(t) = V_m\cos(\omega t)$. Suppose that ω is very large—ideally, approaching infinity. For this voltage, does the inductance approximate either an open or a short circuit? Explain.

P56. At $t = t_0$, the current through a certain inductance is zero. A voltage pulse is applied to the inductance between t_0 and $t_0 + \Delta t$, and the current through the inductance increases to I_f. What can you say about the peak amplitude V_m and area under the pulse waveform (i.e., voltage versus time)? What are the units of the area under the pulse? What must happen to the peak amplitude and area under the pulse as Δt approaches zero, assuming that I_f remains the same?

P57. The energy stored in a 2-H inductor is 400 J and is decreasing at 200 J/s at $t = 4$ s. Determine the voltage magnitude and current magnitude at $t = 4$ s. Does the current enter or leave the positive terminal of the inductor?

P58. Assuming zero initial current, what value of inductance corresponds to an open circuit? Explain your answer. Repeat for a short circuit.

Section 5: Inductances in Series and Parallel

P59. Describe how inductances are combined in series and in parallel. Compare with how resistances are combined.

*P60. Determine the equivalent inductance for each of the series and parallel combinations shown in Figure P60.

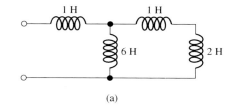

(a)

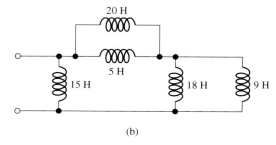

(b)

Figure P60

*P61. Two inductances $L_1 = 1$ H and $L_2 = 2$ H are connected in parallel as shown in

Figure P61. The initial currents are $i_1(0) = 0$ and $i_2(0) = 0$. Find an expression for $i_1(t)$ in terms of $i(t)$, L_1, and L_2. Repeat for $i_2(t)$. Comment.

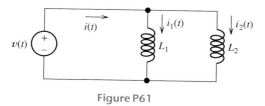

Figure P61

P62. Find the equivalent inductance for each of the series and parallel combinations shown in Figure P62.

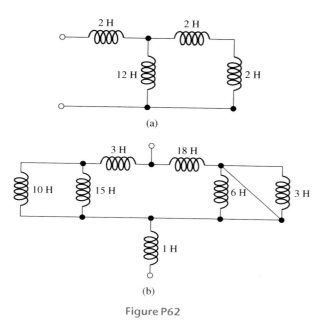

Figure P62

P63. Suppose that we need to combine (in series or in parallel) an unknown inductance L with a second inductance of 4 H to attain an equivalent inductance of 7 H. Should L be placed in series or in parallel with the original inductance? What value is required for L?

P64. Suppose we have three 6-H inductances. What is the maximum inductance that can be obtained by connecting all of the inductances in series and/or parallel? What is the minimum inductance?

P65. We need to combine (in series or in parallel) an unknown inductance L with a second inductance of 4 H to attain an equivalent inductance of 3 H. Should L be placed in series or in parallel with the original inductance? What value is required for L?

Section 6: Practical Inductors

P66. Draw the equivalent circuit for a real inductor, including three parasitic effects.

P67. A 10-mH inductor has a parasitic series resistance of $R_s = 0.5\ \Omega$, as shown in Figure P67. **a.** The current is given by $i(t) = 0.1\sin(20t)$. Find $v_R(t)$, $v_L(t)$, and $v(t)$. In this case, for one-percent accuracy in computing $v(t)$, could the resistance be neglected? **b.** Repeat if $i(t) = 0.1\sin(10^6 t)$.

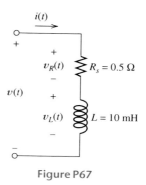

Figure P67

P68. Find $v(t)$, $i_C(t)$, $i(t)$, the energy stored in the capacitance, the energy stored in the inductance, and the total stored energy for the circuit of Figure P68, given that $i_L(t) = \cos(5000t)$ A. (The argument of the cosine function is in radians.) Show that the total stored energy is constant with time. Comment on the results.

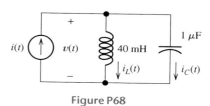

Figure P68

P69. A constant current of 200 mA flows through a real inductor, and the voltage across its external terminals is 400 mV. Which of the circuit parameters of Figure 22 can be deduced from this information and what is its value?

P70. Find $i(t)$, $v_L(t)$, $v(t)$, the energy stored in the capacitance, the energy stored in the inductance, and the total stored energy for the circuit of Figure P70, given that $v_C(t) = 10 \cos(1000t)$ V. (The argument of the cosine function is in radians.) Show that the total stored energy is constant with time. Comment on the results.

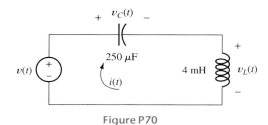

Figure P70

Section 7: Mutual Inductance

P71. Describe briefly the physical basis for mutual inductance.

*P72. **a.** Derive an expression for the equivalent inductance for the circuit shown in Figure P72. **b.** Repeat if the dot for L_2 is moved to the bottom end.

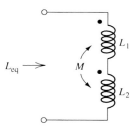

Figure P72

P73. The mutually coupled inductances in Figure P73 have $L_1 = 1$ H, $L_2 = 2$ H, and $M = 1$ H. Furthermore, $i_1(t) = \sin(20t)$ A and $i_2(t) = 0.5 \sin(30t)$ A. **a.** Find expressions for $v_1(t)$ and $v_2(t)$. **b.** Repeat with the dot placed at the bottom of L_2.

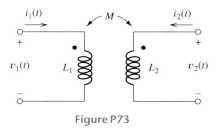

Figure P73

P74. A pair of mutually coupled inductances has $L_1 = 2$ H, $L_2 = 1$ H, $i_1 = 10 \cos(1000t)$ A, $i_2 = 0$, and $v_2 = -5000 \sin(1000t)$ V. Find $v_1(t)$ and the magnitude of the mutual inductance.

P75. Consider the mutually coupled inductors shown in Figure 23(a) with a short connected across the terminals of L_2. Derive an expression for the equivalent inductance seen looking into the terminals of L_1.

P76. Consider the parallel inductors shown in Figure P61, with mutual coupling and the dots at the top ends of L_1 and L_2. Derive an expression for the equivalent inductance seen by the source in terms of L_1, L_2, and M. [*Hint:* Write the circuit equations and manipulate them to obtain an expression of the form $v(t) = L_{eq} di(t)/dt$ in which L_{eq} is a function of L_1, L_2, and M.]

Section 8: Symbolic Integration and Differentiation Using MATLAB

P77. The current through a 200-mH inductance is given by $i_L(t) = \exp(-2t) \sin(4\pi t)$ A in which the angle is in radians. Using your knowledge of calculus, find an expression for the voltage across the inductance. Then, use MATLAB to verify your answer for the voltage and to plot both the current and the voltage for $0 \le t \le 2$ s.

P78. A 1-H inductance has $i_L(0) = 0$ and $v_L(t) = t\exp(-t)$ for $0 \le t$. Using your calculus skills, find an expression for $i_L(t)$. Then, use MATLAB to verify your answer for $i_L(t)$ and to plot $v_L(t)$ and $i_L(t)$ for $0 \le t \le 10$ s.

P79. The current through a 2-μF capacitor is shown in Figure P13. At $t = 0$, the voltage is zero. Write MATLAB commands to determine and plot the current, voltage, power, and stored energy to scale versus time.

P80. The current through a 5-μF capacitor is shown in Figure P16. At $t = 0$, the voltage is $v_C(0) = 0$ V. Write MATLAB commands to determine and plot the current, voltage, power, and stored energy to scale versus time.

P81. The voltage across a 0.5-H inductance is shown in Figure P51. The initial current in the inductance is $i(0) = 0$. Write MATLAB commands to determine and plot the current, voltage, power, and stored energy to scale versus time.

Practice Test

Here is a practice test you can use to check your comprehension of the most important concepts in this chapter. Answers can be found at the end of this chapter and complete solutions are included in the Student Solutions files.

T1. The current flowing through a 10-μF capacitor having terminals labeled a and b is $i_{ab} = 0.3 \exp(-2000t)$ A for $t \geq 0$. Given that $v_{ab}(0) = 0$, find an expression for $v_{ab}(t)$ for $t \geq 0$. Then, find the energy stored in the capacitor for $t = \infty$.

T2. Determine the equivalent capacitance C_{eq} for Figure T2.

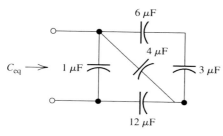

Figure T2

T3. A certain parallel-plate capacitor has plate length of 2 cm and width of 3 cm. The dielectric has a thickness of 0.1 mm and a relative dielectric constant of 80. Determine the capacitance.

T4. A 2-mH inductance has $i_{ab} = 0.3 \sin(2000t)$ A. Find an expression for $v_{ab}(t)$. Then, find the peak energy stored in the inductance.

T5. Determine the equivalent inductance L_{eq} between terminals a and b in Figure T5.

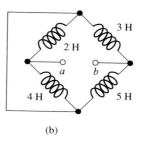

(b)

Figure T5

T6. Figure T6 has $L_1 = 40$ mH, $M = 20$ mH, and $L_2 = 30$ mH. Find expressions for $v_1(t)$ and $v_2(t)$.

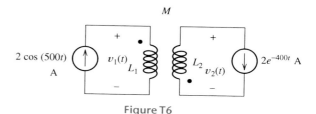

Figure T6

T7. The current flowing through a 20-μF capacitor having terminals labeled a and b is $i_{ab} = 3 \times 10^5 t^2 \exp(-2000t)$ A for $t \geq 0$. Given that $v_{ab}(0) = 5$ V, write a sequence of MATLAB commands to find the expression for $v_{ab}(t)$ for $t \geq 0$ and to produce plots of the current and voltage for $0 \leq t \leq 5$ ms.

Answers for the Practice Test

T1. $v_{ab}(t) = 15 - 15 \exp(-2000t)$ V; $w_C(\infty) = 1.125$ mJ.

T2. $C_{eq} = 5\,\mu$F.

T3. $C = 4248$ pF.

T4. $v_{ab}(t) = 1.2 \cos(2000t)$ V; $w_{peak} = 90\,\mu$J.

T5. $L_{eq} = 3.208$ H.

T6. $v_1(t) = -40 \sin(500t) - 16 \exp(-400t)$ V;

$\quad\quad v_2(t) = 20 \sin(500t) - 24 \exp(-400t)$ V.

T7. One set of commands and the result for $v_{ab}(t)$ are:

```
syms vab iab t
iab = 3*(10^5)*(t^2)*exp(-2000*t);
vab = (1/20e-6)*int(iab,t,0,t)
subplot(2,1,1)
ezplot(iab, [0 5e-3]), title('\iti_a_b\rm (A) versus \itt\rm (s)')
subplot(2,1,2)
ezplot(vab, [0 5e-3]), title('\itv_a_b\rm (V) versus \itt\rm (s)')
```

$$v_{ab} = \frac{15}{4} - \frac{15}{4} \exp(-2000t) - 7500t \exp(-2000t) - 7.5 \times 10^6 t^2 \exp(-2000t)$$

You can test your commands using MATLAB to see if they produce this result for $v_{ab}(t)$ and plots like those in the Student Solutions.

Transients

From Chapter 4 of *Electrical Engineering: Principles and Applications*, Fifth Edition, Allan R. Hambley. Copyright © 2011 by Pearson Education, Inc. Published by Pearson Prentice Hall. All rights reserved.

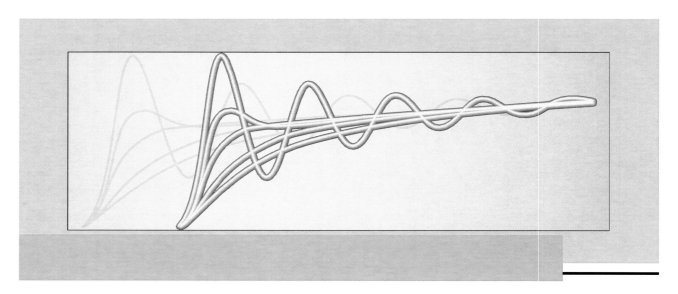

Transients

Study of this chapter will enable you to:

- Solve first-order *RC* or *RL* circuits.
- Understand the concepts of transient response and steady-state response.
- Relate the transient response of first-order circuits to the time constant.
- Solve *RLC* circuits in dc steady-state conditions.
- Solve second-order circuits.
- Relate the step response of a second-order system to its natural frequency and damping ratio.
- Use the MATLAB Symbolic Toolbox to solve differential equations.

Introduction to this chapter:

In this chapter, we study circuits that contain sources, switches, resistances, inductances, and capacitances. The time-varying currents and voltages resulting from the sudden application of sources, usually due to switching, are called **transients**.

In transient analysis, we start by writing circuit equations using concepts such as KCL, KVL, node-voltage analysis, and mesh-current analysis. Because the current–voltage relationships for inductances and capacitances involve integrals and derivatives, we obtain integrodifferential equations. These equations can be converted to pure differential equations by differentiating with respect to time. Thus, the study of transients requires us to solve differential equations.

1 FIRST-ORDER *RC* CIRCUITS

In this section, we consider transients in circuits that contain independent dc sources, resistances, and a single capacitance.

Discharge of a Capacitance through a Resistance

As a first example, consider the circuit shown in Figure 1(a). Prior to $t = 0$, the capacitor is charged to an initial voltage V_i. Then, at $t = 0$, the switch closes and current flows through the resistor, discharging the capacitor.

Writing a current equation at the top node of the circuit after the switch is closed yields

$$C\frac{dv_C(t)}{dt} + \frac{v_C(t)}{R} = 0$$

Multiplying by the resistance gives

$$RC\frac{dv_C(t)}{dt} + v_C(t) = 0 \qquad (1)$$

As expected, we have obtained a differential equation.

Equation 1 indicates that the solution for $v_C(t)$ must be a function that has the same form as its first derivative. Of course, a function with this property is an exponential. Thus, we anticipate that the solution is of the form

$$v_C(t) = Ke^{st} \qquad (2)$$

in which K and s are constants to be determined.

Using Equation 2 to substitute for $v_C(t)$ in Equation 1, we have

$$RCKse^{st} + Ke^{st} = 0 \qquad (3)$$

Solving for s, we obtain

$$s = \frac{-1}{RC} \qquad (4)$$

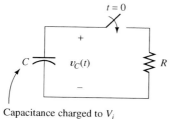

Capacitance charged to V_i
prior to $t = 0$

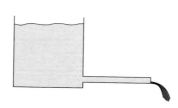

(a) Electrical circuit

(b) Fluid-flow analogy: a filled water tank discharging through a small pipe

Figure 1 A capacitance discharging through a resistance and its fluid-flow analogy. The capacitor is charged to V_i prior to $t = 0$ (by circuitry that is not shown). At $t = 0$, the switch closes and the capacitor discharges through the resistor.

Substituting this into Equation 2, we see that the solution is

$$v_C(t) = Ke^{-t/RC} \tag{5}$$

The voltage across the capacitor cannot change instantaneously when the switch closes.

Referring to Figure 1(a), we reason that the voltage across the capacitor cannot change instantaneously when the switch closes. This is because the current through the capacitance is $i_C(t) = C \, dv_C/dt$. In order for the voltage to change instantaneously, the current would have to be infinite. Since the voltage is finite, the current in the resistance must be finite, and we conclude that the voltage across the capacitor must be continuous. Thus, we write

$$v_C(0+) = V_i \tag{6}$$

in which $v_C(0+)$ represents the voltage immediately after the switch closes. Substituting into Equation 5, we have

$$v_C(0+) = V_i = Ke^0 = K \tag{7}$$

Hence, we conclude that the constant K equals the initial voltage across the capacitor. Finally, the solution for the voltage is

$$v_C(t) = V_i e^{-t/RC} \tag{8}$$

A plot of the voltage is shown in Figure 2. Notice that the capacitor voltage decays exponentially to zero.

The time interval $\tau = RC$ is called the time constant of the circuit.

The time interval

$$\tau = RC \tag{9}$$

is called the **time constant** of the circuit. In one time constant, the voltage decays by the factor $e^{-1} \cong 0.368$. After about five time constants, the voltage remaining on the capacitor is negligible compared with the initial value.

At one time constant, the voltage across a capacitance discharging through a resistance is $e^{-1} \cong 0.368$ times its initial value. After about three to five time constants, the capacitance is almost totally discharged.

An analogous fluid-flow system is shown in Figure 1(b). The tank initially filled with water is analogous to the charged capacitor. Furthermore, the small pipe is analogous to the resistor. At first, when the tank is full, the flow is large and the water level drops fast. As the tank empties, the flow decreases.

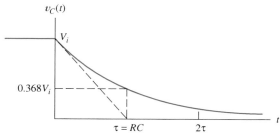

Figure 2 Voltage versus time for the circuit of Figure 1(a). When the switch is closed, the voltage across the capacitor decays exponentially to zero. At one time constant, the voltage is equal to 36.8 percent of its initial value.

In the past, engineers have frequently applied RC circuits in timing applications. For example, suppose that when a garage door opens or closes, a light is to be turned on and is to remain on for 30 s. To achieve this objective, we could design a circuit consisting of (1) a capacitor that is charged to an initial voltage V_i while the door opener is energized, (2) a resistor through which the capacitor discharges, and (3) a sensing circuit that keeps the light on as long as the capacitor voltage is larger than $0.368V_i$. If we choose the time constant $\tau = RC$ to be 30 s, the desired operation is achieved.

Charging a Capacitance from a DC Source through a Resistance

Next, consider the circuit shown in Figure 3. The source voltage V_s is constant — in other words, we have a dc source. The source is connected to the RC circuit by a switch that closes at $t = 0$. We assume that the initial voltage across the capacitor just before the switch closes is $v_C(0-) = 0$. Let us solve for the voltage across the capacitor as a function of time.

We start by writing a current equation at the node that joins the resistor and the capacitor. This yields

$$C\frac{dv_C(t)}{dt} + \frac{v_C(t) - V_s}{R} = 0 \qquad (10)$$

The first term on the left-hand side is the current referenced downward through the capacitor. The second term is the current referenced toward the left through the resistor. KCL requires that the currents leaving the node sum to zero.

Rearranging Equation 10, we obtain

$$RC\frac{dv_C(t)}{dt} + v_C(t) = V_s \qquad (11)$$

As expected, we have obtained a linear first-order differential equation with constant coefficients. As in the previous circuit, the voltage across the capacitance cannot change instantaneously. Thus, we have

$$v_C(0+) = v_C(0-) = 0 \qquad (12)$$

Now, we need to find a solution for $v_C(t)$ that (1) satisfies Equation 11 and (2) matches the initial conditions of the circuit stated in Equation 12. Notice that Equation 11 is the same as Equation 1, except for the constant on the right-hand side. Thus, we expect the solution to be the same as for Equation 1, except for an added constant term. Thus, we are led to try the solution

$$v_C(t) = K_1 + K_2 e^{st} \qquad (13)$$

in which K_1, K_2, and s are constants to be determined.

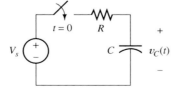

Figure 3 Capacitance charging through a resistance. The switch closes at $t = 0$, connecting the dc source V_s to the circuit.

If we use Equation 13 to substitute for $v_C(t)$ in Equation 11, we obtain

$$(1 + RCs)K_2 e^{st} + K_1 = V_s \tag{14}$$

For equality, the coefficient of e^{st} must be zero. This leads to

$$s = \frac{-1}{RC} \tag{15}$$

From Equation 14, we also have

$$K_1 = V_s \tag{16}$$

Using Equations 15 and 16 to substitute into Equation 13, we obtain

$$v_C(t) = V_s + K_2 e^{-t/RC} \tag{17}$$

in which K_2 remains to be determined.

Now, we use the initial condition (Equation 12) to find K_2. We have

$$v_C(0+) = 0 = V_s + K_2 e^0 = V_s + K_2 \tag{18}$$

from which we find $K_2 = -V_s$. Finally, substituting into Equation 17, we obtain the solution

$$v_C(t) = V_s - V_s e^{-t/RC} \tag{19}$$

When a dc source is contained in the circuit, the total response contains two parts: forced (or steady-state) and transient.

The second term on the right-hand side is called the **transient response**, which eventually decays to negligible values. The first term on the right-hand side is the **steady-state response**, also called the **forced response**, which persists after the transient has decayed.

Here again, the product of the resistance and capacitance has units of seconds and is called the time constant $\tau = RC$. Thus, the solution can be written as

$$v_C(t) = V_s - V_s e^{-t/\tau} \tag{20}$$

A plot of $v_C(t)$ is shown in Figure 4. Notice that $v_C(t)$ starts at 0 and approaches the final value V_s asymptotically as t becomes large. After one time constant, $v_C(t)$ has reached 63.2 percent of its final value. For practical purposes, $v_C(t)$ is equal to its final value V_s after about five time constants. Then, we say that the circuit has reached steady state.

In the case of a capacitance charging from a dc source through a resistance, a straight line tangent to the start of the transient reaches the final value at one time constant.

It can be shown that if the initial slope of v_C is extended, it intersects the final value at one time constant as shown in Figure 4.

We have seen in this section that several time constants are needed to charge or discharge a capacitance. This is the main limitation on the speed at which digital computers can process data. In a typical computer, information is represented by voltages that nominally assume values of either +1.8 or 0 V, depending on the data represented. When the data change, the voltages must change. It is impossible to build circuits that do not have some capacitance that is charged or discharged when voltages change in value. Furthermore, the circuits always have nonzero resistances that limit the currents available for charging or discharging the capacitances. Therefore, a nonzero time constant is associated with each circuit in the computer, limiting its speed.

RC transients are the main limitation on the speed at which computer chips can operate.

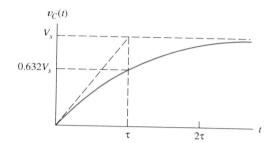

Figure 4 The charging transient for the *RC* circuit of Figure 3.

Exercise 1 Suppose that $R = 5000\ \Omega$ and $C = 1\ \mu\text{F}$ in the circuit of Figure 1(a). Find the time at which the voltage across the capacitor reaches 1 percent of its initial value.

Answer $t = -5\ln(0.01)$ ms $\cong 23$ ms.

Exercise 2 Show that if the initial slope of $v_C(t)$ is extended, it intersects the final value at one time constant, as shown in Figure 4. [The expression for $v_C(t)$ is given in Equation 20.]

2 DC STEADY STATE

The transient terms in the expressions for currents and voltages in *RLC* circuits decay to zero with time. (An exception is *LC* circuits having no resistance.) For dc sources, the steady-state currents and voltages are also constant.

> The transient terms in the expressions for currents and voltages in *RLC* circuits decay to zero with time.

Consider the equation for current through a capacitance:

$$i_C(t) = C\frac{dv_C(t)}{dt}$$

If the voltage $v_C(t)$ is constant, the current is zero. In other words, the capacitance behaves as an open circuit. Thus, we conclude that *for steady-state conditions with dc sources, capacitances behave as open circuits.*

Similarly, for an inductance, we have

$$v_L(t) = L\frac{di_L(t)}{dt}$$

When the current is constant, the voltage is zero. Thus, we conclude that *for steady-state conditions with dc sources, inductances behave as short circuits.*

These observations give us another approach to finding the steady-state solutions to circuit equations for *RLC* circuits with constant sources. First, we replace the capacitors by open circuits and the inductors by short circuits. The circuit then consists of dc sources and resistances. Finally, we solve the equivalent circuit for the steady-state currents and voltages.

> The steps in determining the forced response for *RLC* circuits with dc sources are
> 1. Replace capacitances with open circuits.
> 2. Replace inductances with short circuits.
> 3. Solve the remaining circuit.

| **Example 1** | Steady-State DC Analysis |

Find v_x and i_x for the circuit shown in Figure 5(a) for $t \gg 0$.

Solution After the switch has been closed a long time, we expect the transient response to have decayed to zero. Then the circuit is operating in dc steady-state

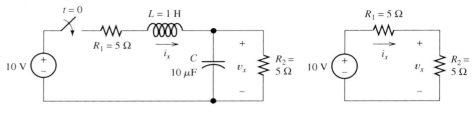

(a) Original circuit   (b) Equivalent circuit for steady state

Figure 5 The circuit and its dc steady-state equivalent for Example 1.

Steps 1 and 2.

Step 3.

conditions. We start our analysis by replacing the inductor by a short circuit and the capacitor by an open circuit. The equivalent circuit is shown in Figure 5(b).

This resistive circuit is readily solved. The resistances R_1 and R_2 are in series. Thus, we have

$$i_x = \frac{10}{R_1 + R_2} = 1\ \text{A}$$

and

$$v_x = R_2 i_x = 5\ \text{V}$$ ∎

Sometimes, we are only interested in the steady-state operation of circuits with dc sources. For example, in analyzing the headlight circuits in an automobile, we are concerned primarily with steady state. On the other hand, we must consider transients in analyzing the operation of the ignition system.

In other applications, we are interested in steady-state conditions with sinusoidal ac sources. For sinusoidal sources, the steady-state currents and voltages are also sinusoidal.

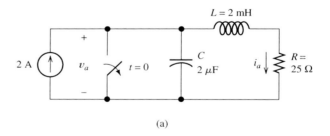

(a)

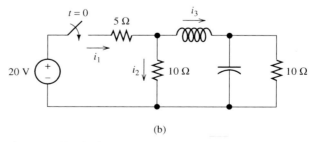

(b)

Figure 6 Circuits for Exercise 3.

Exercise 3 Solve for the steady-state values of the labeled currents and voltages for the circuits shown in Figure 6.

Answer **a.** $v_a = 50$ V, $i_a = 2$ A; **b.** $i_1 = 2$ A, $i_2 = 1$ A, $i_3 = 1$ A. □

3 *RL* CIRCUITS

In this section, we consider circuits consisting of dc sources, resistances, and a single inductance. The methods and solutions are very similar to those we studied for *RC* circuits in Section 1.

The steps involved in solving simple circuits containing dc sources, resistances, and one energy-storage element (inductance or capacitance) are as follows:

1. Apply Kirchhoff's current and voltage laws to write the circuit equation.

2. If the equation contains integrals, differentiate each term in the equation to produce a pure differential equation.

3. Assume a solution of the form $K_1 + K_2 e^{st}$.

4. Substitute the solution into the differential equation to determine the values of K_1 and s. (Alternatively, we can determine K_1 by solving the circuit in steady state as discussed in Section 2.)

5. Use the initial conditions to determine the value of K_2.

6. Write the final solution.

Example 2   *RL* Transient Analysis

Consider the circuit shown in Figure 7. Find the current $i(t)$ and the voltage $v(t)$.

Solution   First, we find the current $i(t)$. Of course, prior to $t = 0$, the switch is open and the current is zero:

$$i(t) = 0 \qquad \text{for } t < 0 \tag{21}$$

After the switch is closed, the current increases in value eventually reaching a steady-state value.

Writing a KVL equation around the loop, we have   Step 1.

$$Ri(t) + L\frac{di}{dt} = V_s \tag{22}$$

Step 2 is not needed in this case.

This is very similar to Equation 11, and we are, therefore, led to try a solution of   Step 3. the same form as that given by Equation 13. Thus, our trial solution is

$$i(t) = K_1 + K_2 e^{st} \tag{23}$$

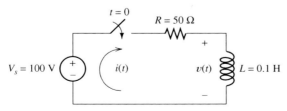

Figure 7 The circuit analyzed in Example 2.

in which K_1, K_2, and s are constants that need to be determined. Following the procedure used in Section 1, we substitute the trial solution into the differential equation, resulting in

$$RK_1 + (RK_2 + sLK_2)e^{st} = V_s \tag{24}$$

from which we obtain

$$K_1 = \frac{V_s}{R} = 2 \tag{25}$$

and

$$s = \frac{-R}{L} \tag{26}$$

Substituting these values into Equation 23 results in

$$i(t) = 2 + K_2 e^{-tR/L} \tag{27}$$

Next, we use the initial conditions to determine the value of K_2. The current in the inductor is zero prior to $t = 0$ because the switch is open. The applied voltage is finite, and the inductor current must be continuous (because $v_L = L\, di/dt$). Thus, immediately after the switch is closed, the current must be zero. Hence, we have

$$i(0+) = 0 = 2 + K_2 e^0 = 2 + K_2 \tag{28}$$

Solving, we find that $K_2 = -2$.

Substituting into Equation 27, we find that the solution for the current is

$$i(t) = 2 - 2e^{-t/\tau} \qquad \text{for } t > 0 \tag{29}$$

in which the time constant is given by

$$\tau = \frac{L}{R} \tag{30}$$

A plot of the current versus time is shown in Figure 8(a). Notice that the current increases from zero to the steady-state value of 2 A. After five time constants, the current is within 99 percent of the final value. As a check, we verify that the steady-state current is 2 A. (As we saw in Section 2, this value can be obtained directly by treating the inductor as a short circuit.)

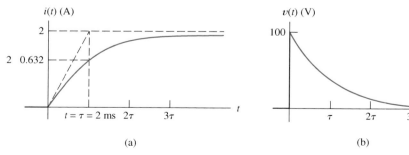

Figure 8 Current and voltage versus time for the circuit of Figure 7.

Now, we consider the voltage $v(t)$. Prior to $t = 0$, with the switch open, the voltage is zero.

$$v(t) = 0 \qquad \text{for } t < 0 \tag{31}$$

After $t = 0$, $v(t)$ is equal to the source voltage minus the drop across R. Thus, we have

$$v(t) = 100 - 50i(t) \qquad \text{for } t > 0 \tag{32}$$

Substituting the expression found earlier for $i(t)$, we obtain

$$v(t) = 100e^{-t/\tau} \tag{33}$$

A plot of $v(t)$ is shown in Figure 8(b).

At $t = 0$, the voltage across the inductor jumps from 0 to 100 V. As the current gradually increases, the drop across the resistor increases, and the voltage across the inductor falls. In steady state, we have $v(t) = 0$ because the inductor behaves as a short circuit. ∎

After solving several circuits with a single energy-storage element, we can use our experience to skip some of the steps listed earlier in the section. We illustrate this in the next example.

Example 3 **RL Transient Analysis**

Consider the circuit shown in Figure 9 in which V_s is a dc source. Assume that the circuit is in steady state prior to $t = 0$. Find expressions for the current $i(t)$ and the voltage $v(t)$.

Solution Prior to $t = 0$, the inductor behaves as a short circuit. Thus, we have

$$v(t) = 0 \qquad \text{for } t < 0$$

and

$$i(t) = \frac{V_s}{R_1} \qquad \text{for } t < 0$$

First, we use dc steady-state analysis to determine the current before the switch opens.

Before the switch opens, current circulates clockwise through V_s, R_1, and the inductance. When the switch opens, current continues to flow through the inductance, but the return path is through R_2. Then, a voltage appears across R_2 and the inductance, causing the current to decay.

Since there are no sources driving the circuit after the switch opens, the steady-state solution is zero for $t > 0$. Hence, the solution for $i(t)$ is given by

$$i(t) = Ke^{-t/\tau} \qquad \text{for } t > 0 \tag{34}$$

After the switch opens, the source is disconnected from the circuit so the steady-state solution for $t > 0$ is zero.

in which the time constant is

$$\tau = \frac{L}{R_2} \tag{35}$$

Unless an infinite voltage appears across the inductance, the current must be continuous. Recall that prior to $t = 0$, $i(t) = V_s/R_1$. Consequently, just after the switch opens, we have

$$i(0+) = \frac{V_s}{R_1} = Ke^{-0} = K$$

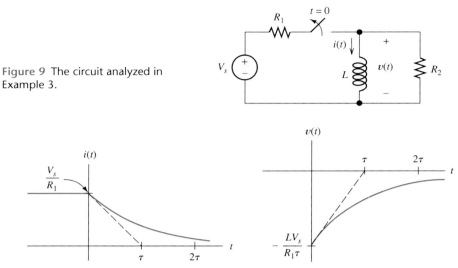

Figure 9 The circuit analyzed in Example 3.

Figure 10 The current and voltage for the circuit of Figure 9.

Substituting the value of K into Equation 34, we find that the current is

$$i(t) = \frac{V_s}{R_1}e^{-t/\tau} \qquad \text{for } t > 0 \qquad (36)$$

The voltage is given by

$$v(t) = L\frac{di(t)}{dt}$$
$$= 0 \qquad \text{for } t < 0$$
$$= -\frac{LV_s}{R_1\tau}e^{-t/\tau} \qquad \text{for } t > 0$$

Plots of the voltage and current are shown in Figure 10. ■

Exercise 4 For the circuit of Example 3 (Figure 9), assume that $V_s = 15$ V, $R_1 = 10$ Ω, $R_2 = 100$ Ω, and $L = 0.1$ H. **a.** What is the value of the time constant (after the switch opens)? **b.** What is the maximum magnitude of $v(t)$? **c.** How does the maximum magnitude of $v(t)$ compare to the source voltage? **d.** Find the time t at which $v(t)$ is one-half of its value immediately after the switch opens.
Answer **a.** $\tau = 1$ ms; **b.** $|v(t)|_{\max} = 150$ V; **c.** the maximum magnitude of $v(t)$ is 10 times the value of V_s; **d.** $t = \tau \ln(2) = 0.693$ ms. □

Exercise 5 Consider the circuit shown in Figure 11, in which the switch opens at $t = 0$. Find expressions for $v(t)$, $i_R(t)$, and $i_L(t)$ for $t > 0$. Assume that $i_L(t)$ is zero before the switch opens.
Answer $v(t) = 20e^{-t/0.2}$, $i_R(t) = 2e^{-t/0.2}$, $i_L(t) = 2 - 2e^{-t/0.2}$. □

Exercise 6 Consider the circuit shown in Figure 12. Assume that the switch has been closed for a very long time prior to $t = 0$. Find expressions for $i(t)$ and $v(t)$.

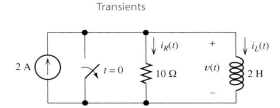

Figure 11 The circuit for Exercise 5.

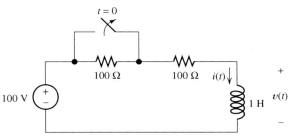

Figure 12 The circuit for Exercise 6.

Answer

$$i(t) = 1.0 \qquad \text{for } t < 0$$
$$= 0.5 + 0.5e^{-t/\tau} \qquad \text{for } t > 0$$
$$v(t) = 0 \qquad \text{for } t < 0$$
$$= -100e^{-t/\tau} \qquad \text{for } t > 0$$

where the time constant is $\tau = 5$ ms. □

4 *RC* AND *RL* CIRCUITS WITH GENERAL SOURCES

Now that we have gained some familiarity with *RL* and *RC* circuits, we discuss their solution in general. In this section, we treat circuits that contain one energy-storage element, either an inductance or a capacitance.

Consider the circuit shown in Figure 13(a). The circuit inside the box can be any combination of resistances and sources. The single inductance *L* is shown explicitly. Recall that we can find a Thévenin equivalent for circuits consisting of sources and resistances. The Thévenin equivalent is an independent voltage source $v_t(t)$ in series with the Thévenin resistance *R*. Thus, any circuit composed of sources, resistances, and one inductance has the equivalent circuit shown in Figure 13(b). (Of course, we could reduce any circuit containing sources, resistances, and a single capacitance in a similar fashion.)

Writing a KVL equation for Figure 13(b), we obtain

$$L\frac{di(t)}{dt} + Ri(t) = v_t(t) \tag{37}$$

If we divide through by the resistance *R*, we have

$$\frac{L}{R}\frac{di(t)}{dt} + i(t) = \frac{v_t(t)}{R} \tag{38}$$

183

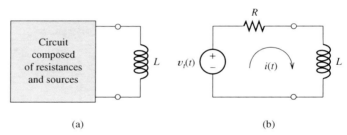

(a)   (b)

Figure 13 A circuit consisting of sources, resistances, and one inductance has an equivalent circuit consisting of a voltage source and a resistance in series with the inductance.

In general, the equation for any circuit containing one inductance or one capacitance can be put into the form

$$\tau \frac{dx(t)}{dt} + x(t) = f(t) \tag{39}$$

Then, we need to find solutions to Equation 39 that are consistent with the initial conditions (such as the initial current in the inductance).

The constant τ (which turns out to be the time constant) is a function of only the resistances and the inductance (or capacitance). The sources result in the term $f(t)$, which is called the **forcing function**. If we have a circuit without sources (such as Figure 1), the forcing function is zero. For dc sources, the forcing function is constant.

Equation 39 is called a first-order differential equation because the highest-order derivative is first order. It is a linear equation because it does not involve powers or other nonlinear functions of $x(t)$ or its derivatives. Thus, to solve an *RL* (or *RC*) circuit, we must find the general solution of a linear first-order differential equation with constant coefficients.

Solution of the Differential Equation

The general solution to Equation 39 consists of two parts.

An important result in differential equations states that the general solution to Equation 39 consists of two parts. The first part is called the **particular solution** $x_p(t)$ and is any expression that satisfies Equation 39. Thus,

The particular solution (also called the forced response) is any expression that satisfies the equation.

$$\tau \frac{dx_p(t)}{dt} + x_p(t) = f(t) \tag{40}$$

The particular solution is also called the **forced response** because it depends on the forcing function (which in turn is due to the independent sources).

In order to have a solution that satisfies the initial conditions, we must add the complementary solution to the particular solution.

(Even though the particular solution satisfies the differential equation, it may not be consistent with the initial conditions, such as the initial voltage on a capacitance or current through an inductance. By adding another term, known as the complementary solution, we obtain a general solution that satisfies both the differential equation and meets the initial conditions.)

For the forcing functions that we will encounter, we can often select the form of the particular solution by inspection. Usually, the particular solution includes terms with the same functional forms as the terms found in the forcing function and its derivatives.

Sinusoidal functions of time are one of the most important types of forcing functions in electrical engineering. For example, consider the forcing function

$$f(t) = 10 \cos(200t)$$

Because the derivatives of sine and cosine functions are also sine and cosine functions, we would try a particular solution of the form

$$x_p(t) = A \cos(200t) + B \sin(200t)$$

where A and B are constants that must be determined. We find these constants by substituting the proposed solution into the differential equation and requiring the two sides of the equation to be identical. This leads to equations that can be solved for A and B.

The second part of the general solution is called the **complementary solution** $x_c(t)$ and is the solution of the **homogeneous equation**

$$\tau \frac{dx_c(t)}{dt} + x_c(t) = 0 \tag{41}$$

The homogeneous equation is obtained by setting the forcing function to zero.

We obtain the homogeneous equation by setting the forcing function to zero. Thus, the form of the complementary solution does not depend on the sources. It is also called the **natural response** because it depends on the passive circuit elements. The complementary solution must be added to the particular solution in order to obtain a general solution that matches the initial values of the currents and voltages.

The complementary solution (also called the natural response) is obtained by solving the homogeneous equation.

We can rearrange the homogeneous equation into this form:

$$\frac{dx_c(t)/dt}{x_c(t)} = \frac{-1}{\tau} \tag{42}$$

Integrating both sides of Equation 42, we have

$$\ln[x_c(t)] = \frac{-t}{\tau} + c \tag{43}$$

in which c is the constant of integration. Equation 43 is equivalent to

$$x_c(t) = e^{(-t/\tau + c)} = e^c e^{-t/\tau}$$

Then, if we define $K = e^c$, we have the complementary solution

$$x_c(t) = K e^{-t/\tau} \tag{44}$$

Step-by-Step Solution

Next, we summarize an approach to solving circuits containing a resistance, a source, and an inductance (or a capacitance):

1. Write the circuit equation and reduce it to a first-order differential equation.

2. Find a particular solution. The details of this step depend on the form of the forcing function. We illustrate several types of forcing functions in examples, exercises, and problems.

3. Obtain the complete solution by adding the particular solution to the complementary solution given by Equation 44, which contains the arbitrary constant K.

4. Use initial conditions to find the value of K.

We illustrate this procedure with an example.

Example 4   Transient Analysis of an *RC* Circuit with a Sinusoidal Source

Solve for the current in the circuit shown in Figure 14. The capacitor is initially charged so that $v_C(0+) = 1$ V.

Solution   First, we write a voltage equation for $t > 0$. Traveling clockwise and summing voltages, we obtain

Step 1: Write the circuit equation and reduce it to a first-order differential equation.

$$Ri(t) + \frac{1}{C}\int_0^t i(t)\,dt + v_C(0) - 2\sin(200t) = 0$$

We convert this to a differential equation by taking the derivative of each term. Of course, the derivative of the integral is simply the integrand. Because $v_C(0)$ is a constant, its derivative is zero. Thus, we have

$$R\frac{di(t)}{dt} + \frac{1}{C}i(t) = 400\cos(200t) \tag{45}$$

Multiplying by C, we get

$$RC\frac{di(t)}{dt} + i(t) = 400\,C\cos(200t) \tag{46}$$

Substituting values for R and C, we obtain

$$5 \times 10^{-3}\frac{di(t)}{dt} + i(t) = 400 \times 10^{-6}\cos(200t) \tag{47}$$

Step 2: Find a particular solution.

The second step is to find a particular solution $i_p(t)$. Often, we start by guessing at the form of $i_p(t)$, possibly including some unknown constants. Then, we substitute our guess into the differential equation and solve for the constants. In the present case, since the derivatives of $\sin(200t)$ and $\cos(200t)$ are $200\cos(200t)$ and $-200\sin(200t)$, respectively, we try a particular solution of the form

The particular solution for a sinusoidal forcing function always has the form given by Equation 48.

$$i_p(t) = A\cos(200t) + B\sin(200t) \tag{48}$$

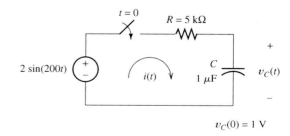

Figure 14 A first-order *RC* circuit with a sinusoidal source. See Example 4.

where A and B are constants to be determined so that i_p is indeed a solution to Equation 47.

Substituting the proposed solution into Equation 47, we obtain

$$-A\sin(200t) + B\cos(200t) + A\cos(200t) + B\sin(200t)$$
$$= 400 \times 10^{-6}\cos(200t)$$

However, the left-hand side of this equation is required to be identical to the right-hand side. Equating the coefficients of the sine functions, we have

$$-A + B = 0 \tag{49}$$

Equating the coefficients of the cosine functions, we get

$$B + A = 400 \times 10^{-6} \tag{50}$$

These equations can be readily solved, yielding

$$A = 200 \times 10^{-6} = 200\,\mu A$$

and

$$B = 200 \times 10^{-6} = 200\,\mu A$$

Substituting these values into Equation 48, we obtain the particular solution

$$i_p(t) = 200\cos(200t) + 200\sin(200t)\,\mu A \tag{51}$$

which can also be written as

$$i_p(t) = 200\sqrt{2}\cos(200t - 45°)$$

We obtain the homogeneous equation by substituting 0 for the forcing function in Equation 46. Thus, we have

$$RC\frac{di(t)}{dt} + i(t) = 0 \tag{52}$$

The complementary solution is

$$i_c(t) = Ke^{-t/RC} = Ke^{-t/\tau} \tag{53}$$

Adding the particular solution and the complementary solution, we obtain the general solution

$$i(t) = 200\cos(200t) + 200\sin(200t) + Ke^{-t/RC}\,\mu A \tag{54}$$

Finally, we determine the value of the constant K by using the initial conditions. The voltages and currents immediately after the switch closes are shown in Figure 15. The source voltage is 0 V and the voltage across the capacitor is

We substitute Equation 48 into the differential equation, and solve for A and B.

Step 3: Obtain the complete solution by adding the particular solution to the complementary solution.

Step 4: Use initial conditions to find the value of K.

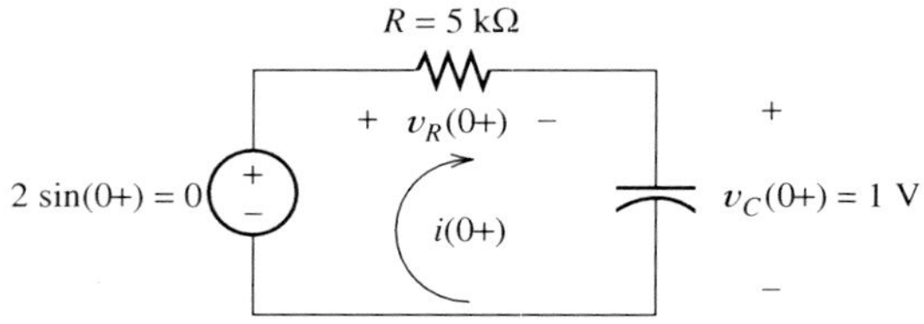

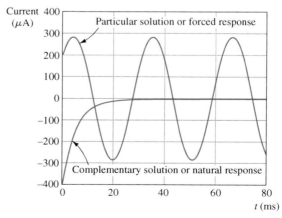

Figure 15 The voltages and currents for the circuit of Figure 14 immediately after the switch closes.

$v_C(0+) = 1$. Consequently, the voltage across the resistor must be $v_R(0+) = -1$ V. Thus, we get

$$i(0+) = \frac{v_R(0+)}{R} = \frac{-1}{5000} = -200 \ \mu A$$

Substituting $t = 0$ into Equation 54, we obtain

$$i(0+) = -200 = 200 + K \ \mu A \tag{55}$$

Solving, we find that $K = -400 \ \mu A$. Substituting this into Equation 54, we have the solution

$$i(t) = 200 \cos(200t) + 200 \sin(200t) - 400e^{-t/RC} \ \mu A \tag{56}$$

Plots of the particular solution and of the complementary solution are shown in Figure 16. The time constant for this circuit is $\tau = RC = 5$ ms. Notice that the natural response decays to negligible values in about 25 ms. As expected, the natural response has decayed in about five time constants. Furthermore, notice that for a sinusoidal forcing function, the forced response is also sinusoidal and persists after the natural response has decayed.

A plot of the complete solution is shown in Figure 17. ∎

Notice that the forced response is sinusoidal for a sinusoidal forcing function.

Exercise 7   Repeat Example 4 if the source voltage is changed to $2 \cos(200t)$ and the initial voltage on the capacitor is $v_C(0) = 0$. The circuit with these changes is shown in Figure 18.

Figure 16 The complementary solution and the particular solution for Example 4.

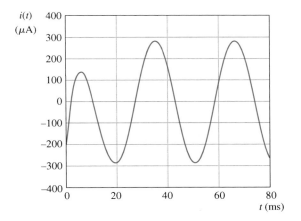

Figure 17 The complete solution
for Example 4.

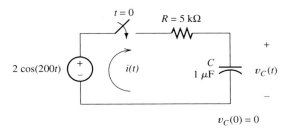

Figure 18 The circuit for
Exercise 7.

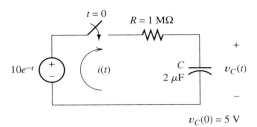

Figure 19 The circuit for
Exercise 8.

Answer $i(t) = -200\sin(200t) + 200\cos(200t) + 200e^{-t/RC}$ μA, in which $\tau = RC = 5$ ms.   □

Exercise 8 Solve for the current in the circuit shown in Figure 19 after the switch closes. [*Hint:* Try a particular solution of the form $i_p(t) = Ae^{-t}$.]
Answer $i(t) = 20e^{-t} - 15e^{-t/2}$ μA.   □

5 SECOND-ORDER CIRCUITS

In this section, we consider circuits that contain two energy-storage elements. In particular, we look at circuits that have one inductance and one capacitance, either in series or in parallel.

Differential Equation

To derive the general form of the equations that we encounter in circuits with two energy-storage elements, consider the series circuit shown in Figure 20(a). Writing

189

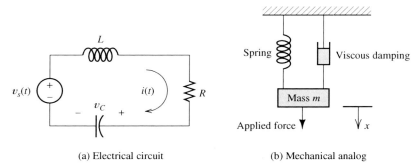

(a) Electrical circuit   (b) Mechanical analog

Figure 20 The series *RLC* circuit and its mechanical analog.

a KVL equation, we have

$$L\frac{di(t)}{dt} + Ri(t) + \frac{1}{C}\int_0^t i(t)dt + v_C(0) = v_s(t) \tag{57}$$

We convert the integrodifferential equation to a pure differential equation by differentiating with respect to time.

Taking the derivative with respect to time, we get

$$L\frac{d^2i(t)}{dt^2} + R\frac{di(t)}{dt} + \frac{1}{C}i(t) = \frac{dv_s(t)}{dt} \tag{58}$$

Dividing through by L, we obtain

$$\frac{d^2i(t)}{dt^2} + \frac{R}{L}\frac{di(t)}{dt} + \frac{1}{LC}i(t) = \frac{1}{L}\frac{dv_s(t)}{dt} \tag{59}$$

Now, we define the **damping coefficient** as

$$\alpha = \frac{R}{2L} \tag{60}$$

and the **undamped resonant frequency** as

$$\omega_0 = \frac{1}{\sqrt{LC}} \tag{61}$$

The **forcing function** is

$$f(t) = \frac{1}{L}\frac{dv_s(t)}{dt} \tag{62}$$

Using these definitions, we find that Equation 59 can be written as

$$\frac{d^2i(t)}{dt^2} + 2\alpha\frac{di(t)}{dt} + \omega_0^2 i(t) = f(t) \tag{63}$$

If a circuit contains two energy-storage elements (after substituting all possible series or parallel equivalents), the circuit equations can always be reduced to the form given by Equation 63.

This is a linear second-order differential equation with constant coefficients. Thus, we refer to circuits having two energy-storage elements as second-order circuits. (An exception occurs if we can combine the energy-storage elements in series or parallel. For example, if we have two capacitors in parallel, we can combine them into a single equivalent capacitance, and then we would have a first-order circuit.)

Mechanical Analog

The mechanical analog of the series RLC circuit is shown in Figure 20(b). The displacement x of the mass is analogous to electrical charge, the velocity dx/dt is analogous to current, and force is analogous to voltage. The mass plays the role of the inductance, the spring plays the role of the capacitance, and the damper plays the role of the resistance. The equation of motion for the mechanical system can be put into the form of Equation 63.

Based on an intuitive consideration of Figure 20, we can anticipate that the sudden application of a constant force (dc voltage) can result in a displacement (current) that either approaches steady-state conditions asymptotically or oscillates before settling to the steady-state value. The type of behavior depends on the relative values of the mass, spring constant, and damping coefficient.

Solution of the Second-Order Equation

We will see that the circuit equations for currents and voltages in circuits having two energy-storage elements can always be put into the form of Equation 63. Thus, let us consider the solution of

$$\frac{d^2x(t)}{dt^2} + 2\alpha\frac{dx(t)}{dt} + \omega_0^2 x(t) = f(t) \tag{64}$$

where we have used $x(t)$ for the variable, which could represent either a current or a voltage.

Here again, the general solution $x(t)$ to this equation consists of two parts: a particular solution $x_p(t)$ plus the complementary solution $x_c(t)$ and is expressed as

$$x(t) = x_p(t) + x_c(t) \tag{65}$$

Particular Solution. The particular solution is any expression $x_p(t)$ that satisfies the differential equation

$$\frac{d^2x_p(t)}{dt^2} + 2\alpha\frac{dx_p(t)}{dt} + \omega_0^2 x_p(t) = f(t) \tag{66}$$

The particular solution is also called the **forced response**. (Usually, we eliminate any terms from $x_p(t)$ that produce a zero net result when substituted into the left-hand side of Equation 66. In other words, we eliminate any terms that have the same form as the homogeneous solution.)

We will be concerned primarily with either constant (dc) or sinusoidal (ac) forcing functions. For dc sources, we can find the particular solution directly from the circuit by replacing the inductances by short circuits, replacing the capacitances by open circuits, and solving. This technique was discussed in Section 2.

For dc sources, we can find the particular solution by performing a dc steady-state analysis as discussed in Section 2.

Complementary Solution. The complementary solution $x_c(t)$ is found by solving the homogeneous equation, which is obtained by substituting 0 for the forcing function $f(t)$. Thus, the homogeneous equation is

$$\frac{d^2x_c(t)}{dt^2} + 2\alpha\frac{dx_c(t)}{dt} + \omega_0^2 x_c(t) = 0 \tag{67}$$

In finding the solution to the homogeneous equation, we start by substituting the trial solution $x_c(t) = Ke^{st}$. This yields

$$s^2 K e^{st} + 2\alpha s K e^{st} + \omega_0^2 K e^{st} = 0 \tag{68}$$

Factoring, we obtain

$$(s^2 + 2\alpha s + \omega_0^2) K e^{st} = 0 \tag{69}$$

Since we want to find a solution Ke^{st} that is nonzero, we must have

$$s^2 + 2\alpha s + \omega_0^2 = 0 \tag{70}$$

This is called the **characteristic equation**.

The **damping ratio** is defined as

$$\zeta = \frac{\alpha}{\omega_0} \tag{71}$$

The form of the
complementary solution
depends on the value of the
damping ratio.

The form of the complementary solution depends on the value of the damping ratio. The roots of the characteristic equation are given by

$$s_1 = -\alpha + \sqrt{\alpha^2 - \omega_0^2} \tag{72}$$

and

$$s_2 = -\alpha - \sqrt{\alpha^2 - \omega_0^2} \tag{73}$$

We have three cases depending on the value of the damping ratio ζ compared with unity.

If the damping ratio is greater
than unity, we say that the
circuit is overdamped, the
roots of the characteristic
equation are real, and the
complementary solution has
the form given in
Equation 74.

1. *Overdamped case* ($\zeta > 1$). If $\zeta > 1$ (or equivalently, if $\alpha > \omega_0$), the roots of the characteristic equation are real and distinct. Then the complementary solution is

$$x_c(t) = K_1 e^{s_1 t} + K_2 e^{s_2 t} \tag{74}$$

In this case, we say that the circuit is **overdamped**.

If the damping ratio equals
unity, the circuit is critically
damped, the roots of the
characteristic equation are
real and equal, and the
complementary solution has
the form given in
Equation 75.

2. *Critically damped case* ($\zeta = 1$). If $\zeta = 1$ (or equivalently, if $\alpha = \omega_0$), the roots are real and equal. Then, the complementary solution is

$$x_c(t) = K_1 e^{s_1 t} + K_2 t e^{s_1 t} \tag{75}$$

In this case, we say that the circuit is **critically damped**.

If the damping ratio is less
than unity, the roots of the
characteristic equation are
complex conjugates, and the
complementary solution has
the form given in
Equation 77.

3. *Underdamped case* ($\zeta < 1$). Finally, if $\zeta < 1$ (or equivalently, if $\alpha < \omega_0$), the roots are complex. (By the term *complex*, we mean that the roots involve the imaginary number $\sqrt{-1}$.) In other words, the roots are of the form

$$s_1 = -\alpha + j\omega_n \quad \text{and} \quad s_2 = -\alpha - j\omega_n$$

in which $j = \sqrt{-1}$ and the **natural frequency** is given by

$$\omega_n = \sqrt{\omega_0^2 - \alpha^2} \tag{76}$$

(In electrical engineering, we use j rather than i to stand for the imaginary number $\sqrt{-1}$ because we use i for current.)

For complex roots, the complementary solution is of the form

$$x_c(t) = K_1 e^{-\alpha t} \cos(\omega_n t) + K_2 e^{-\alpha t} \sin(\omega_n t) \tag{77}$$

In this case, we say that the circuit is **underdamped**.

Analysis of a Second-Order Circuit with a DC Source

A dc source is connected to a series RLC circuit by a switch that closes at $t = 0$ as shown in Figure 21. The initial conditions are $i(0) = 0$ and $v_C(0) = 0$. Write the differential equation for $v_C(t)$. Solve for $v_C(t)$ if $R = 300, 200$, and $100\ \Omega$.

Solution   First, we can write an expression for the current in terms of the voltage across the capacitance:

$$i(t) = C\frac{dv_C(t)}{dt} \tag{78}$$

First, we write the circuit equations and reduce them to the form given in Equation 63.

Then, we write a KVL equation for the circuit:

$$L\frac{di(t)}{dt} + Ri(t) + v_C(t) = V_s \tag{79}$$

Using Equation 78 to substitute for $i(t)$, we get

$$LC\frac{d^2 v_C(t)}{dt^2} + RC\frac{dv_C(t)}{dt} + v_C(t) = V_s \tag{80}$$

Dividing through by LC, we have

$$\frac{d^2 v_C(t)}{dt^2} + \frac{R}{L}\frac{dv_C(t)}{dt} + \frac{1}{LC}v_C(t) = \frac{V_s}{LC} \tag{81}$$

As expected, the differential equation for $v_C(t)$ has the same form as Equation 63.

Next, we find the particular solution. Since we have a dc source, we can find this part of the solution by replacing the inductance by a short circuit and the capacitance by an open circuit. This is shown in Figure 22. Then the current is zero, the drop across the resistance is zero, and the voltage across the capacitance (open circuit) is equal to the dc source voltage. Therefore, the particular solution is

Next, we find the particular solution by solving the circuit for dc steady-state conditions.

$$v_{Cp}(t) = V_s = 10\ \text{V} \tag{82}$$

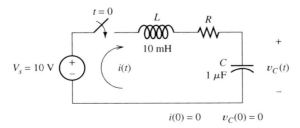

Figure 21   The circuit for Example 5.

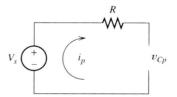

Figure 22 The equivalent circuit for Figure 21 under steady-state conditions. The inductor has been replaced by a short circuit and the capacitor by an open circuit.

(It can be verified that this is a particular solution by substituting it into Equation 81.) Notice that in this circuit the particular solution for $v_C(t)$ is the same for all three values of resistance.

Next, we find the complementary solution for each value of R. For each resistance value, we

1. Determine the damping ratio and roots of the characteristic equation.

2. Select the appropriate form for the homogeneous solution, depending on the value of the damping ratio.

3. Add the homogeneous solution to the particular solution and determine the values of the coefficients (K_1 and K_2), based on the initial conditions.

Next, we find the homogeneous solution and general solution for each value of R. For all three cases, we have

$$\omega_0 = \frac{1}{\sqrt{LC}} = 10^4 \qquad (83)$$

Case I ($R = 300\ \Omega$)

In this case, we get

$$\alpha = \frac{R}{2L} = 1.5 \times 10^4 \qquad (84)$$

The damping ratio is $\zeta = \alpha/\omega_0 = 1.5$. Because we have $\zeta > 1$, this is the overdamped case. The roots of the characteristic equation are given by Equations 72 and 73. Substituting values, we find that

$$
\begin{aligned}
s_1 &= -\alpha + \sqrt{\alpha^2 - \omega_0^2} \\
&= -1.5 \times 10^4 - \sqrt{(1.5 \times 10^4)^2 - (10^4)^2} \\
&= -2.618 \times 10^4
\end{aligned}
$$

and

$$
\begin{aligned}
s_2 &= -\alpha - \sqrt{\alpha^2 - \omega_0^2} \\
&= -0.3820 \times 10^4
\end{aligned}
$$

The homogeneous solution has the form of Equation 74. Adding the particular solution given by Equation 82 to the homogeneous solution, we obtain the general solution

$$v_C(t) = 10 + K_1 e^{s_1 t} + K_2 e^{s_2 t} \qquad (85)$$

Now, we must find values of K_1 and K_2 so the solution matches the known initial conditions in the circuit. It was given that the initial voltage on the capacitance is zero. Hence,

$$v_C(0) = 0$$

Evaluating Equation 85 at $t = 0$, we obtain

$$10 + K_1 + K_2 = 0 \qquad (86)$$

Furthermore, the initial current was given as $i(0) = 0$. Since the current through the capacitance is given by

$$i(t) = C \frac{dv_C(t)}{dt}$$

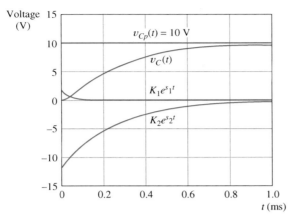

Figure 23 Solution for $R = 300\ \Omega$.

we conclude that

$$\frac{dv_C(0)}{dt} = 0$$

Taking the derivative of Equation 85 and evaluating at $t = 0$, we have

$$s_1 K_1 + s_2 K_2 = 0 \tag{87}$$

Now, we can solve Equations 86 and 87 for the values of K_1 and K_2. The results are $K_1 = 1.708$ and $K_2 = -11.708$. Substituting these values into Equation 85, we have the solution

$$v_C(t) = 10 + 1.708 e^{s_1 t} - 11.708 e^{s_2 t}$$

Plots of each of the terms of this equation and the complete solution are shown in Figure 23.

Case II ($R = 200\ \Omega$)

In this case, we get

$$\alpha = \frac{R}{2L} = 10^4 \tag{88}$$

Now, we repeat the steps for $R = 200\ \Omega$.

Because $\zeta = \alpha/\omega_0 = 1$, this is the critically damped case. The roots of the characteristic equation are given by Equations 72 and 73. Substituting values, we have

$$s_1 = s_2 = -\alpha + \sqrt{\alpha^2 - \omega_0^2} = -\alpha = -10^4$$

The homogeneous solution has the form of Equation 75. Adding the particular solution (Equation 82) to the homogeneous solution, we find that

$$v_C(t) = 10 + K_1 e^{s_1 t} + K_2 t e^{s_1 t} \tag{89}$$

As in case I, the initial conditions require $v_C(0) = 0$ and $dv_C(0)/dt = 0$. Thus, substituting $t = 0$ into Equation 89, we get

$$10 + K_1 = 0 \tag{90}$$

Differentiating Equation 89 and substituting $t = 0$ yields

$$s_1 K_1 + K_2 = 0 \tag{91}$$

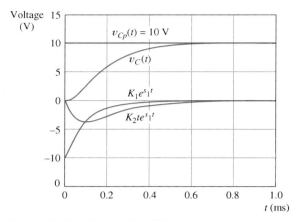

Figure 24 Solution for $R = 200 \ \Omega$.

Solving Equations 90 and 91 yields $K_1 = -10$ and $K_2 = -10^5$. Thus, the solution is

$$v_C(t) = 10 - 10e^{s_1 t} - 10^5 t e^{s_1 t} \qquad (92)$$

Plots of each of the terms of this equation and the complete solution are shown in Figure 24.

Case III ($R = 100 \ \Omega$)

Finally, we repeat the solution for $R = 100 \ \Omega$.

For this value of resistance, we have

$$\alpha = \frac{R}{2L} = 5000 \qquad (93)$$

Because $\zeta = \alpha/\omega_0 = 0.5$, this is the underdamped case. Using Equation 76, we compute the natural frequency:

$$\omega_n = \sqrt{\omega_0^2 - \alpha^2} = 8660 \qquad (94)$$

The homogeneous solution has the form of Equation 77. Adding the particular solution found earlier to the homogeneous solution, we obtain the general solution:

$$v_C(t) = 10 + K_1 e^{-\alpha t} \cos(\omega_n t) + K_2 e^{-\alpha t} \sin(\omega_n t) \qquad (95)$$

As in the previous cases, the initial conditions are $v_C(0) = 0$ and $dv_C(0)/dt = 0$. Evaluating Equation 95 at $t = 0$, we obtain

$$10 + K_1 = 0 \qquad (96)$$

Differentiating Equation 95 and evaluating at $t = 0$, we have

$$-\alpha K_1 + \omega_n K_2 = 0 \qquad (97)$$

Solving Equations 96 and 97, we obtain $K_1 = -10$ and $K_2 = -5.774$. Thus, the complete solution is

$$v_C(t) = 10 - 10e^{-\alpha t} \cos(\omega_n t) - 5.774 e^{-\alpha t} \sin(\omega_n t) \qquad (98)$$

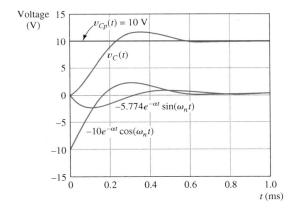

Figure 25 Solution for $R = 100\ \Omega$.

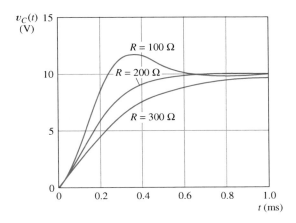

Figure 26 Solutions for all three resistances.

Plots of each of the terms of this equation and the complete solution are shown in Figure 25.

Figure 26 shows the complete response for all three values of resistance. ∎

Normalized Step Response of Second-Order Systems

When we suddenly apply a constant source to a circuit, we say that the forcing function is a **step function**. A unit step function, denoted by $u(t)$, is shown in Figure 27. By definition, we have

$$u(t) = 0 \quad t < 0$$
$$ = 1 \quad t \geq 0$$

For example, if we apply a dc voltage of A volts to a circuit by closing a switch, the applied voltage is a step function, given by

$$v(t) = Au(t)$$

This is illustrated in Figure 28.

We often encounter situations, such as Example 5, in which step forcing functions are applied to second-order systems described by a differential equation

Figure 27 A unit step function $u(t)$.
For $t < 0$, $u(t) = 0$. For $t \geq 0$, $u(t) = 1$.

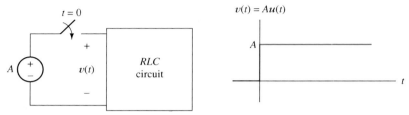

Figure 28 Applying a dc voltage by closing a switch results in a forcing function that is a step function.

of the form

$$\frac{d^2x(t)}{dt^2} + 2\alpha\frac{dx(t)}{dt} + \omega_0^2 x(t) = Au(t) \tag{99}$$

The differential equation is characterized by its undamped resonant frequency ω_0 and damping ratio $\zeta = \alpha/\omega_0$. [Of course, the solution for $x(t)$ also depends on the initial conditions.] Normalized solutions are shown in Figure 29 for the initial conditions $x(0) = 0$ and $x'(0) = 0$.

The system response for small values of the damping ratio ζ displays **overshoot** and **ringing** before settling to the steady-state value. On the other hand, if the damping ratio is large (compared to unity), the response takes a relatively long time to closely approach the final value.

Sometimes, we want to design a second-order system that quickly settles to steady state. Then we try to design for a damping ratio close to unity. For example, the control system for a robot arm could be a second-order system. When a step signal calls for the arm to move, we probably want it to achieve the final position in the minimum time without excessive overshoot and ringing.

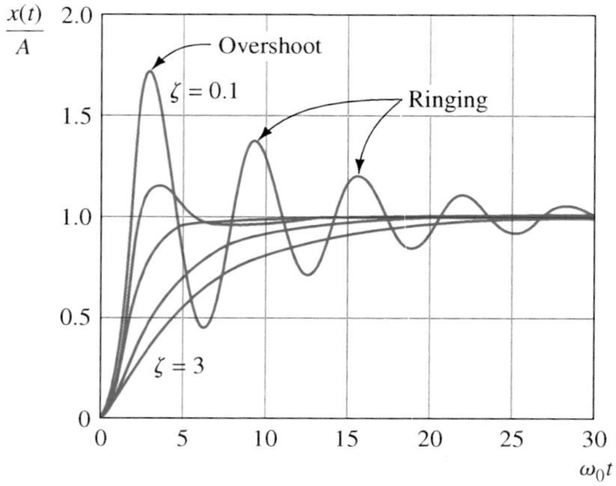

Frequently, electrical control systems and mechanical systems are best designed with a damping ratio close to unity. For example, when the suspension system on your automobile becomes severely underdamped, it is time for new shock absorbers.

Figure 29 Normalized step responses for second-order systems described by Equation 99 with damping ratios of $\zeta = 0.1, 0.5, 1, 2,$ and 3. The initial conditions are assumed to be $x(0) = 0$ and $x'(0) = 0$.

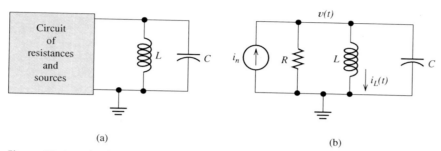

(a)   (b)

Figure 30 Any circuit consisting of sources, resistances, and a parallel LC combination can be reduced to the equivalent circuit shown in (b).

Circuits with Parallel L and C

The solution of circuits having an inductance and capacitance in parallel is very similar to the series case. Consider the circuit shown in Figure 30(a). The circuit inside the box is assumed to consist of sources and resistances. We can find a Norton equivalent circuit for any two-terminal circuit composed of resistances and sources. The equivalent circuit is shown in Figure 30(b).

We can analyze this circuit by writing a KCL equation at the top node of Figure 30(b) which results in

$$C\frac{dv(t)}{dt} + \frac{1}{R}v(t) + \frac{1}{L}\int_0^t v(t)\,dt + i_L(0) = i_n(t) \tag{100}$$

This can be converted into a pure differential equation by taking the derivative with respect to time:

$$C\frac{d^2v(t)}{dt^2} + \frac{1}{R}\frac{dv(t)}{dt} + \frac{1}{L}v(t) = \frac{di_n(t)}{dt} \tag{101}$$

Dividing through by the capacitance, we have

$$\frac{d^2v(t)}{dt^2} + \frac{1}{RC}\frac{dv(t)}{dt} + \frac{1}{LC}v(t) = \frac{1}{C}\frac{di_n(t)}{dt} \tag{102}$$

Now, if we define the damping coefficient

$$\alpha = \frac{1}{2RC} \tag{103}$$

the undamped resonant frequency

$$\omega_0 = \frac{1}{\sqrt{LC}} \tag{104}$$

and the forcing function

$$f(t) = \frac{1}{C}\frac{di_n(t)}{dt} \tag{105}$$

the differential equation can be written as

$$\frac{d^2v(t)}{dt^2} + 2\alpha\frac{dv(t)}{dt} + \omega_0^2 v(t) = f(t) \tag{106}$$

Notice that the equation for the damping coefficient of the parallel RLC circuit is different from that for the series circuit.

This equation has exactly the same form as Equation 64. Therefore, transient analysis of circuits with parallel LC elements is very similar to that of series LC circuits. However, notice that the equation for the damping coefficient α is different for the parallel circuit (in which $\alpha = 1/2RC$) than for the series circuit (in which $\alpha = R/2L$).

Exercise 9 Consider the circuit shown in Figure 31 on page 195 with $R = 25\ \Omega$. **a.** Compute the undamped resonant frequency, the damping coefficient, and the damping ratio. **b.** The initial conditions are $v(0-) = 0$ and $i_L(0-) = 0$. Show that this requires that $v'(0+) = 10^6$ V/s. **c.** Find the particular solution for $v(t)$. **d.** Find the general solution for $v(t)$, including the numerical values of all parameters.

$v(0-)$ and $i_L(0-)$ are the voltage and current values immediately before the switch opens.

Answer **a.** $\omega_0 = 10^5, \alpha = 2 \times 10^5$, and $\zeta = 2$; **b.** KCL requires that $i_C(0) = 0.1$ A $= Cv'(0)$, thus $v'(0) = 10^6$; **c.** $v_p(t) = 0$; **d.** $v(t) = 2.89(e^{-0.268 \times 10^5 t} - e^{-3.73 \times 10^5 t})$. □

PRACTICAL APPLICATION 1

Electronics and the Art of Automotive Maintenance

Throughout much of the history of the automobile, ignition systems have been designed as a straightforward application of electrical transients. The basic ignition system used for many years is shown in Figure PA1. The coil is a pair of mutually coupled inductors known as the primary and the secondary. The points form a switch that opens and closes as the engine rotates, opening at the instant that an ignition spark is needed by one of the cylinders. While the points are closed, current builds up relatively slowly in the primary winding of the coil. Then, when the points open, the current is rapidly interrupted. The resulting high rate of change of current induces a large voltage across the secondary winding, which is connected to the appropriate spark plug by the distributor. The resistance is needed to limit the current in case the engine stops with the points closed.

The capacitor prevents the voltage across the points from rising too rapidly when they open. (Recall that the voltage across a capacitance cannot change instantaneously.) Otherwise, arcing would occur across the points, causing them to become burned and pitted. By slowing the rise of voltage, the capacitor gives the gap between the points time to become wide enough to withstand the voltage across them. (Even so, the peak voltage across the points is many times the battery voltage.)

The primary inductance, current-limiting resistance, and capacitance form an underdamped series RLC circuit. Thus, an oscillatory current flows through the primary when the points open, inducing the requisite voltage in the secondary.

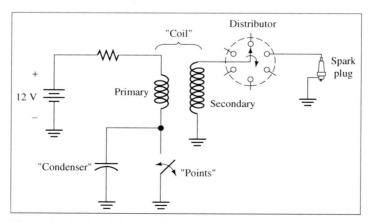

Figure PA1 Classic ignition for an internal-combustion engine.

In its early forms, the ignition system had mechanical or vacuum systems to make adjustments to the timing, depending on engine speed and throttle setting. In more recent years, the availability of complex electronics at reasonable costs plus the desire to adjust the ignition to obtain good performance and low pollution levels with varying air temperature, fuel quality, air pressure, engine temperature, and other factors have greatly affected the design of ignition systems. The basic principles remain the same as in the days of the classic automobile, but a complex network of electrical sensors, a digital computer, and an electronic switch have replaced the points and simple vacuum advance.

The complexity of modern engineering designs has become somewhat intimidating, even to practicing engineers. In the 1960s, as a new engineering graduate, I could study the design of an ignition system, a radio, or a home appliance, readily spotting and repairing malfunctions with the aid of a few tools and standard parts. Nowadays, if my car should fail to start due to ignition malfunction, at the end of a fishing trip into the backwoods of northern Michigan, I might very well have to walk back to civilization. Nevertheless, the improvements in performance provided by modern electronics make up for its difficulty of repair.

Figure PA2

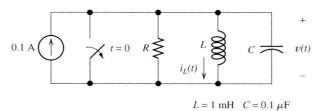

$L = 1 \text{ mH} \quad C = 0.1 \ \mu\text{F}$

Figure 31 Circuit for Exercises 9, 10, and 11.

Exercise 10 Repeat Exercise 9 for $R = 50 \ \Omega$.
Answer **a.** $\omega_0 = 10^5$, $\alpha = 10^5$, and $\zeta = 1$; **b.** KCL requires that $i_C(0) = 0.1 \text{ A} = Cv'(0)$, thus $v'(0) = 10^6$; **c.** $v_p(t) = 0$; **d.** $v(t) = 10^6 t e^{-10^5 t}$.   □

Exercise 11 Repeat Exercise 9 for $R = 250 \ \Omega$.

Answer **a.** $\omega_0 = 10^5$, $\alpha = 0.2 \times 10^5$, and $\zeta = 0.2$; **b.** KCL requires that $i_C(0) = 0.1$ A $= Cv'(0)$, thus $v'(0) = 10^6$; **c.** $v_p(t) = 0$; **d.** $v(t) = 10.21e^{-2 \times 10^4 t} \sin(97.98 \times 10^3 t)$.

□

6 TRANSIENT ANALYSIS USING THE MATLAB SYMBOLIC TOOLBOX

The MATLAB Symbolic Toolbox greatly facilitates the solution of transients in electrical circuits. It makes the solution of systems of differential equations almost as easy as arithmetic using a calculator. A step-by-step process for solving a circuit in this manner is

1. Write the differential-integral equations for the mesh currents, node voltages, or other circuit variables of interest.
2. If necessary, differentiate the equations to eliminate integrals.
3. Analyze the circuit at $t = 0+$ (i.e., immediately after switches operate) to determine initial conditions for the circuit variables and their derivatives. For a first-order equation, we need the initial value of the circuit variable. For a second-order equation we need the initial values of the circuit variable and its first derivative.
4. Enter the equations and initial values into the dsolve command in MATLAB.

We illustrate with a few examples.

Example 6   Computer-Aided Solution of a First-Order Circuit

Solve for $v_L(t)$ in the circuit of Figure 32(a). (*Note:* This example runs with MATLAB versions R2008a or R2008b.)

Solution   First, we write a KCL equation at the node joining the resistance and inductance.

$$\frac{v_L(t) - 20\cos(100t)}{R} + \frac{1}{L}\int_0^t v_L(t)dt + i_L(0) = 0$$

Taking the derivative of the equation to eliminate the integral, multiplying each term by R, and substituting values, we eventually obtain

$$\frac{dv_L(t)}{dt} + 100v_L(t) = -2000\sin(100t)$$

Next, we need to determine the initial value of v_L. Because the switch is open prior to $t = 0$, the initial current in the inductance is zero prior to $t = 0$. Furthermore, the current cannot change instantaneously in this circuit. Thus, we have $i_L(0+) = 0$. Immediately after the switch closes, the voltage source has a value of 20 V, and the current flowing in the circuit is zero, resulting in zero volts across the resistor. Then KVL yields $v_L(0+) = 20$ V. This is illustrated in Figure 32(b).

Now, we can write the MATLAB commands. As usual, we show the commands in **boldface**, comments in regular font, and MATLAB responses in color.

```
>> clear
>> syms VL t
```

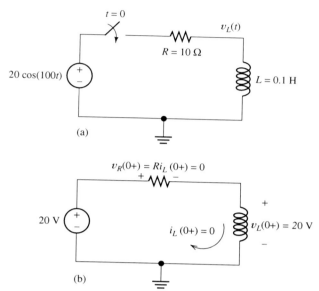

(a)

(b)

Figure 32 (a) Circuit of Example 6. (b) Circuit conditions at $t = 0+$.

```
>> % Enter the equation and initial value in the dsolve command.
>> % DVL represents the derivative of VL with respect to time.
>> VL = dsolve('DVL + 100*VL = -2000*sin(100*t)', 'VL(0) = 20');
>> % Print answer with 4 decimal place accuracy for the constants:
>> vpa(VL,4)
    ans =
    10.*cos(100.*t)-10.*sin(100.*t)+10.*exp(-100.*t)
```

In standard mathematical notation, the result becomes

$$v_L(t) = 10\cos(100t) - 10\sin(100t) + 10\exp(-100t)$$

An m-file named Example_4_6 containing the commands for this example can be found in the MATLAB folder. ∎

Example 7　Computer-Aided Solution of a Second-Order Circuit

The switch in the circuit of Figure 33(a) is closed for a long time prior to $t = 0$. Assume that $i_L(0+) = 0$. Use MATLAB to solve for $i_L(t)$ and plot the result for $0 \le t \le 2$ ms. (*Note:* As of early 2009, this example runs with Version R2008a but not with R2008b.)

Solution　Because this circuit contains two nodes and three meshes, node-voltage analysis is simpler than mesh analysis. We will solve for $v(t)$ and then take $1/L$ times the integral of the voltage to obtain the current through the inductance.

We start the node-voltage analysis by writing the KCL equation at the top node of the circuit (with the switch open).

$$C\frac{dv(t)}{dt} + \frac{v(t)}{R} + \frac{1}{L}\int_0^t v(t)dt + i_L(0+) = 0.2\exp(-1000t)$$

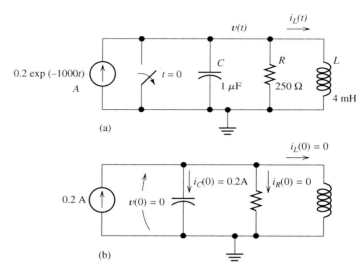

Figure 33 (a) Circuit of Example 7. (b) Circuit conditions at $t = 0+$.

Taking the derivative of the equation to eliminate the integral and substituting values, we eventually obtain

$$10^{-6}\frac{d^2v(t)}{dt^2} + 4 \times 10^{-3}\frac{dv(t)}{dt} + 250v(t) = -200\exp(-1000t)$$

Because this is a second-order equation, we need the initial value for both $v(t)$ and its first derivative. The circuit conditions at $t = 0+$ are shown in Figure 33(b). The problem states that the initial current in the inductance is zero. The initial voltage $v(0+)$ is zero, because, with the switch closed, the capacitor is shorted. When the switch opens, the voltage remains zero, because an infinite current would be required to change the capacitor voltage instantaneously. Furthermore, the current flowing through the resistor is zero because the voltage across it is zero. Thus, the 0.2 A from the source must flow through the capacitor, and we have

$$C\frac{dv(0+)}{dt} = 0.2$$

We have established that $v(0+) = 0$ and $v'(0+) = dv(0+)/dt = 0.2 \times 10^6$ V/s.

After the voltage is found, the current is given by

$$i_L(t) = \frac{1}{L}\int_0^t v(t)dt = 250\int_0^t v(t)dt$$

We use the following MATLAB commands to obtain the solution.

```
>> clear
>> syms ILV t
>> % Enter the equation and initial values in the dsolve command.
>> % D2V represents the second derivative of V.
>> V = dsolve('(1e-6)*D2V + (4e-3)*DV + 250*V = -200*exp(-1000*t)',...
            'DV(0)=0.2e6', 'V(0)=0');
>> % Calculate the inductor current by integrating V with respect to t
>> % from 0 to t and multiplying by 1/L:
>> IL = (250)*int(V,t,0,t);
```

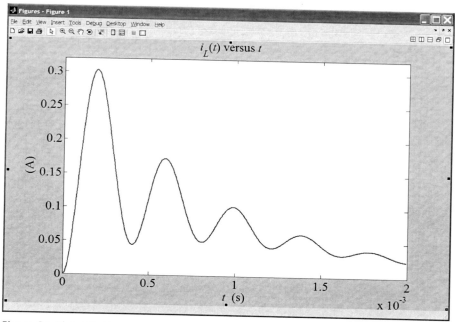

Figure 34 Plot of $i_L(t)$ versus t.

```
>> % Display the expression for current to 4 decimal place accuracy:
>> pretty(vpa(IL,4))
-0.2024exp(-2000. t)cos(15680. t) - 0.01290exp(-2000. t)sin(15680. t)
        + 0.2024 exp(-1000. t)
>> ezplot(IL,[0 2e-3])
```

In standard mathematical notation, the result is

$$i_L(t) = -0.2024 \exp(-2000t) \cos(15680t) -$$
$$0.01290 \exp(-2000t) \sin(15680t) + 0.2024 \exp(-1000t)$$

The plot (after some editing to dress it up) is shown in Figure 34. An m-file named Example_4_7 containing the commands for this example can be found in the MATLAB folder. ■

Solving Systems of Linear Differential Equations

So far in this chapter, each of our examples has involved a single differential equation. Circuits that require two or more circuit variables (such as node voltages or mesh currents) result in systems of differential equations. While these systems can be rather formidable to solve by traditional methods, the MATLAB Symbolic Toolbox can solve them with relative ease.

Example 8	Computer-Aided Solution of a System of Differential Equations

Use MATLAB to solve for the node voltages in the circuit of Figure 35. The circuit has been connected for a long time prior to $t = 0$ with the switch open, so the initial

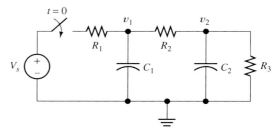

Figure 35 Circuit of Example 8.

$V_s = 10\text{ V} \quad R_1 = R_2 = R_3 = 1\text{ M}\Omega \quad C_1 = C_2 = 1\ \mu\text{F}$

values of the node voltages are zero. (*Note:* This example runs with versions R2008a or R2008b.)

Solution First, we write the KCL equations at nodes 1 and 2.

$$C_1 \frac{dv_1(t)}{dt} + \frac{v_1(t) - V_s}{R_1} + \frac{v_1(t) - v_2(t)}{R_2} = 0$$

$$C_2 \frac{dv_2(t)}{dt} + \frac{v_2(t) - v_1(t)}{R_2} + \frac{v_2(t)}{R_3} = 0$$

Now substituting values, multiplying each term by 10^6, and rearranging terms, we have

$$\frac{dv_1(t)}{dt} + 2v_1(t) - v_2(t) = 10$$

$$\frac{dv_2(t)}{dt} + 2v_2(t) - v_1(t) = 0$$

The MATLAB commands and results are:

```
>> clear
>> syms v1 v2 t
>> [v1 v2] = dsolve('Dv1 + 2*v1 - v2 = 10','Dv2 + 2*v2 -v1 = 0',...
                    'v1(0) = 0','v2(0)= 0');
>> v1
        v1 =
        -5*exp(-t)-5/3*exp(-3*t)+20/3
>> v2
        v2 =
        -5*exp(-t)+5/3*exp(-3*t)+10/3
```

Thus, the node voltages are given by

$$v_1(t) = 20/3 - 5\exp(-t) - (5/3)\exp(-3t)$$

$$v_2(t) = 10/3 - 5\exp(-t) + (5/3)\exp(-3t)$$

It is always a good idea to perform a few checks on our answers. First, we can verify that the MATLAB results are both zero at $t = 0$ as required by the initial conditions. Furthermore, at $t = \infty$, the capacitors act as open circuits, and the voltage division principle yields $v_1(\infty) = 20/3\text{ V}$ and $v_2(\infty) = 10/3$. The expressions delivered by MATLAB also yield these values. ∎

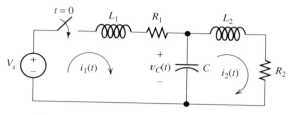

$V_s = 2$ V $L_1 = L_2 = 1$ mH $R_1 = R_2 = 1\,\Omega$ $C = 10\,\mu F$

Figure 36 Circuit of Example 9.

Example 9   Computer-Aided Solution of a System of Differential Equations

Use MATLAB to solve for the mesh currents and $v_C(t)$ in the circuit of Figure 36. The circuit has been connected for a long time prior to $t = 0$, so the initial values of the capacitor voltage and inductor currents are zero. Determine the constants in the equations to four decimal place accuracy. (*Note:* This example runs with either R2008a or R2008b. However, it is slow and gives the answer in an awkward form with R2008b.)

Solution   We will solve for the mesh currents and then compute the capacitor voltage as

$$v_C(t) = \frac{1}{C}\int_0^t [i_1(t) - i_2(t)]dt$$

The first step in solving for the mesh currents is to write the KVL equations around meshes 1 and 2.

$$L_1\frac{di_1(t)}{dt} + R_1 i_1(t) + \frac{1}{C}\int_0^t [i_1(t) - i_2(t)]dt = V_s \qquad (107)$$

$$L_2\frac{di_2(t)}{dt} + R_2 i_2(t) + \frac{1}{C}\int_0^t [i_2(t) - i_1(t)]dt = 0 \qquad (108)$$

Because the equations contain integrals, we differentiate each term with respect to time.

$$L_1\frac{d^2 i_1(t)}{dt^2} + R_1\frac{di_1(t)}{dt} + \frac{1}{C}i_1(t) - \frac{1}{C}i_2(t) = 0$$

$$L_2\frac{d^2 i_2(t)}{dt^2} + R_2\frac{di_2(t)}{dt} + \frac{1}{C}i_2(t) - \frac{1}{C}i_1(t) = 0$$

Then, we substitute component values to obtain:

$$10^{-3}\frac{d^2 i_1(t)}{dt^2} + \frac{di_1(t)}{dt} + 10^5 i_1(t) - 10^5 i_2(t) = 0$$

$$10^{-3}\frac{d^2 i_2(t)}{dt^2} + \frac{di_2(t)}{dt} + 10^5 i_2(t) - 10^5 i_1(t) = 0$$

We have second-order equations, so we need the values of $i_1(0+), i_2(0+), i_1'(0+)$, and $i_2'(0+)$. Because the switch was open for a long time prior to $t = 0$, we know that the currents in the inductors are zero before the switch opens. Furthermore, the currents are not forced to change instantaneously in this circuit, so we have $i_1(0+) = 0$ and $i_2(0+) = 0$. Also, the voltage across the capacitance is zero prior to $t = 0$ and at $t = 0+$. Then, at $t = 0+$, the mesh equations (Equations 107 and 108) simplify to:

$$L_1 \frac{di_1(0+)}{dt} = V_s$$

$$L_2 \frac{di_2(0+)}{dt} = 0$$

Thus, we have $i_1'(0+) = V_s/L_1 = 2000 \, \text{A/s}$, and $i_2'(0+) = 0$.

Now, we are ready to apply the MATLAB commands:

```
>> clear
>> syms i1 i2 t vc
>> [i1 i2] = dsolve('(1e-3)*D2i1 + Di1 + (1e5)*i1 - (1e5)*i2 = 0',...
                    '(1e-3)*D2i2 + Di2 + (1e5)*i2 - (1e5)*i1 = 0',...
                    'i1(0)= 0, Di1(0)= 2000, i2(0) = 0, Di2(0) =0');
>> vpa(i1, 4) % Display answer to 4 decimal place accuracy.
     ans =
     1.-1.*exp(-1000.*t)+.7076e-1*exp(-500.*t)*sin(.1414e5*t)
>> vpa(i2, 4) % Display answer to 4 decimal place accuracy.
     ans =
     1.-1.*exp(-1000.*t)-.7076e-1*exp(-500.*t)*sin(.1414e5*t)
>> % Next calculate vc by integrating the difference between the
>> % results for i1 and i2:
>> vc = int((1e5)*(i1-i2),t,0,t);
>> vc = vpa(vc,4) % Display answer to 4 decimal place accuracy.
     vc =
     1.-1.*exp(-500.*t)*cos(.1414e5*t)-.3539e-1*exp(-500.*t)*sin(.1414e5*t)
```

Thus, the results are:

$$i_1(t) = 1 - \exp(-1000t) + 0.07076 \exp(-500t) \sin(14.14 \times 10^3 t) \, \text{A}$$

$$i_2(t) = 1 - \exp(-1000t) - 0.07076 \exp(-500t) \sin(14.14 \times 10^3 t) \, \text{A}$$

$$v_C(t) = 1 - \exp(-500t) \cos(14.14 \times 10^3 t) - 0.03539 \exp(-500t) \sin(14.14 \times 10^3 t) \, \text{V}$$

As a partial check, we can verify that the results meet the initial conditions and the conditions in steady state at $t = \infty$. ∎

Exercise 12 Use the MATLAB Symbolic Toolbox to solve Example 4, obtaining the result given in Equation 56 and a plot similar to Figure 17.

Answer A sequence of commands that produces the solution and the plot is:

```
clear
syms ix t R C vCinitial w
ix = dsolve('(R*C)*Dix + ix = (w*C)*2*cos(w*t)', 'ix(0)=-vCinitial/R');
ians =subs(ix,[R C vCinitial w],[5000 1e-6 1 200]);
pretty(vpa(ians, 4))
ezplot(ians,[0 80e-3])
```

An m-file named Exercise_4_12 containing these commands can be found in the MATLAB folder. (Runs with either R2008a or R2008b.) □

Exercise 13 Use the MATLAB Symbolic Toolbox to solve Example 5 obtaining the results given in the example for $v_C(t)$ and a plot similar to Figure 26.

Answer A list of commands that produces the solution and the plot is:

```
clear
syms vc t
% Case I, R = 300:
vc = dsolve('(1e-8)*D2vc + (1e-6)*300*Dvc+ vc =10', 'vc(0) = 0','Dvc(0)=0');
vpa(vc,4)
ezplot(vc, [0 1e-3])
hold on % Turn hold on so all plots are on the same axes
% Case II, R = 200:
vc = dsolve('(1e-8)*D2vc + (1e-6)*200*Dvc+ vc =10', 'vc(0) = 0','Dvc(0)=0');
vpa(vc,4)
ezplot(vc, [0 1e-3])
% Case III, R = 100:
vc = dsolve('(1e-8)*D2vc + (1e-6)*100*Dvc+ vc =10', 'vc(0) = 0','Dvc(0)=0');
vpa(vc,4)
ezplot(vc, [0 1e-3])
```

An m-file named Exercise_4_13 containing these commands resides in the MATLAB folder. (Runs with either R2008a or R2008b.)

Summary

1. The transient part of the response for a circuit containing sources, resistances, and a single energy-storage element (L or C) is of the form $Ke^{-t/\tau}$. The time constant is given by $\tau = RC$ or by $\tau = L/R$, where R is the Thévenin resistance seen looking back into the circuit from the terminals of the energy-storage element.

2. In dc steady-state conditions, inductors behave as short circuits and capacitors behave as open circuits. We can find the steady-state (forced) response for dc sources by analyzing the dc equivalent circuit.

3. To find the transient currents and voltages, we must solve linear differential equations with constant coefficients. The solutions are the sum of two parts. The particular solution, also called the forced response, depends on the sources, as well as the other circuit elements. The homogeneous solution, also called the natural response, depends on the passive elements (R, L, and C), but not on the sources. In circuits that contain resistances, the natural response eventually decays to zero.

4. The natural response of a second-order circuit containing a series or parallel combination of inductance and capacitance depends on the damping ratio and undamped resonant frequency.

If the damping ratio is greater than unity, the circuit is overdamped, and the natural response is of the form

$$x_c(t) = K_1 e^{s_1 t} + K_2 e^{s_2 t}$$

If the damping ratio equals unity, the circuit is critically damped, and the natural response is of the form

$$x_c(t) = K_1 e^{s_1 t} + K_2 t e^{s_1 t}$$

If the damping ratio is less than unity, the circuit is underdamped, and the natural response is of the form

$$x_c(t) = K_1 e^{-\alpha t} \cos(\omega_n t) + K_2 e^{-\alpha t} \sin(\omega_n t)$$

The normalized step response for second-order systems is shown in Figure 29 for several values of the damping ratio.

5. The MATLAB Symbolic Toolbox is a powerful tool for solving the equations for transient circuits. A step-by-step procedure is given in this chapter.

Note: **You can check the answers to many of the problems in this chapter by using a computer-aided circuit-analysis program such as Multisim** **from National Instruments or OrCAD Capture from Cadence Inc.**

Problems

Section 1: First-Order *RC* Circuits

P1. Suppose we have a capacitance C discharging through a resistance R. Define and give an expression for the time constant. To attain a long time constant, do we need large or small values for R? For C?

*P2. The dielectric materials used in real capacitors are not perfect insulators. A resistance called a leakage resistance in parallel with the capacitance can model this imperfection. A 100-μF capacitor is initially charged to 100 V. We want 90 percent of the initial energy to remain after one minute. What is the limit on the leakage resistance for this capacitor?

*P3. The initial voltage across the capacitor shown in Figure P3 is $v_C(0+) = -10$ V. Find an expression for the voltage across the capacitor as a function of time. Also, determine the time t_0 at which the voltage crosses zero.

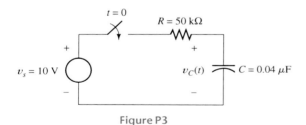

Figure P3

*P4. A 100-μF capacitance is initially charged to 1000 V. At $t = 0$, it is connected to a 1-kΩ resistance. At what time t_2 has 50 percent of the initial energy stored in the capacitance been dissipated in the resistance?

*P5. At $t = 0$, a charged 10-μF capacitance is connected to a voltmeter, as shown in Figure P5. The meter can be modeled as a resistance. At $t = 0$, the meter reads 50 V. At $t = 30$ s,

the reading is 25 V. Find the resistance of the voltmeter.

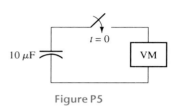

Figure P5

*P6. At time t_1, a capacitance C is charged to a voltage of V_1. Then, the capacitance discharges through a resistance R. Write an expression for the voltage across the capacitance as a function of time for $t > t_1$ in terms of R, C, V_1, and t_1.

P7. Given an initially charged capacitance that begins to discharge through a resistance at $t = 0$, what percentage of the initial voltage remains at two time constants? What percentage of the initial stored energy remains?

P8. The initial voltage across the capacitor shown in Figure P3 is $v_C(0+) = 0$. Find an expression for the voltage across the capacitor as a function of time, and sketch to scale versus time.

P9. In physics, the half-life is often used to characterize exponential decay of physical quantities such as radioactive substances. The half-life is the time required for the quantity to decay to half of its initial value. The time constant for the voltage on a capacitance discharging through a resistance is $\tau = RC$. Find an expression for the half-life of the voltage in terms of R and C.

P10. We know that a 50-μF capacitance is charged to an unknown voltage V_i at $t = 0$. The capacitance is in parallel with a 3-kΩ resistance.

---

* Denotes that answers are contained in the Student Solutions files.

At $t = 100$ ms, the voltage across the capacitance is 5 V. Determine the value of V_i.

P11. We know that the capacitor shown in Figure P11 is charged to a voltage of 10 V prior to $t = 0$. **a.** Find expressions for the voltage across the capacitor $v_C(t)$ and the voltage across the resistor $v_R(t)$ for all time. **b.** Find an expression for the power delivered to the resistor. **c.** Integrate the power from $t = 0$ to $t = \infty$ to find the energy delivered. **d.** Show that the energy delivered to the resistor is equal to the energy stored in the capacitor prior to $t = 0$.

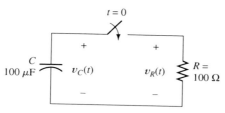

Figure P11

P12. The purchasing power P of a certain unit of currency declines by 3 percent per year. Determine the time constant associated with the purchasing power of this currency.

P13. Derive an expression for $v_C(t)$ in the circuit of Figure P13 and sketch $v_C(t)$ to scale versus time.

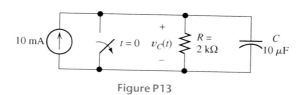

Figure P13

P14. Suppose that at $t = 0$, we connect an uncharged 10-μF capacitor to a charging circuit consisting of a 2500-V voltage source in series with a 2-MΩ resistance. At $t = 40$ s, the capacitor is disconnected from the charging circuit and connected in parallel with a 5-MΩ resistor. Determine the voltage across the capacitor at $t = 40$ s and at $t = 100$ s. (*Hint:* You may find it convenient to redefine

the time variable to be $t' = t - 40$ for the discharge interval so that the discharge starts at $t' = 0$.)

P15 . Suppose we have a capacitance C that is charged to an initial voltage V_i. Then at $t = 0$, a resistance R is connected across the capacitance. Write an expression for the current. Then, integrate the current from $t = 0$ to $t = \infty$, and show that the result is equal to the initial charge stored on the capacitance.

P16. A person shuffling across a dry carpet can be approximately modeled as a charged 100-pF capacitance with one end grounded. If the person touches a grounded metallic object such as a water faucet, the capacitance is discharged and the person experiences a brief shock. Typically, the capacitance may be charged to 20,000 V and the resistance (mainly of one's finger) is 100 Ω. Determine the peak current during discharge and the time constant of the shock.

P17. Consider the circuit of Figure P17, in which the switch instantaneously moves back and forth between contacts A and B, spending 2 seconds in each position. Thus, the capacitor repeatedly charges for 2 seconds and then discharges for 2 seconds. Assume that $v_C(0) = 0$ and that the switch moves to position A at $t = 0$. Determine $v_C(2)$, $v_C(4)$, $v_C(6)$, and $v_C(8)$.

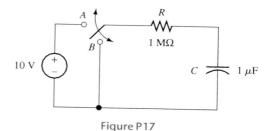

Figure P17

P18. Consider the circuit shown in Figure P18. Prior to $t = 0$, $v_1 = 100$ V, and $v_2 = 0$. **a.** Immediately after the switch is closed, what is the value of the current [i.e., what is the value of $i(0+)$]? **b.** Write the KVL equation for the circuit in terms of the current and initial voltages. Take the derivative to obtain a differential equation. **c.** What is the value of the time constant in this circuit? **d.** Find an expression for the current as a function of time. **e.** Find the value that v_2 approaches as t becomes very large.

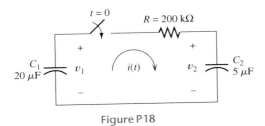

Figure P18

Section 2: DC Steady State

P19. List the steps for dc steady-state analysis of *RLC* circuits.

P20. Explain why we replace capacitances with open circuits and inductances with short circuits in dc steady-state analysis.

*P21. Solve for the steady-state values of i_1, i_2, and i_3 for the circuit shown in Figure P21.

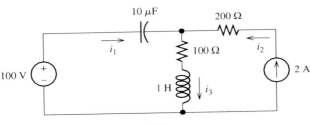

Figure P21

*P22. Consider the circuit shown in Figure P22. What is the steady-state value of v_C after the switch opens? Determine how long it takes after the switch opens before v_C is within 1 percent of its steady-state value.

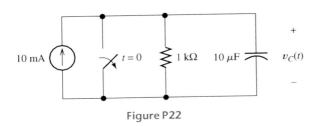

Figure P22

*P23. In the circuit of Figure P23, the switch is in position *A* for a long time prior to $t = 0$. Find expressions for $v_R(t)$ and sketch it to scale for $-2 \le t \le 10\,\text{s}$.

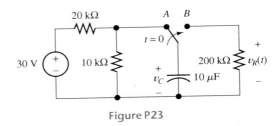

Figure P23

P24. The circuit shown in Figure P24 has been set up for a long time prior to $t = 0$ with the switch closed. Find the value of v_C prior to $t = 0$. Find the steady-state value of v_C after the switch has been opened for a long time.

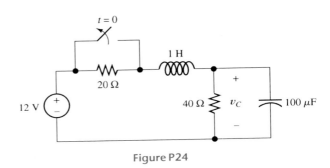

Figure P24

P25. Solve for the steady-state values of i_1, i_2, i_3, i_4, and v_C for the circuit shown in Figure P25, assuming that the switch has been closed for a long time.

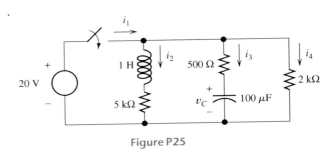

Figure P25

P26. The circuit shown in Figure P26 is operating in steady state. Determine the values of i_L, v_x, and v_C.

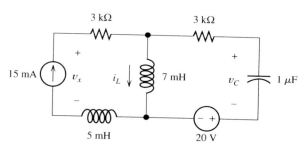

Figure P26

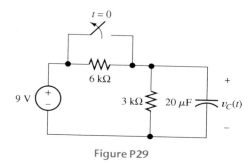

Figure P29

P27. The circuit of Figure P27 has been connected for a very long time. Determine the values of v_C and i_R.

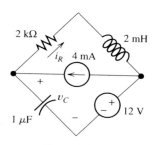

Figure P27

P28. Consider the circuit of Figure P28 in which the switch has been closed for a long time prior to $t = 0$. Determine the values of $v_C(t)$ before $t = 0$ and a long time after $t = 0$. Also, determine the time constant after the switch opens and expressions for $v_C(t)$. Sketch $v_C(t)$ to scale versus time for $-0.2 \le t \le 0.5$ s.

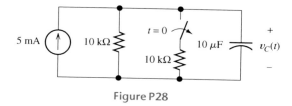

Figure P28

P29. For the circuit shown in Figure P29, the switch is closed for a long time prior to $t = 0$. Find expressions for $v_C(t)$ and sketch it to scale for $-80 \le t \le 160$ ms.

P30. Consider the circuit of Figure P30 in which the switch has been closed for a long time prior to $t = 0$. Determine the values of $v_C(t)$ before $t = 0$ and a long time after $t = 0$. Also, determine the time constant after the switch opens and expressions for $v_C(t)$. Sketch $v_C(t)$ to scale versus time for $-4 \le t \le 16$ s.

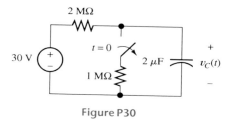

Figure P30

Section 3: *RL* Circuits

P31. Give the expression for the time constant of a circuit consisting of an inductance with an initial current in series with a resistance R. To attain a long time constant, do we need large or small values for R? For L?

P32. A circuit consists of switches that open or close at $t = 0$, resistances, dc sources, and a single energy storage element, either an inductance or a capacitance. We wish to solve for a current or a voltage $x(t)$ as a function of time for $t \ge 0$. Write the general form for the solution. How is each unknown in the solution determined?

*P33. The circuit shown in Figure P33 is operating in steady state with the switch closed prior to $t = 0$. Find $i(t)$ for $t < 0$ and for $t \ge 0$.

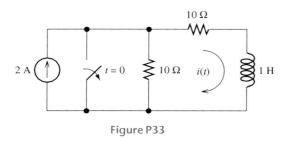

Figure P33

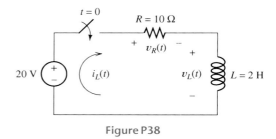

Figure P38

*P34. Consider the circuit shown in Figure P34. The initial current in the inductor is $i_L(0-) = -0.2$ A. Find expressions for $i_L(t)$ and $v(t)$ for $t \geq 0$ and sketch to scale versus time.

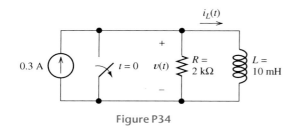

Figure P34

P35. Repeat Problem P34 given $i_L(0-) = 0$ A.

*P36. Real inductors have series resistance associated with the wire used to wind the coil. Suppose that we want to store energy in a 10-H inductor. Determine the limit on the series resistance so the energy remaining after one hour is at least 75 percent of the initial energy.

P37. Determine expressions for and sketch $i_s(t)$ to scale versus time for $-0.2 \leq t \leq 1.0$ s for the circuit of Figure P37.

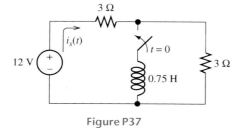

Figure P37

P38. For the circuit shown in Figure P38, find an expression for the current $i_L(t)$ and sketch it to scale versus time. Also, find an expression for $v_L(t)$ and sketch it to scale versus time.

P39. The circuit shown in Figure P39 is operating in steady state with the switch closed prior to $t = 0$. Find expressions for $i_L(t)$ for $t < 0$ and for $t \geq 0$. Sketch $i_L(t)$ to scale versus time.

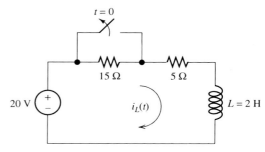

Figure P39

P40. Consider the circuit shown in Figure P40. A voltmeter (VM) is connected across the inductance. The switch has been closed for a long time. When the switch is opened, an arc appears across the switch contacts. Explain why. Assuming an ideal switch and inductor, what voltage appears across the inductor when the switch is opened? What could happen to the voltmeter when the switch opens?

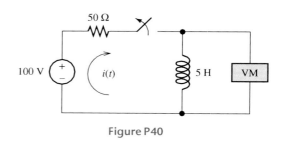

Figure P40

P41. Due to components not shown in the figure, the circuit of Figure P41 has $i_L(0) = I_t$.
a. Write an expression for $i_L(t)$ for $t \geq 0$.
b. Find an expression for the power delivered to the resistance as a function of time.
c. Integrate the power delivered to the resistance from $t = 0$ to $t = \infty$, and show that the result is equal to the initial energy stored in the inductance.

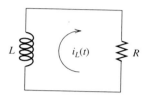

Figure P41

P42. The switch shown in Figure P42 has been closed for a long time prior to $t = 0$, then it opens at $t = 0$ and closes again at $t = 1$ s. Find $i_L(t)$ for all t.

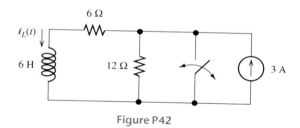

Figure P42

P43. Determine expressions for and sketch $v_R(t)$ to scale versus time for the circuit of Figure P43. The circuit is operating in steady state with the switch closed prior to $t = 0$. Consider the time interval $-1 \leq t \leq 5$ ms.

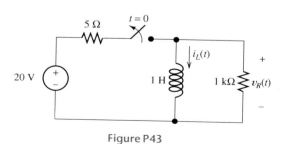

Figure P43

Section 4: *RC* and *RL* Circuits with General Sources

P44. What are the steps in solving a circuit having a resistance, a source, and an inductance (or capacitance)?

*P45. Write the differential equation for $i_L(t)$ and find the complete solution for the circuit of Figure P45. [*Hint:* Try a particular solution of the form $i_{Lp}(t) = Ae^{-t}$.]

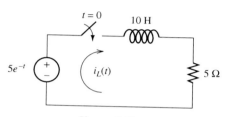

Figure P45

*P46. Solve for $v_C(t)$ for $t > 0$ in the circuit of Figure P46. [*Hint:* Try a particular solution of the form $v_{Cp}(t) = Ae^{-3t}$.]

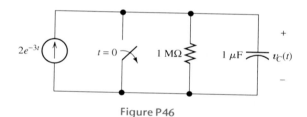

Figure P46

*P47. Solve for $v(t)$ for $t > 0$ in the circuit of Figure P47, given that the inductor current is zero prior to $t = 0$. [*Hint:* Try a particular solution of the form $v_p = A\cos(10t) + B\sin(10t)$.]

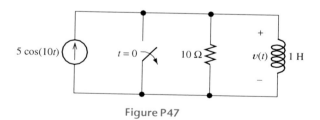

Figure P47

P48. Solve for $i_L(t)$ for $t > 0$ in the circuit of Figure P48. You will need to make an educated guess as to the form of the particular solution. (*Hint:* The particular solution includes terms with the same functional forms as the terms found in the forcing function and its derivatives.)

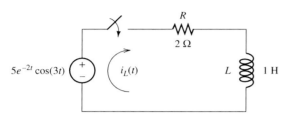

Figure P48

P49. Consider the circuit shown in Figure P49. The voltage source is known as a **ramp function,** which is defined by

$$v(t) = \begin{cases} 0 & \text{for } t < 0 \\ t & \text{for } t \geq 0 \end{cases}$$

Assume that $v_C(0) = 0$. Derive an expression for $v_C(t)$ for $t \geq 0$. Sketch $v_C(t)$ to scale versus time. [*Hint:* Write the differential equation for $v_C(t)$ and assume a particular solution of the form $v_{Cp}(t) = A + Bt$.]

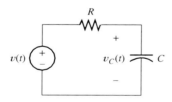

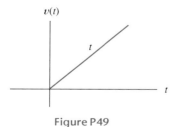

Figure P49

P50. Consider the circuit shown in Figure P50. The initial current in the inductor is $i_s(0+) = 0$. Write the differential equation for

$i_s(t)$ and solve. [*Hint:* Try a particular solution of the form $i_{sp}(t) = A\cos(300t) + B\sin(300t)$.]

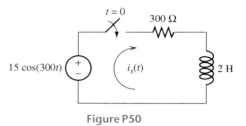

Figure P50

P51. The voltage source shown in Figure P51 is called a ramp function. Assume that $i_L(0) = 0$. Write the differential equation for $i_L(t)$, and find the complete solution. [*Hint:* Try a particular solution of the form $i_p(t) = A + Bt$.]

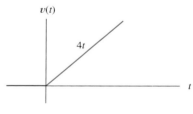

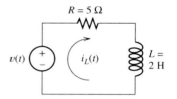

Figure P51

P52. Determine the form of the particular solution for the differential equation

$$2\frac{dv(t)}{dt} + v(t) = 5t\sin(t)$$

Then, find the particular solution. (*Hint:* The particular solution includes terms with the same functional forms as the terms found in the forcing function and its derivatives.)

P53. Determine the form of the particular solution for the differential equation

$$\frac{dv(t)}{dt} + 3v(t) = t^2\exp(-t)$$

Then, find the particular solution. (*Hint:* The particular solution includes terms with the same functional forms as the terms found in the forcing function and its derivatives.)

P54. Consider the circuit shown in Figure P54.
a. Write the differential equation for $i(t)$.
b. Find the time constant and the form of the complementary solution.
c. Usually, for an exponential forcing function like this, we would try a particular solution of the form $i_p(t) = K\exp(-2t)$. Why doesn't that work in this case?
d. Find the particular solution. [*Hint:* Try a particular solution of the form $i_p(t) = Kt\exp(-2t)$.]
e. Find the complete solution for $i(t)$.

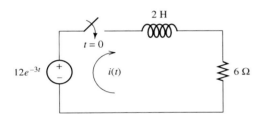

Figure P54

P55. Consider the circuit shown in Figure P55.
a. Write the differential equation for $v(t)$.
b. Find the time constant and the form of the complementary solution.
c. Usually, for an exponential forcing function like this, we would try a particular solution of the form $v_p(t) = K\exp(-10t)$. Why doesn't that work in this case?
d. Find the particular solution. [*Hint:* Try a particular solution of the form $i_p(t) = Kt\exp(-10t)$.]
e. Find the complete solution for $i(t)$.

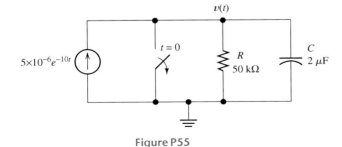

Figure P55

Section 5: Second-Order Circuits

P56. How can first- or second-order circuits be identified by inspecting the circuit diagrams?

P57. How can an underdamped second-order system be identified? What form does its complementary solution take? Repeat for a critically damped system and for an overdamped system.

P58. What is a unit step function?

P59. Discuss two methods that can be used to determine the particular solution of a circuit with constant dc sources.

P60. Sketch a step response for a second-order system that displays considerable overshoot and ringing. In what types of circuits do we find pronounced overshoot and ringing?

*P61. A dc source is connected to a series RLC circuit by a switch that closes at $t = 0$, as shown in Figure P61. The initial conditions are $i(0+) = 0$ and $v_C(0+) = 0$. Write the differential equation for $v_C(t)$. Solve for $v_C(t)$, if $R = 80\,\Omega$.

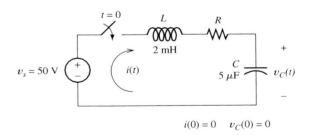

$i(0) = 0 \qquad v_C(0) = 0$

Figure P61

*P62. Repeat Problem P61 for $R = 40\,\Omega$.

*P63. Repeat Problem P61 for $R = 20\,\Omega$.

P64. Consider the circuit shown in Figure P64 in which the switch has been open for a long time prior to $t = 0$ and we are given $R = 25\,\Omega$. a. Compute the undamped resonant frequency, the damping coefficient, and the damping ratio of the circuit after the switch closes. b. Assume that the capacitor is initially charged by a 25-V dc source not shown in the figure, so we have $v(0+) = 25\,\text{V}$. Determine the values of $i_L(0+)$ and $v'(0+)$. c. Find the particular solution for $v(t)$. d. Find

217

the general solution for $v(t)$, including the numerical values of all parameters.

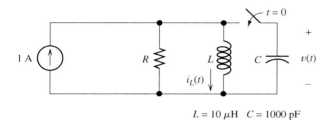

$L = 10\ \mu\text{H} \quad C = 1000\ \text{pF}$

Figure P64

P65. Repeat Problem P64 for $R = 50\ \Omega$.

P66. Repeat Problem P64 for $R = 500\ \Omega$.

P67. Solve for $i(t)$ for $t > 0$ in the circuit of Figure P67, with $R = 50\ \Omega$, given that $i(0+) = 0$ and $v_C(0+) = 20\ \text{V}$. [*Hint:* Try a particular solution of the form $i_p(t) = A\cos(100t) + B\sin(100t)$.]

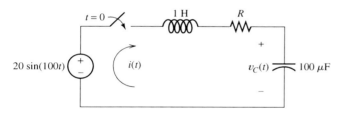

Figure P67

P68. Repeat Problem P67 with $R = 200\ \Omega$.

P69. Repeat Problem P67 with $R = 400\ \Omega$.

P70. Consider the circuit shown in Figure P70.
   a. Write the differential equation for $v(t)$.

   b. Find the damping coefficient, the natural frequency, and the form of the complementary solution.

   c. Usually, for a sinusoidal forcing function, we try a particular solution of the form $v_p(t) = A\cos(10^4 t) + B\sin(10^4 t)$. Why doesn't that work in this case?

   d. Find the particular solution. [*Hint:* Try a particular solution of the form $v_p(t) = At\cos(10^4 t) + B\,t\sin(10^4 t)$.]

   e. Find the complete solution for $v(t)$.

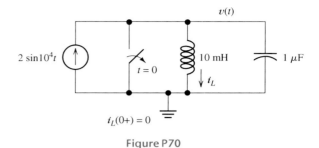

$i_L(0+) = 0$

Figure P70

Section 6: Transient Analysis Using the MATLAB Symbolic Toolbox

P71. Use MATLAB to derive an expression for $v_C(t)$ in the circuit of Figure P13 and plot $v_C(t)$ versus time for $0 < t < 100\ \text{ms}$.

P72. Consider the circuit shown in Figure P49. The voltage source is known as a **ramp function,** which is defined by

$$v(t) = \begin{cases} 0 & \text{for } t < 0 \\ t & \text{for } t \geq 0 \end{cases}$$

or more compactly as $v(t) = tu(t)$. Use MATLAB to derive an expression for $v_C(t)$ in terms of R, C, and t. Next, substitute $R = 1\ \text{M}\Omega$ and $C = 1\ \mu\text{F}$. Then, plot $v_C(t)$ and $v(t)$ on the same axes for $-2 < t < 5\ \text{s}$. [*Hint:* In MATLAB, $u(t)$ is expressed as heaviside(t).]

P73. Consider the circuit shown in Figure P50 in which the switch is open for a long time prior to $t = 0$. The initial current is $i_s(0+) = 0$. Write the differential equation for $i_s(t)$ and use MATLAB to solve. Then, plot $i_s(t)$ for t ranging from 0 to 80 ms. (*Hint:* Avoid using lowercase "i" as the first letter of the dependent variable, instead use "Is" for the current in MATLAB.)

P74. Consider the circuit shown in Figure P64 in which the switch has been open for a long time prior to $t = 0$ and we are given $R = 25\ \Omega$. **a.** Write the differential equation for $v(t)$. **b.** Assume that the capacitor is initially charged by a 50-V dc source not shown in the figure, so we have $v(0+) = 50\ \text{V}$. Determine the values of $i_L(0+)$ and $v'(0+)$. **c.** Use MATLAB to find the general solution for $v(t)$.

P75. Consider the circuit shown in Figure P70. **a.** Write the differential equation for $v(t)$.

b. Determine the values for $v(0+)$ and $v'(0+)$.

c. Use MATLAB to find the complete solution for $v(t)$.

P76. Use MATLAB to solve for the mesh currents in the circuit of Figure P76. The circuit has been connected for a long time prior to $t = 0$ with the switch open, so the initial values of the inductor currents are zero.

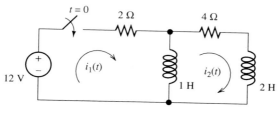

Figure P76

P77. The circuit shown in Figure P77 has been operating for a long time prior to $t = 0$ with the switch open. Use MATLAB to solve for the node voltages. Give the answers with four decimal place accuracy for all constants.

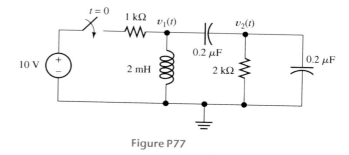

Figure P77

Practice Test

Here is a practice test you can use to check your comprehension of the most important concepts in this chapter. Answers can be found at the end of this chapter and complete solutions are included in the Student Solutions files.

T1. Consider the circuit shown in Figure T1. The circuit has been operating for a long time with the switch closed prior to $t = 0$. **a.** Determine the values of $i_L, i_1, i_2, i_3,$ and v_C just before the switch opens. **b.** Determine the values of i_L, $i_1, i_2, i_3,$ and v_C immediately after the switch opens. **c.** Find $i_L(t)$ for $t > 0$. **d.** Find $v_C(t)$ for $t > 0$.

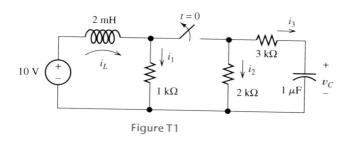

Figure T1

T2. Consider the circuit shown in Figure T2.
a. Write the differential equation for $i(t)$.

b. Find the time constant and the form of the complementary solution.

c. Find the particular solution.

d. Find the complete solution for $i(t)$.

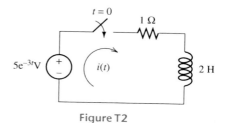

Figure T2

T3. Consider the circuit shown in Figure T3 in which the initial inductor current and capacitor voltage are both zero.
a. Write the differential equation for $v_C(t)$.

b. Find the particular solution.

c. Is this circuit overdamped, critically damped, or underdamped? Find the form of the complementary solution.

d. Find the complete solution for $v_C(t)$.

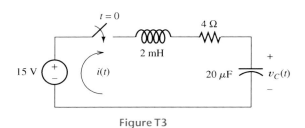

Figure T3

T4. Write the MATLAB commands to obtain the solution for the differential equation of question T3 with four decimal place accuracy for the constants.

Answers for the Practice Test

T1. a. $i_1(0-) = 10\,\text{mA}$, $i_2(0-) = 5\,\text{mA}$, $i_3(0-) = 0$, $i_L(0-) = 15\,\text{mA}$, $v_C(0-) = 10\,\text{V}$

   b. $i_1(0+) = 15\,\text{mA}$, $i_2(0+) = 2\,\text{mA}$, and $i_3(0+) = -2\,\text{mA}$, $i_L(0+) = 15\,\text{mA}$, $v_C(0+) = 10\,\text{V}$

   c. $i_L(t) = 10 + 5\ \exp(-5 \times 10^5 t)\,\text{mA}$

   d. $v_C(t) = 10\ \exp(-200t)\,\text{V}$

T2. a. $2\frac{di(t)}{dt} + i(t) = 5\ \exp(-3t)$.

   b. $\tau = L/R = 2\,\text{s}$, $i_c(t) = A\exp(-0.5t)\,\text{A}$.

   c. $i_p(t) = -\exp(-3t)\,\text{A}$.

   d. $i(t) = \exp(-0.5t) - \exp(-3t)\,\text{A}$.

T3. a. $\frac{d^2 v_C(t)}{dt^2} + 2000\frac{dv_C(t)}{dt} + 25 \times 10^6 v_C(t) = 375 \times 10^6$

   b. $v_{Cp}(t) = 15\,\text{V}$

   c. Underdamped; $v_{Cc}(t) = K_1\exp(-1000t)\cos(4899t) + K_2\exp(-1000t)\sin(4899t)$

   d. $v_C(t) = 15 - 15\ \exp(-1000t)\cos(4899t) - (3.062)\exp(-1000t)\sin(4899t)\,\text{V}$

T4. The commands are

```
syms vC t
S = dsolve('D2vC + 2000*DvC + (25e6)*vC = 375e6', 'vC(0) = 0, DvC(0) = 0');
simple(vpa(S,4))
```

The commands are stored in the m-file named T_4 that can be found in the Hambley MATLAB folder.

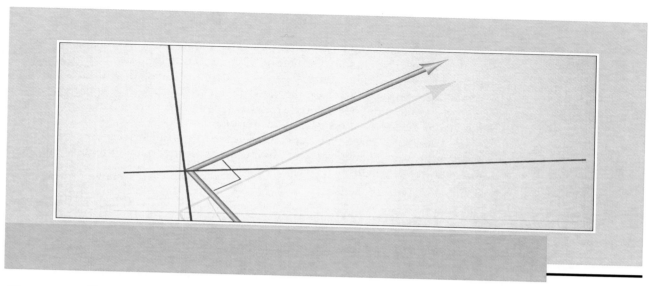

Steady-State Sinusoidal Analysis

Study of this chapter will enable you to:

- Identify the frequency, angular frequency, peak value, rms value, and phase of a sinusoidal signal.

- Determine the root-mean-square (rms) value of any periodic current or voltage.

- Solve steady-state ac circuits, using phasors and complex impedances.

- Compute power for steady-state ac circuits.

- Find Thévenin and Norton equivalent circuits.

- Determine load impedances for maximum power transfer.

- Discuss the advantages of three-phase power distribution.

- Solve balanced three-phase circuits.

Introduction to this chapter:

Circuits with sinusoidal sources have many important applications. For example, electric power is distributed to residences and businesses by sinusoidal currents and voltages. Furthermore, sinusoidal signals have many uses in radio communication. Finally, a branch of mathematics known as Fourier analysis shows that all signals of practical interest are composed of sinusoidal components. Thus, the study of circuits with sinusoidal sources is a central theme in electrical engineering.

From Chapter 5 of *Electrical Engineering: Principles and Applications*, Fifth Edition, Allan R. Hambley. Copyright © 2011 by Pearson Education, Inc. Published by Pearson Prentice Hall. All rights reserved.

The response of a network has two parts: the forced response and the natural response. In most circuits, the natural response decays rapidly to zero. The forced response for sinusoidal sources persists indefinitely and, therefore, is called the steady-state response. Because the natural response quickly decays, the steady-state response is often of highest interest. In this chapter, we learn efficient methods for finding the steady-state responses for sinusoidal sources.

We also study three-phase circuits, which are used in electric power-distribution systems. Most engineers who work in industrial settings need to understand three-phase power distribution.

1 SINUSOIDAL CURRENTS AND VOLTAGES

A sinusoidal voltage is shown in Figure 1 and is given by

$$v(t) = V_m \cos(\omega t + \theta) \tag{1}$$

where V_m is the **peak value** of the voltage, ω is the **angular frequency** in radians per second, and θ is the **phase angle**.

Sinusoidal signals are periodic, repeating the same pattern of values in each **period** T. Because the cosine (or sine) function completes one cycle when the angle increases by 2π radians, we get

$$\omega T = 2\pi \tag{2}$$

The **frequency** of a periodic signal is the number of cycles completed in one second. Thus, we obtain

$$f = \frac{1}{T} \tag{3}$$

We refer to ω as angular frequency with units of radians per second and f simply as frequency with units of hertz (Hz).

The units of frequency are hertz (Hz). (Actually, the physical units of hertz are equivalent to inverse seconds.) Solving Equation 2 for the angular frequency, we have

$$\omega = \frac{2\pi}{T} \tag{4}$$

Using Equation 3 to substitute for T, we find that

$$\omega = 2\pi f \tag{5}$$

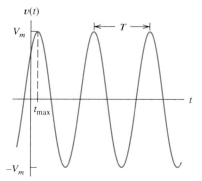

Figure 1 A sinusoidal voltage waveform given by $v(t) = V_m \cos (\omega t + \theta)$. *Note:* Assuming that θ is in degrees, we have $t_{max} = \frac{-\theta}{360} \times T$. For the waveform shown, θ is $-45°$.

Throughout our discussion, the argument of the cosine (or sine) function is of the form

$$\omega t + \theta$$

We assume that the angular frequency ω has units of radians per second (rad/s). However, we sometimes give the phase angle θ in degrees. Then, the argument has mixed units. If we wanted to evaluate $\cos(\omega t + \theta)$ for a particular value of time, we would have to convert θ to radians before adding the terms in the argument. Usually, we find it easier to visualize an angle expressed in degrees, and mixed units are not a problem.

Electrical engineers often write the argument of a sinusoid in mixed units: ωt is in radians and the phase angle θ is in degrees.

For uniformity, we express sinusoidal functions by using the cosine function rather than the sine function. The functions are related by the identity

$$\sin(z) = \cos(z - 90°) \tag{6}$$

For example, when we want to find the phase angle of

$$v_x(t) = 10 \sin(200t + 30°)$$

we first write it as

$$v_x(t) = 10 \cos(200t + 30° - 90°)$$

$$= 10 \cos(200t - 60°)$$

Thus, we state that the phase angle of $v_x(t)$ is $-60°$.

Root-Mean-Square Values

Consider applying a periodic voltage $v(t)$ with period T to a resistance R. The power delivered to the resistance is given by

$$p(t) = \frac{v^2(t)}{R} \tag{7}$$

Furthermore, the energy delivered in one period is given by

$$E_T = \int_0^T p(t)\, dt \tag{8}$$

The average power P_{avg} delivered to the resistance is the energy delivered in one cycle divided by the period. Thus,

$$P_{avg} = \frac{E_T}{T} = \frac{1}{T} \int_0^T p(t)\, dt \tag{9}$$

Using Equation 7 to substitute into Equation 9, we obtain

$$P_{avg} = \frac{1}{T} \int_0^T \frac{v^2(t)}{R}\, dt \tag{10}$$

This can be rearranged as

$$P_{\text{avg}} = \frac{\left[\sqrt{\frac{1}{T} \int_0^T v^2(t)\, dt}\right]^2}{R} \tag{11}$$

Now, we define the **root-mean-square** (rms) value of the periodic voltage $v(t)$ as

$$V_{\text{rms}} = \sqrt{\frac{1}{T} \int_0^T v^2(t)\, dt} \tag{12}$$

Using this equation to substitute into Equation 11, we get

$$P_{\text{avg}} = \frac{V_{\text{rms}}^2}{R} \tag{13}$$

Power calculations are facilitated by using rms values for voltage or current.

Thus, if the rms value of a periodic voltage is known, it is relatively easy to compute the average power that the voltage can deliver to a resistance. The rms value is also called the **effective value**.

Similarly for a periodic current $i(t)$, we define the rms value as

$$I_{\text{rms}} = \sqrt{\frac{1}{T} \int_0^T i^2(t)\, dt} \tag{14}$$

and the average power delivered if $i(t)$ flows through a resistance is given by

$$P_{\text{avg}} = I_{\text{rms}}^2 R \tag{15}$$

RMS Value of a Sinusoid

Consider a sinusoidal voltage given by

$$v(t) = V_m \cos(\omega t + \theta) \tag{16}$$

To find the rms value, we substitute into Equation 12, which yields

$$V_{\text{rms}} = \sqrt{\frac{1}{T} \int_0^T V_m^2 \cos^2(\omega t + \theta)\, dt} \tag{17}$$

Next, we use the trigonometric identity

$$\cos^2(z) = \frac{1}{2} + \frac{1}{2}\cos(2z) \tag{18}$$

to write Equation 17 as

$$V_{\text{rms}} = \sqrt{\frac{V_m^2}{2T} \int_0^T [1 + \cos(2\omega t + 2\theta)]\, dt} \tag{19}$$

Integrating, we get

$$V_{\text{rms}} = \sqrt{\frac{V_m^2}{2T} \left[t + \frac{1}{2\omega} \sin(2\omega t + 2\theta) \right]_0^T} \tag{20}$$

Evaluating, we have

$$V_{\text{rms}} = \sqrt{\frac{V_m^2}{2T} \left[T + \frac{1}{2\omega} \sin(2\omega T + 2\theta) - \frac{1}{2\omega} \sin(2\theta) \right]} \tag{21}$$

Referring to Equation 2, we see that $\omega T = 2\pi$. Thus, we obtain

$$\frac{1}{2\omega} \sin(2\omega T + 2\theta) - \frac{1}{2\omega} \sin(2\theta) = \frac{1}{2\omega} \sin(4\pi + 2\theta) - \frac{1}{2\omega} \sin(2\theta)$$

$$= \frac{1}{2\omega} \sin(2\theta) - \frac{1}{2\omega} \sin(2\theta)$$

$$= 0$$

Therefore, Equation 21 reduces to

$$V_{\text{rms}} = \frac{V_m}{\sqrt{2}} \tag{22}$$

This is a useful result that we will use many times in dealing with sinusoids.

Usually in discussing sinusoids, the rms or effective value is given rather than the peak value. For example, ac power in residential wiring is distributed as a 60-Hz 115-V rms sinusoid (in the United States). Most people are aware of this, but probably few know that 115 V is the rms value and that the peak value is $V_m = V_{\text{rms}} \times \sqrt{2} = 115 \times \sqrt{2} \cong 163$ V. (Actually, 115 V is the nominal residential distribution voltage. It can vary from approximately 105 to 130 V.)

Keep in mind that $V_{\text{rms}} = V_m/\sqrt{2}$ applies to sinusoids. To find the rms value of other periodic waveforms, we would need to employ the definition given by Equation 12.

> The rms value for a sinusoid is the peak value divided by the square root of two. This is not true for other periodic waveforms such as square waves or triangular waves.

Power Delivered to a Resistance by a Sinusoidal Source

Suppose that a voltage given by $v(t) = 100\cos(100\pi t)$ V is applied to a 50-Ω resistance. Sketch $v(t)$ to scale versus time. Find the rms value of the voltage and the average power delivered to the resistance. Find the power as a function of time and sketch to scale.

Solution By comparison of the expression given for $v(t)$ with Equation 1, we see that $\omega = 100\pi$. Using Equation 5, we find that the frequency is $f = \omega/2\pi = 50$ Hz. Then, the period is $T = 1/f = 20$ ms. A plot of $v(t)$ versus time is shown in Figure 2(a).

The peak value of the voltage is $V_m = 100$ V. Thus, the rms value is $V_{\text{rms}} = V_m/\sqrt{2} = 70.71$ V. Then, the average power is

$$P_{\text{avg}} = \frac{V_{\text{rms}}^2}{R} = \frac{(70.71)^2}{50} = 100 \text{ W}$$

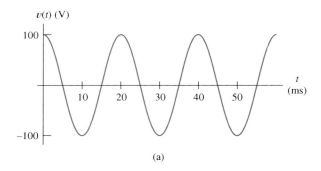

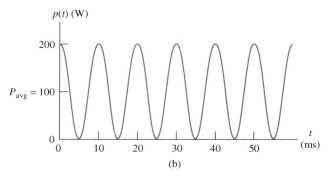

Figure 2 Voltage and power versus time for Example 1.

The power as a function of time is given by

$$p(t) = \frac{v^2(t)}{R} = \frac{100^2 \cos^2(100\pi t)}{50} = 200 \cos^2(100\pi t) \text{ W}$$

A plot of $p(t)$ versus time is shown in Figure 2(b). Notice that the power fluctuates from 0 to 200 W. However, the average power is 100 W, as we found by using the rms value. ∎

For a sinusoidal current flowing in a resistance, power fluctuates periodically from zero to twice the average value.

RMS Values of Nonsinusoidal Voltages or Currents

Sometimes we need to determine the rms values of periodic currents or voltages that are not sinusoidal. We can accomplish this by applying the definition given by Equation 12 or 14 directly.

Example 2 RMS Value of a Triangular Voltage

The voltage shown in Figure 3(a) is known as a triangular waveform. Determine its rms value.

Solution First, we need to determine the equations describing the waveform between $t = 0$ and $t = T = 2$ s. As illustrated in Figure 3(b), the equations for the first period of the triangular wave are

$$v(t) = \begin{cases} 3t & for \quad 0 \leq t \leq 1 \\ 6 - 3t & for \quad 1 \leq t \leq 2 \end{cases}$$

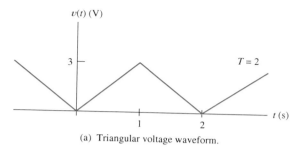

(a) Triangular voltage waveform.

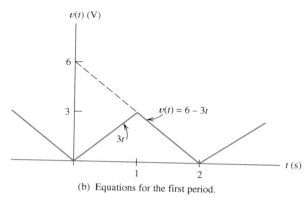

(b) Equations for the first period.

Figure 3 Triangular voltage waveform of Example 2.

Equation 12 gives the rms value of the voltage.

$$V_{\text{rms}} = \sqrt{\frac{1}{T} \int_0^T v^2(t)\,dt}$$

Dividing the interval into two parts and substituting for $v(t)$, we have

$$V_{\text{rms}} = \sqrt{\frac{1}{2}\left[\int_0^1 9t^2\,dt + \int_1^2 (6-3t)^2\,dt\right]}$$

$$V_{\text{rms}} = \sqrt{\frac{1}{2}\left[3t^3|_{t=0}^{t=1} + (36t - 18t^2 + 3t^3)|_{t=1}^{t=2}\right]}$$

Evaluating, we find

$$V_{\text{rms}} = \sqrt{\frac{1}{2}[3 + (72 - 36 - 72 + 18 + 24 - 3)]} = \sqrt{3}\ \text{V}$$

■

The integrals in this example are easy to carry out manually. However, when the integrals are more difficult, we can obtain answers using the MATLAB Symbolic Toolbox. Here are the MATLAB commands needed to perform the integrals in this example:

```
>> syms Vrms t
>> Vrms = sqrt((1/2)*(int(9*t^2,t,0,1) + int((6-3*t)^2,t,1,2)))
     Vrms =
     3^(1/2)
```

227

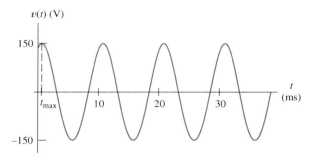

$v(t)$ (V)

150

t_{max} 10   20   30 t (ms)

−150

Figure 4 Answer for Exercise 1(c).

Exercise 1 Suppose that a sinusoidal voltage is given by

$$v(t) = 150 \cos(200\pi t - 30°) \text{ V}$$

a. Find the angular frequency, the frequency in hertz, the period, the peak value, and the rms value. Also, find the first value of time t_{max} after $t = 0$ such that $v(t)$ attains its positive peak. **b.** If this voltage is applied to a 50-Ω resistance, compute the average power delivered. **c.** Sketch $v(t)$ to scale versus time.

Answer **a.** $\omega = 200\pi$, $f = 100$ Hz, $T = 10$ ms, $V_m = 150$ V, $V_{rms} = 106.1$ V, $t_{max} = \frac{30°}{360°} \times T = 0.833$ ms; **b.** $P_{avg} = 225$ W; **c.** a plot of $v(t)$ versus time is shown in Figure 4. □

Exercise 2 Express $v(t) = 100 \sin(300\pi t + 60°)$ V as a cosine function.
Answer $v(t) = 100 \cos(300\pi t - 30°)$ V. □

Exercise 3 Suppose that the ac line voltage powering a computer has an rms value of 110 V and a frequency of 60 Hz, and the peak voltage is attained at $t = 5$ ms. Write an expression for this ac voltage as a function of time.
Answer $v(t) = 155.6 \cos(377t - 108°)$ V. □

2 PHASORS

In the next several sections, we will see that sinusoidal steady-state analysis is greatly facilitated if the currents and voltages are represented as vectors (called **phasors**) in the complex-number plane. In preparation for this material, you may wish to review complex-number arithmetic.

We start with a study of convenient methods for adding (or subtracting) sinusoidal waveforms. We often need to do this in applying Kirchhoff's voltage law (KVL) or Kirchhoff's current law (KCL) to ac circuits. For example, in applying KVL to a network with sinusoidal voltages, we might obtain the expression

$$v(t) = 10 \cos(\omega t) + 5 \sin(\omega t + 60°) + 5 \cos(\omega t + 90°) \tag{23}$$

To obtain the peak value of $v(t)$ and its phase angle, we need to put Equation 23 into the form

$$v(t) = V_m \cos(\omega t + \theta) \tag{24}$$

This could be accomplished by repeated substitution, using standard trigonometric identities. However, that method is too tedious for routine work. Instead, we will see that we can represent each term on the right-hand side of Equation 23 by a vector in the complex-number plane known as a **phasor**. Then, we can add the phasors with relative ease and convert the sum into the desired form.

Phasor Definition

For a sinusoidal voltage of the form

$$v_1(t) = V_1 \cos(\omega t + \theta_1)$$

we define the phasor as

$$\mathbf{V}_1 = V_1 \angle \theta_1$$

Thus, the phasor for a sinusoid is a complex number having a magnitude equal to the peak value and having the same phase angle as the sinusoid. We use boldface letters for phasors. (Actually, engineers are not consistent in choosing the magnitudes of phasors. In this chapter, we take the peak values for the magnitudes of phasors, which is the prevailing custom in circuit-analysis courses for electrical engineers. However, power-system engineers take the rms values for the phasor magnitudes. We will take care to label rms phasors as such when we encounter them.)

> Phasors are complex numbers that represent sinusoidal voltages or currents. The magnitude of a phasor equals the peak value and the angle equals the phase of the sinusoid (written as a cosine).

If the sinusoid is of the form

$$v_2(t) = V_2 \sin(\omega t + \theta_2)$$

we first convert to a cosine function by using the trigonometric identity

$$\sin(z) = \cos(z - 90°) \tag{25}$$

Thus, we have

$$v_2(t) = V_2 \cos(\omega t + \theta_2 - 90°)$$

and the phasor is

$$\mathbf{V}_2 = V_2 \angle \theta_2 - 90°$$

Phasors are obtained for sinusoidal currents in a similar fashion. Thus, for the currents

$$i_1(t) = I_1 \cos(\omega t + \theta_1)$$

and

$$i_2(t) = I_2 \sin(\omega t + \theta_2)$$

the phasors are

$$\mathbf{I}_1 = I_1 \angle \theta_1$$

and

$$\mathbf{I}_2 = I_2 \angle \theta_2 - 90°$$

respectively.

Adding Sinusoids Using Phasors

Now, we illustrate how we can use phasors to combine the terms of the right-hand side of Equation 23. In this discussion, we proceed in small logical steps to illustrate clearly why sinusoids can be added by adding their phasors. Later, we streamline the procedure for routine work.

Our first step in combining the terms in Equation 23 is to write all the sinusoids as cosine functions by using Equation 25. Thus, Equation 23 can be written as

$$v(t) = 10\cos(\omega t) + 5\cos(\omega t + 60° - 90°) + 5\cos(\omega t + 90°) \tag{26}$$

$$v(t) = 10\cos(\omega t) + 5\cos(\omega t - 30°) + 5\cos(\omega t + 90°) \tag{27}$$

Referring to Euler's formula, we see that we can write

$$\cos(\theta) = \text{Re}\left(e^{j\theta}\right) = \text{Re}[\cos(\theta) + j\sin(\theta)] \tag{28}$$

where the notation Re( ) means that we retain only the real part of the quantity inside the parentheses. Thus, we can rewrite Equation 27 as

$$v(t) = 10\,\text{Re}\left[e^{j\omega t}\right] + 5\,\text{Re}\left[e^{j(\omega t - 30°)}\right] + 5\,\text{Re}\left[e^{j(\omega t + 90°)}\right] \tag{29}$$

When we multiply a complex number Z by a real number A, both the real and imaginary parts of Z are multiplied by A. Thus, Equation 29 becomes

$$v(t) = \text{Re}\left[10e^{j\omega t}\right] + \text{Re}\left[5e^{j(\omega t - 30°)}\right] + \text{Re}\left[5e^{j(\omega t + 90°)}\right] \tag{30}$$

Next, we can write

$$v(t) = \text{Re}\left[10e^{j\omega t} + 5e^{j(\omega t - 30°)} + 5e^{j(\omega t + 90°)}\right] \tag{31}$$

because the real part of the sum of several complex quantities is equal to the sum of the real parts. If we factor out the common term $e^{j\omega t}$, Equation 31 becomes

$$v(t) = \text{Re}\left[\left(10 + 5e^{-j30°} + 5^{j90°}\right)e^{j\omega t}\right] \tag{32}$$

Putting the complex numbers into polar form, we have

$$v(t) = \text{Re}\left[(10\ \underline{/0°} + 5\ \underline{/-30°} + 5\ \underline{/90°})e^{j\omega t}\right] \tag{33}$$

Now, we can combine the complex numbers as

$$
\begin{aligned}
10\ \underline{/0°} + 5\ \underline{/-30°} + 5\ \underline{/90°} &= 10 + 4.33 - j2.50 + j5 \\
&= 14.33 + j2.5 \\
&= 14.54\ \underline{/9.90°} \\
&= 14.54e^{j9.90°}
\end{aligned}
\tag{34}
$$

Using this result in Equation 33, we have

$$v(t) = \text{Re}\left[\left(14.54e^{j9.90°}\right)e^{j\omega t}\right]$$

which can be written as

$$v(t) = \text{Re}\left[14.54e^{j(\omega t + 9.90°)}\right] \tag{35}$$

Now, using Equation 28, we can write this as

$$v(t) = 14.54\cos(\omega t + 9.90°) \tag{36}$$

Thus, we have put the original expression for $v(t)$ into the desired form. The terms on the left-hand side of Equation 34 are the phasors for the terms on the right-hand side of the original expression for $v(t)$. Notice that the essential part of the work needed to combine the sinusoids is to add the phasors.

Streamlined Procedure for Adding Sinusoids

From now on, to add sinusoids, we will first write the phasor for each term in the sum, add the phasors by using complex-number arithmetic, and then write the simplified expression for the sum.

To add sinusoids, we find the phasor for each term, add the phasors by using complex-number arithmetic, express the sum in polar form, and then write the corresponding sinusoidal time function.

Example 3   Using Phasors to Add Sinusoids

Suppose that

$$v_1(t) = 20\cos(\omega t - 45°)$$

$$v_2(t) = 10\sin(\omega t + 60°)$$

Reduce the sum $v_s(t) = v_1(t) + v_2(t)$ to a single term.

Solution   The phasors are

In using phasors to add sinusoids, all of the terms must have the same frequency.

$$\mathbf{V}_1 = 20 \angle{-45°}$$

$$\mathbf{V}_2 = 10 \angle{-30°}$$

Step 1: Determine the phasor for each term.

Notice that we have subtracted 90° to find the phase angle for $\mathbf{V}_2$ because $v_2(t)$ is a sine function rather than a cosine function.

Next, we use complex-number arithmetic to add the phasors and convert the sum to polar form:

Step 2: Use complex arithmetic to add the phasors.

$$\mathbf{V}_s = \mathbf{V}_1 + \mathbf{V}_2$$

$$= 20 \angle{-45°} + 10 \angle{-30°}$$

$$= 14.14 - j14.14 + 8.660 - j5$$

Step 3: Convert the sum to polar form.

$$= 22.80 - j19.14$$

$$= 29.77 \angle{-40.01°}$$

Now, we write the time function corresponding to the phasor $\mathbf{V}_s$.

Step 4: Write the result as a time function.

$$v_s(t) = 29.77\cos(\omega t - 40.01°)$$

■

Exercise 4   Reduce the following expressions by using phasors:

$$v_1(t) = 10\cos(\omega t) + 10\sin(\omega t)$$

$$i_1(t) = 10\cos(\omega t + 30°) + 5\sin(\omega t + 30°)$$

$$i_2(t) = 20\sin(\omega t + 90°) + 15\cos(\omega t - 60°)$$

Answer

$$v_1(t) = 14.14\cos(\omega t - 45°)$$

$$i_1(t) = 11.18\cos(\omega t + 3.44°)$$

$$i_2(t) = 30.4\cos(\omega t - 25.3°)$$

□

Phasors as Rotating Vectors

Consider a sinusoidal voltage given by

$$v(t) = V_m\cos(\omega t + \theta)$$

In developing the phasor concept, we write

$$v(t) = \text{Re}\left[V_m e^{j(\omega t+\theta)}\right]$$

The complex quantity inside the brackets is

$$V_m e^{j(\omega t+\theta)} = V_m \ \angle{\omega t + \theta}$$

Sinusoids can be visualized as the real-axis projection of vectors rotating in the complex plane. The phasor for a sinusoid is a snapshot of the corresponding rotating vector at $t = 0$.

This can be visualized as a vector of length V_m that rotates counterclockwise in the complex plane with an angular velocity of ω rad/s. Furthermore, the voltage $v(t)$ is the real part of the vector, which is illustrated in Figure 5. As the vector rotates, its projection on the real axis traces out the voltage as a function of time. The phasor is simply a "snapshot" of this rotating vector at $t = 0$.

Phase Relationships

We will see that the phase relationships between currents and voltages are often important. Consider the voltages

$$v_1(t) = 3\cos(\omega t + 40°)$$

and

$$v_2(t) = 4\cos(\omega t - 20°)$$

The corresponding phasors are

To determine phase relationships from a phasor diagram, consider that the phasors rotate counterclockwise. Then, when standing at a fixed point, if $\mathbf{V}_1$ arrives first followed by $\mathbf{V}_2$ after a rotation of θ, we say that $\mathbf{V}_1$ leads $\mathbf{V}_2$ by θ. Alternatively, we could say that $\mathbf{V}_2$ lags $\mathbf{V}_1$ by θ. (Usually, we take θ as the smaller angle between the two phasors.)

$$\mathbf{V}_1 = 3 \ \angle{40°}$$

and

$$\mathbf{V}_2 = 4 \ \angle{-20°}$$

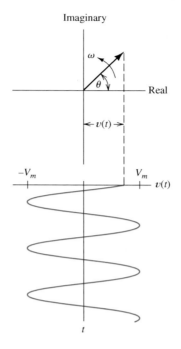

Imaginary

Real

$v(t)$

$-V_m$ V_m

$v(t)$

t

Figure 5 A sinusoid can be represented as the real part of a vector rotating counterclockwise in the complex plane.

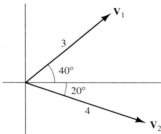

$\mathbf{V}_1$

3

40°

20°

4

$\mathbf{V}_2$

Figure 6 Because the vectors rotate counterclockwise, $\mathbf{V}_1$ leads $\mathbf{V}_2$ by 60° (or, equivalently, $\mathbf{V}_2$ lags $\mathbf{V}_1$ by 60°).

The phasor diagram is shown in Figure 6. Notice that the angle between $\mathbf{V}_1$ and $\mathbf{V}_2$ is 60°. Because the complex vectors rotate counterclockwise, we say that $\mathbf{V}_1$ *leads* $\mathbf{V}_2$ by 60°. (An alternative way to state the phase relationship is to state that $\mathbf{V}_2$ *lags* $\mathbf{V}_1$ by 60°.)

We have seen that the voltages versus time can be obtained by tracing the real part of the rotating vectors. The plots of $v_1(t)$ and $v_2(t)$ versus ωt are shown in Figure 7. Notice that $v_1(t)$ reaches its peak 60° earlier than $v_2(t)$. This is the meaning of the statement that $v_1(t)$ leads $v_2(t)$ by 60°.

To determine phase relationships between sinusoids from their plots versus time, find the shortest time interval t_p between positive peaks of the two waveforms. Then, the phase angle is $\theta = (t_p/T) \times 360°$. If the peak of $v_1(t)$ occurs first, we say that $v_1(t)$ leads $v_2(t)$ or that $v_2(t)$ lags $v_1(t)$.

Exercise 5   Consider the voltages given by

$$v_1(t) = 10\cos(\omega t - 30°)$$
$$v_2(t) = 10\cos(\omega t + 30°)$$
$$v_3(t) = 10\sin(\omega t + 45°)$$

State the phase relationship between each pair of the voltages. (*Hint:* Find the phasor for each voltage and draw the phasor diagram.)

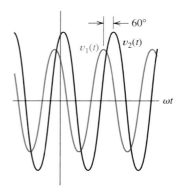

Figure 7 The peaks of $v_1(t)$ occur $60°$ before the peaks of $v_2(t)$. In other words, $v_1(t)$ leads $v_2(t)$ by $60°$.

Answer

v_1 lags v_2 by $60°$ (or v_2 leads v_1 by $60°$)

v_1 leads v_3 by $15°$ (or v_3 lags v_1 by $15°$)

v_2 leads v_3 by $75°$ (or v_3 lags v_2 by $75°$)

$\square$

3 COMPLEX IMPEDANCES

In this section, we learn that by using phasors to represent sinusoidal voltages and currents, we can solve sinusoidal steady-state circuit problems with relative ease. Except for the fact that we use complex arithmetic, sinusoidal steady-state analysis is virtually the same as the analysis of resistive circuits.

Inductance

Consider an inductance in which the current is a sinusoid given by

$$i_L(t) = I_m \sin(\omega t + \theta) \tag{37}$$

Recall that the voltage across an inductance is

$$v_L(t) = L\frac{di_L(t)}{dt} \tag{38}$$

Substituting Equation 37 into Equation 38 and reducing, we obtain

$$v_L(t) = \omega L I_m \cos(\omega t + \theta) \tag{39}$$

Now, the phasors for the current and voltage are

$$\mathbf{I}_L = I_m \ \underline{/\theta - 90°} \tag{40}$$

and

$$\mathbf{V}_L = \omega L I_m \ \underline{/\theta} = V_m \ \underline{/\theta} \tag{41}$$

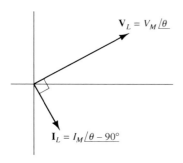

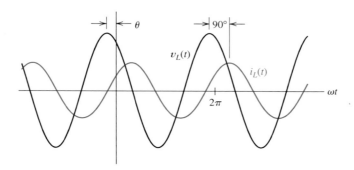

(a) Phasor diagram   (b) Current and voltage versus time

Figure 8 Current lags voltage by 90° in a pure inductance.

The phasor diagram of the current and voltage is shown in Figure 8(a). The corresponding waveforms of current and voltage are shown in Figure 8(b). *Notice that the current lags the voltage by 90° for a pure inductance.*

Equation 41 can be written in the form

$$\mathbf{V}_L = (\omega L \ \underline{/90°}) \times I_m \ \underline{/\theta - 90°} \tag{42}$$

Using Equation 40 to substitute into Equation 42, we find that

$$\mathbf{V}_L = (\omega L \ \underline{/90°}) \times \mathbf{I}_L \tag{43}$$

which can also be written as

$$\mathbf{V}_L = j\omega L \times \mathbf{I}_L \tag{44}$$

We refer to the term $j\omega L = \omega L \ \underline{/90°}$ as the **impedance** of the inductance and denote it as Z_L. Thus, we have

$$Z_L = j\omega L = \omega L \ \underline{/90°} \tag{45}$$

and

$$\mathbf{V}_L = Z_L\mathbf{I}_L \tag{46}$$

Thus, the phasor voltage is equal to the impedance times the phasor current. This is Ohm's law in phasor form. However, for an inductance, the impedance is an imaginary number, whereas resistance is a real number. (Impedances that are pure imaginary are also called **reactances**.)

Capacitance

In a similar faashion for a capacitance, we can show that if the current and voltage are sinusoidal, the phasors are related by

$$\mathbf{V}_C = Z_C\mathbf{I}_C \tag{47}$$

in which the impedance of the capacitance is

$$Z_C = -j\frac{1}{\omega C} = \frac{1}{j\omega C} = \frac{1}{\omega C} \ \underline{/-90°} \tag{48}$$

Current lags voltage by 90° for a pure inductance.

Equation 46 shows that phasor voltage and phasor current for an inductance are related in a manner analogous to Ohm's law.

PRACTICAL APPLICATION 1

Electronics and the Art of Automotive Maintenance

Several types of radio systems, based on the phase relationships between signals received from several radio transmitters, have been developed for navigation, surveying, and accurate time dissemination.

An early system of this type is called LORAN. The objective of this system is for receivers to be able to determine their latitudes and longitudes. In its simplest form, a LORAN system consists of a chain of three transmitters (a master and two slaves), which periodically broadcast 10-cycle pulses of 100-kHz sine waves in a precise phase relationship. Because the signals travel at the speed of light, the signal received from each transmitter is phase shifted in proportion to the distance from that transmitter to the receiver.

The signal from the first (or master) transmitter gives the receiver a phase reference. Then, the phases of the two slave signals are measured. Thus, the receiver determines the differential time delay between the master and each slave. The difference in time delay between the master and a given slave establishes a line of position (LOP) as illustrated in Figure PA1. For example, if the time delays of the signals from the master and slave 1 are equal (i.e., zero differential delay), the line of position is the perpendicular bisector of the line between the master and slave 1. If the time delay from the master is smaller by a given amount, the line of position turns out to be a hyperbola.

The receiver location is the intersection of the lines of position for two slaves as illustrated in Figure PA2. LORAN is capable of establishing positions to within several hundred meters.

In a more modern and sophisticated system known as the *Global Positioning System* (GPS), signals are broadcast from a network of 24 satellites. By comparing the phases of the signals received, a receiver (containing a special-purpose computer) can establish its position to within several meters and set an internal clock to an accuracy on the order of 0.01 μs. These receivers are available at a cost of several hundred dollars and are widely used by flyers, boaters, and hikers.

By using several high-quality GPS receivers, we find that it is possible to make distance measurements that are accurate enough for surveying purposes. For example, researchers have been making remote measurements of the height of the Greenland ice cap to assess the possible effects of global warming. A ground-based GPS receiver at a known position and altitude provides reference measurements, another GPS receiver in an airplane flown over the ice cap establishes its position and altitude relative to the reference, and finally, a radar measures the distance from the airplane down to the ice cap. Remarkably, these ice-cap height measurements are repeatable to within several centimeters.

The simple concept of phase relationships has applications in systems that are useful to the general public, civil engineers, and scientists.

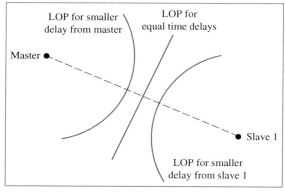

Figure PA1

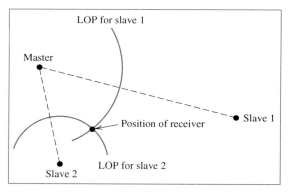

Figure PA2

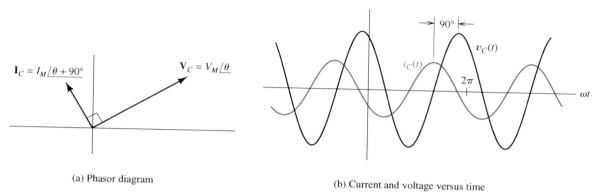

(a) Phasor diagram

(b) Current and voltage versus time

Figure 9 Current leads voltage by 90° in a pure capacitance.

Notice that the impedance of a capacitance is also a pure imaginary number.
   Suppose that the phasor voltage is

$$\mathbf{V}_C = V_m \ \angle\theta$$

Then, the phasor current is

$$\mathbf{I}_C = \frac{\mathbf{V}_C}{Z_C} = \frac{V_m \ \angle\theta}{(1/\omega C) \ \angle{-90°}} = \omega C V_m \ \angle{\theta + 90°}$$

$$\mathbf{I}_C = I_m \ \angle{\theta + 90°}$$

where $I_m = \omega C V_m$. The phasor diagram for current and voltage in a pure capacitance
is shown in Figure 9(a). The corresponding plots of current and voltage versus time
are shown in Figure 9(b). Notice that the current leads the voltage by 90°. (On
the other hand, current lags voltage for an inductance. This is easy to remember if
you know *ELI* the *ICE* man. The letter *E* is sometimes used to stand for *electromotive force*, which is another term for voltage, *L* and *C* are used for inductance and
capacitance, respectively, and *I* is used for current.)

Current leads voltage by 90°
for a pure capacitance.

Resistance

For a resistance, the phasors are related by

$$\mathbf{V}_R = R\mathbf{I}_R \tag{49}$$

Because resistance is a real number, the current and voltage are in phase, as illustrated
in Figure 10.

Current and voltage are in
phase for a resistance.

Exercise 6   A voltage $v_L(t) = 100\cos(200t)$ is applied to a 0.25-H inductance.
(Notice that $\omega = 200$.) **a.** Find the impedance of the inductance, the phasor current,
and the phasor voltage. **b.** Draw the phasor diagram.
Answer   a. $Z_L = j50 = 50 \ \angle{90°}$, $\mathbf{I}_L = 2 \ \angle{-90°}$, $\mathbf{V}_L = 100 \ \angle{0°}$; **b.** the phasor
diagram is shown in Figure 11(a).   □

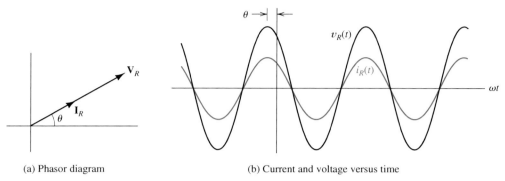

(a) Phasor diagram   (b) Current and voltage versus time

Figure 10 For a pure resistance, current and voltage are in phase.

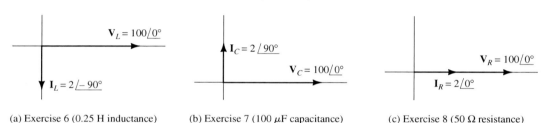

(a) Exercise 6 (0.25 H inductance)   (b) Exercise 7 (100 μF capacitance)   (c) Exercise 8 (50 Ω resistance)

Figure 11 Answers for Exercises 6, 7, and 8. The scale has been expanded for the currents compared with the voltages so the current phasors can be easily seen.

Exercise 7 A voltage $v_C(t) = 100\cos(200t)$ is applied to a 100-μF capacitance.
a. Find the impedance of the capacitance, the phasor current, and the phasor voltage.
b. Draw the phasor diagram.
Answer a. $Z_C = -j50 = 50\ \angle{-90°}$, $\mathbf{I}_C = 2\ \angle{90°}$, $\mathbf{V}_C = 100\ \angle{0°}$; **b.** the phasor diagram is shown in Figure 11(b). □

Exercise 8 A voltage $v_R(t) = 100\cos(200t)$ is applied to a 50-Ω resistance. **a.** Find the phasor for the current and the phasor voltage. **b.** Draw the phasor diagram.
Answer a. $\mathbf{I}_R = 2\ \angle{0°}$, $\mathbf{V}_R = 100\ \angle{0°}$; **b.** the phasor diagram is shown in Figure 11(c). □

4 CIRCUIT ANALYSIS WITH PHASORS AND COMPLEX IMPEDANCES

Kirchhoff's Laws in Phasor Form

Recall that KVL requires that the voltages sum to zero for any closed path in an electrical network. A typical KVL equation is

$$v_1(t) + v_2(t) - v_3(t) = 0 \tag{50}$$

If the voltages are sinusoidal, they can be represented by phasors. Then, Equation 50 becomes

$$\mathbf{V}_1 + \mathbf{V}_2 - \mathbf{V}_3 = 0 \tag{51}$$

Thus, we can apply KVL directly to the phasors. The sum of the phasor voltages equals zero for any closed path.

Similarly, KCL can be applied to currents in phasor form. The sum of the phasor currents entering a node must equal the sum of the phasor currents leaving.

Circuit Analysis Using Phasors and Impedances

We have seen that phasor currents and voltages are related by complex impedances, and Kirchhoff's laws apply in phasor form. Except for the fact that the voltages, currents, and impedances can be complex, the equations are exactly like those of resistive circuits.

A step-by-step procedure for steady-state analysis of circuits with sinusoidal sources is

1. Replace the time descriptions of the voltage and current sources with the corresponding phasors. (All of the sources must have the same frequency.)
2. Replace inductances by their complex impedances $Z_L = j\omega L = \omega L \angle 90°$. Replace capacitances by their complex impedances $Z_C = 1/(j\omega C) = (1/\omega C) \angle -90°$. Resistances have impedances equal to their resistances.
3. Analyze the circuit and perform the calculations with complex arithmetic.

Example 4 Steady-State AC Analysis of a Series Circuit

Find the steady-state current for the circuit shown in Figure 12(a). Also, find the phasor voltage across each element and construct a phasor diagram.

Solution From the expression given for the source voltage $v_S(t)$, we see that the peak voltage is 100 V, the angular frequency is $\omega = 500$, and the phase angle is 30°. The phasor for the voltage source is

$$\mathbf{V}_S = 100 \angle 30°$$

The complex impedances of the inductance and capacitance are

$$Z_L = j\omega L = j500 \times 0.3 = j150 \ \Omega$$

and

$$Z_C = -j\frac{1}{\omega C} = -j\frac{1}{500 \times 40 \times 10^{-6}} = -j50 \ \Omega$$

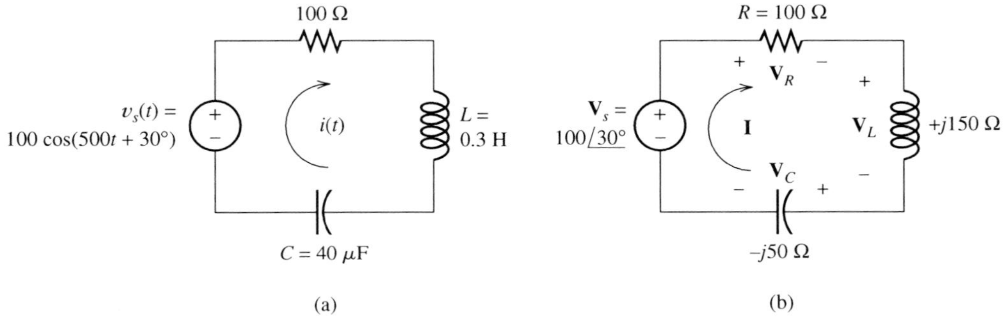

(a)   (b)

Figure 12 Circuit for Example 4.

Step 1: Replace the time description of the voltage source with the corresponding phasor.

Step 2: Replace inductances and capacitances with their complex impedances.

The transformed circuit is shown in Figure 12(b). All three elements are in series. Thus, we find the equivalent impedance of the circuit by adding the impedances of all three elements:

$$Z_{\text{eq}} = R + Z_L + Z_C$$

Substituting values, we have

$$Z_{\text{eq}} = 100 + j150 - j50 = 100 + j100$$

Converting to polar form, we obtain

$$Z_{\text{eq}} = 141.4 \ \underline{/45°}$$

Now, we can find the phasor current by dividing the phasor voltage by the equivalent impedance, resulting in

$$\mathbf{I} = \frac{\mathbf{V}_s}{Z} = \frac{100 \ \underline{/30°}}{141.4 \ \underline{/45°}} = 0.707 \ \underline{/-15°}$$

As a function of time, the current is

$$i(t) = 0.707 \cos(500t - 15°)$$

Next, we can find the phasor voltage across each element by multiplying the phasor current by the respective impedance:

$$\mathbf{V}_R = R \times \mathbf{I} = 100 \times 0.707 \ \underline{/-15°} = 70.7 \ \underline{/-15°}$$
$$\mathbf{V}_L = j\omega L \times \mathbf{I} = \omega L \ \underline{/90°} \times \mathbf{I} = 150 \ \underline{/90°} \times 0.707 \ \underline{/-15°}$$
$$= 106.1 \ \underline{/75°}$$
$$\mathbf{V}_C = -j\frac{1}{\omega C} \times \mathbf{I} = \frac{1}{\omega C} \ \underline{/-90°} \times \mathbf{I} = 50 \ \underline{/-90°} \times 0.707 \ \underline{/-15°}$$
$$= 35.4 \ \underline{/-105°}$$

The phasor diagram for the current and voltages is shown in Figure 13. Notice that the current $\mathbf{I}$ lags the source voltage $\mathbf{V}_s$ by 45°. As expected, the voltage $\mathbf{V}_R$ and current $\mathbf{I}$ are in phase for the resistance. For the inductance, the voltage $\mathbf{V}_L$ leads the current $\mathbf{I}$ by 90°. For the capacitance, the voltage $\mathbf{V}_C$ lags the current by 90°. ∎

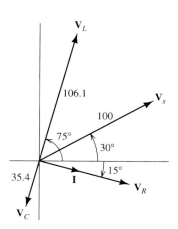

Figure 13 Phasor diagram for Example 4.

Example 5   Series and Parallel Combinations of Complex Impedances

Consider the circuit shown in Figure 14(a). Find the voltage $v_C(t)$ in steady state. Find the phasor current through each element, and construct a phasor diagram showing the currents and the source voltage.

Solution The phasor for the voltage source is $\mathbf{V}_s = 10 \ \angle{-90°}$. [Notice that $v_s(t)$ is a sine function rather than a cosine function, and it is necessary to subtract 90° from the phase.] The angular frequency of the source is $\omega = 1000$. The impedances of the inductance and capacitance are

$$Z_L = j\omega L = j1000 \times 0.1 = j100 \ \Omega$$

and

$$Z_C = -j\frac{1}{\omega C} = -j\frac{1}{1000 \times 10 \times 10^{-6}} = -j100 \ \Omega$$

The transformed network is shown in Figure 14(b).

To find $\mathbf{V}_C$, we will first combine the resistance and the impedance of the capacitor in parallel. Then, we will use the voltage-division principle to compute the voltage across the RC combination. The impedance of the parallel RC circuit is

$$Z_{RC} = \frac{1}{1/R + 1/Z_C} = \frac{1}{1/100 + 1/(-j100)}$$

$$= \frac{1}{0.01 + j0.01} = \frac{1 \ \angle{0°}}{0.01414 \ \angle{45°}} = 70.71 \ \angle{-45°}$$

Converting to rectangular form, we have

$$Z_{RC} = 50 - j50$$

The equivalent network is shown in Figure 14(c).

Step 1: Replace the time description of the voltage source with the corresponding phasor.

Step 2: Replace inductances and capacitances with their complex impedances.

Step 3: Use complex arithmetic to analyze the circuit.

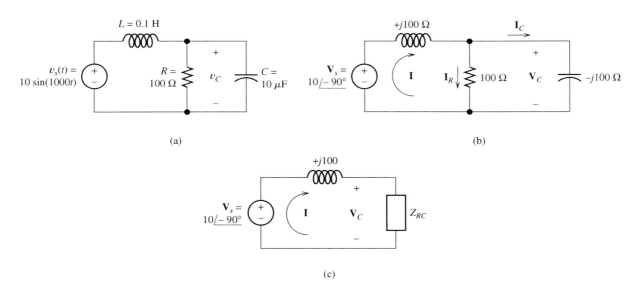

(a)   (b)

(c)

Figure 14 Circuit for Example 5.

Now, we use the voltage-division principle to obtain

$$\mathbf{V}_C = \mathbf{V}_s \frac{Z_{RC}}{Z_L + Z_{RC}} = 10 \ \angle{-90°} \ \frac{70.71 \ \angle{-45°}}{j100 + 50 - j50}$$

$$= 10 \ \angle{-90°} \ \frac{70.71 \ \angle{-45°}}{50 + j50} = 10 \ \angle{-90°} \ \frac{70.71 \ \angle{-45°}}{70.71 \ \angle{45°}}$$

$$= 10 \ \angle{-180°}$$

Converting the phasor to a time function, we have

$$v_C(t) = 10\cos(1000t - 180°) = -10\cos(1000t)$$

Next, we compute the current in each element yielding

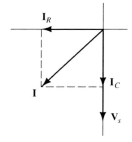

$$\mathbf{I} = \frac{\mathbf{V}_s}{Z_L + Z_{RC}} = \frac{10 \ \angle{-90°}}{j100 + 50 - j50} = \frac{10 \ \angle{-90°}}{50 + j50}$$

$$= \frac{10 \ \angle{-90°}}{70.71 \ \angle{45°}} = 0.1414 \ \angle{-135°}$$

$$\mathbf{I}_R = \frac{\mathbf{V}_C}{R} = \frac{10 \ \angle{-180°}}{100} = 0.1 \ \angle{-180°}$$

$$\mathbf{I}_C = \frac{\mathbf{V}_C}{Z_C} = \frac{10 \ \angle{-180°}}{-j100} = \frac{10 \ \angle{-180°}}{100 \ \angle{-90°}} = 0.1 \ \angle{-90°}$$

Figure 15 Phasor diagram for Example 5.

The phasor diagram is shown in Figure 15. ∎

Node-Voltage Analysis

We can perform node-voltage analysis by using phasors. We illustrate with an example.

Example 6   Steady-State AC Node-Voltage Analysis

Use the node-voltage technique to find $v_1(t)$ in steady state for the circuit shown in Figure 16(a).

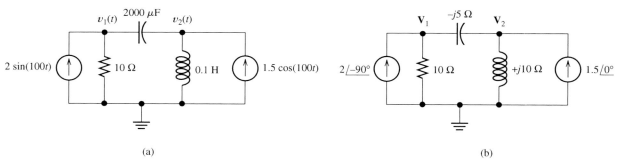

(a)   (b)

Figure 16 Circuit for Example 6.

Solution The transformed network is shown in Figure 16(b). We obtain two equations by applying KCL at node 1 and at node 2. This yields

$$\frac{\mathbf{V}_1}{10} + \frac{\mathbf{V}_1 - \mathbf{V}_2}{-j5} = 2 \underline{/-90°}$$

$$\frac{\mathbf{V}_2}{j10} + \frac{\mathbf{V}_2 - \mathbf{V}_1}{-j5} = 1.5 \underline{/0°}$$

These equations can be put into the standard form

$$(0.1 + j0.2)\mathbf{V}_1 - j0.2\mathbf{V}_2 = -j2$$

$$-j0.2\mathbf{V}_1 + j0.1\mathbf{V}_2 = 1.5$$

Now, we solve for $\mathbf{V}_1$ yielding

$$\mathbf{V}_1 = 16.1 \underline{/29.7°}$$

Then, we convert the phasor to a time function and obtain

$$v_1(t) = 16.1 \cos(100t + 29.7°)$$

■

Mesh-Current Analysis

In a similar fashion, you can use phasors to carry out mesh-current analysis in ac circuits. Exercise 11 gives you a chance to try this approach.

Exercise 9 Consider the circuit shown in Figure 17(a). **a.** Find $i(t)$. **b.** Construct a phasor diagram showing all three voltages and the current. **c.** What is the phase relationship between $v_s(t)$ and $i(t)$?
Answer a. $i(t) = 0.0283 \cos(500t - 135°)$; **b.** the phasor diagram is shown in Figure 17(b); **c.** $i(t)$ lags $v_s(t)$ by 45°. ☐

Exercise 10 Find the phasor voltage and the phasor current through each element in the circuit of Figure 18.
Answer $\mathbf{V} = 277 \underline{/-56.3°}, \mathbf{I}_C = 5.55 \underline{/33.7°}, \mathbf{I}_L = 1.39 \underline{/-146.3°},$
$\mathbf{I}_R = 2.77 \underline{/-56.3°}.$ ☐

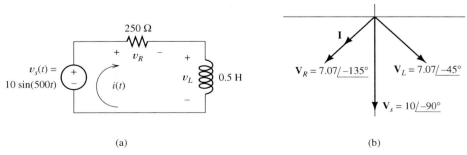

(a)　　　　　　　　　　(b)

Figure 17 Circuit and phasor diagram for Exercise 9.

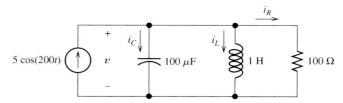

Figure 18 Circuit for Exercise 10.

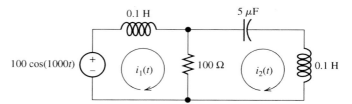

Figure 19 Circuit for Exercise 11.

Exercise 11 Solve for the mesh currents shown in Figure 19.
Answer $i_1(t) = 1.414 \cos(1000t - 45°), i_2(t) = \cos(1000t)$. □

5 POWER IN AC CIRCUITS

Consider the situation shown in Figure 20. A voltage $v(t) = V_m \cos(\omega t)$ is applied to a network composed of resistances, inductances, and capacitances (i.e., an RLC network). The phasor for the voltage source is $\mathbf{V} = V_m \angle 0°$, and the equivalent impedance of the network is $Z = |Z| \angle \theta = R + jX$. The phasor current is

$$\mathbf{I} = \frac{\mathbf{V}}{Z} = \frac{V_m \angle 0°}{|Z| \angle \theta} = I_m \angle -\theta \qquad (52)$$

where we have defined

$$I_m = \frac{V_m}{|Z|} \qquad (53)$$

Before we consider the power delivered by the source to a general load, it is instructive to consider a pure resistive load, a pure inductive load, and a pure capacitive load.

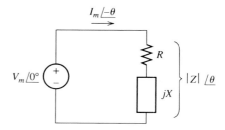

Figure 20 A voltage source delivering power to a load impedance $Z = R + jX$.

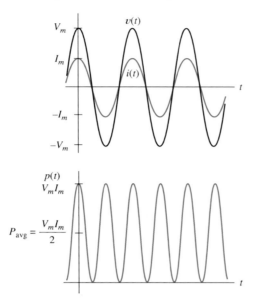

Figure 21 Current, voltage, and power versus time for a purely resistive load.

Current, Voltage, and Power for a Resistive Load

First, consider the case in which the network is a pure resistance. Then, $\theta = 0$, and we have

$$v(t) = V_m \cos(\omega t)$$

$$i(t) = I_m \cos(\omega t)$$

$$p(t) = v(t)i(t) = V_m I_m \cos^2(\omega t)$$

Plots of these quantities are shown in Figure 21. Notice that the current is in phase with the voltage (i.e., they both reach their peak values at the same time). Because $p(t)$ is positive at all times, we conclude that energy flows continually in the direction from the source to the load (where it is converted to heat). Of course, the value of the power rises and falls with the voltage (and current) magnitude.

Average power is absorbed by resistances in ac circuits.

Current, Voltage, and Power for an Inductive Load

Next, consider the case in which the load is a pure inductance for which $Z = \omega L \; \underline{/90°}$. Thus, $\theta = 90°$, and we get

$$v(t) = V_m \cos(\omega t)$$

$$i(t) = I_m \cos(\omega t - 90°) = I_m \sin(\omega t)$$

$$p(t) = v(t)i(t) = V_m I_m \cos(\omega t) \sin(\omega t)$$

Using the trigonometric identity $\cos(x) \sin(x) = (1/2) \sin(2x)$, we find that the expression for the power becomes

$$p(t) = \frac{V_m I_m}{2} \sin(2\omega t)$$

Power surges into and out of inductances in ac circuits. The average power absorbed by inductances is zero.

Plots of the current, voltage, and power are shown in Figure 22(a). Notice that the current lags the voltage by 90°. Half of the time the power is positive, showing

245

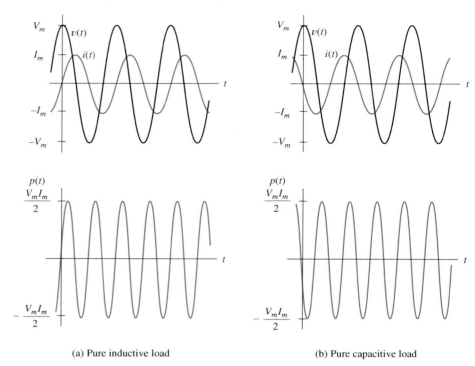

(a) Pure inductive load   (b) Pure capacitive load

Figure 22 Current, voltage, and power versus time for pure energy-storage elements.

that energy is delivered to the inductance, where it is stored in the magnetic field. For the other half of the time, power is negative, showing that the inductance returns energy to the source. Notice that the average power is zero. In this case, we say that **reactive power** flows from the source to the load.

Current, Voltage, and Power for a Capacitive Load

Next, consider the case in which the load is a pure capacitance for which $Z = (1/\omega C) \; \angle{-90^\circ}$. Then, $\theta = -90^\circ$, and we have

$$v(t) = V_m \cos(\omega t)$$
$$i(t) = I_m \cos(\omega t + 90^\circ) = -I_m \sin(\omega t)$$
$$p(t) = v(t)i(t) = -V_m I_m \cos(\omega t) \sin(\omega t)$$
$$= -\frac{V_m I_m}{2} \sin(2\omega t)$$

Power surges into and out of capacitances in ac circuits. The average power absorbed by capacitances is zero.

Plots of the current, voltage, and power are shown in Figure 22(b). Here again, the average power is zero, and we say that reactive power flows. Notice, however, that the power for the capacitance carries the opposite sign as that for the inductance. Thus, we say that reactive power is positive for an inductance and is negative for a capacitance. If a load contains both inductance and capacitance with reactive powers of equal magnitude, the reactive powers cancel.

Importance of Reactive Power

Even though no average power is consumed by a pure energy-storage element (inductance or capacitance), reactive power is still of concern to power-system engineers because transmission lines, transformers, fuses, and other elements must be capable of withstanding the current associated with reactive power. It is possible to have loads composed of energy-storage elements that draw large currents requiring heavy-duty wiring, even though little average power is consumed. Therefore, electric-power companies charge their industrial customers for reactive power (but at a lower rate) as well as for total energy delivered.

The power flow back and forth to inductances and capacitances is called reactive power. Reactive power flow is important because it causes power dissipation in the lines and transformers of a power distribution system.

Power Calculations for a General Load

Now, let us consider the voltage, current, and power for a general RLC load for which the phase θ can be any value from $-90°$ to $+90°$. We have

$$v(t) = V_m \cos(\omega t) \tag{54}$$

$$i(t) = I_m \cos(\omega t - \theta) \tag{55}$$

$$p(t) = V_m I_m \cos(\omega t) \cos(\omega t - \theta) \tag{56}$$

Using the trigonometric identity

$$\cos(\omega t - \theta) = \cos(\theta) \cos(\omega t) + \sin(\theta) \sin(\omega t)$$

we can put Equation 56 into the form

$$p(t) = V_m I_m \cos(\theta) \cos^2(\omega t) + V_m I_m \sin(\theta) \cos(\omega t) \sin(\omega t) \tag{57}$$

Using the identities

$$\cos^2(\omega t) = \frac{1}{2} + \frac{1}{2} \cos(2\omega t)$$

and

$$\cos(\omega t) \sin(\omega t) = \frac{1}{2} \sin(2\omega t)$$

we find that Equation 57 can be written as

$$p(t) = \frac{V_m I_m}{2} \cos(\theta)[1 + \cos(2\omega t)] + \frac{V_m I_m}{2} \sin(\theta) \sin(2\omega t) \tag{58}$$

Notice that the terms involving $\cos(2\omega t)$ and $\sin(2\omega t)$ have average values of zero. Thus, the average power P is given by

$$P = \frac{V_m I_m}{2} \cos(\theta) \tag{59}$$

Using the fact that $V_{\text{rms}} = V_m/\sqrt{2}$ and $I_{\text{rms}} = I_m/\sqrt{2}$, we can write the expression for average power as

$$P = V_{\text{rms}} I_{\text{rms}} \cos(\theta) \tag{60}$$

As usual, the units of power are watts (W).

Power Factor

The term $\cos(\theta)$ is called the **power factor**:

$$PF = \cos(\theta) \tag{61}$$

Power factor is the cosine of the angle θ by which the current lags the voltage. (If the current leads the voltage, the angle is negative.)

To simplify our discussion, we assumed a voltage having zero phase. In general, the phase of the voltage may have a value other than zero. Then, θ should be taken as the phase of the voltage θ_v minus the phase of the current θ_i, or

$$\theta = \theta_v - \theta_i \tag{62}$$

Sometimes, θ is called the **power angle**.

Often, power factor is expressed as a percentage.

If the current lags the voltage, the power factor is said to be inductive or lagging. If the current leads the voltage, the power factor is said to be capacitive or leading.

Often, power factor is stated as a percentage. Also, it is common to state whether the current leads (capacitive load) or lags (inductive load) the voltage. A typical power factor would be stated to be 90 percent lagging, which means that $\cos(\theta) = 0.9$ and that the current lags the voltage.

Reactive Power

In ac circuits, energy flows into and out of energy storage elements (inductances and capacitances). For example, when the voltage magnitude across a capacitance is increasing, energy flows into it, and when the voltage magnitude decreases, energy flows out. Similarly, energy flows into an inductance when the current flowing through it increases in magnitude. Although instantaneous power can be very large, the net energy transferred per cycle is zero for either an ideal capacitance or inductance.

When a capacitance and an inductance are in parallel (or series) energy flows into one, while it flows out of the other. Thus, the power flow of a capacitance tends to cancel that of an inductance at each instant in time.

The peak instantaneous power associated with the energy storage elements contained in a general load is called **reactive power** and is given by

$$Q = V_{\text{rms}} I_{\text{rms}} \sin(\theta) \tag{63}$$

where θ is the power angle given by Equation 62, V_{rms} is the effective (or rms) voltage across the load, and I_{rms} is the effective current through the load. (Notice that if we had a purely resistive load, we would have $\theta = 0$ and $Q = 0$.)

The units of reactive power Q are VARs.

The physical units of reactive power are watts. However, to emphasize the fact that Q does not represent the flow of net energy, its units are usually given as *V*olt *A*mperes *R*eactive (VARs).

Apparent Power

Apparent power equals the product of rms current and rms voltage. The units for apparent power are stated as volt-amperes (VA).

Another quantity of interest is the **apparent power**, which is defined as the product of the effective voltage and the effective current, or

$$\text{apparent power} = V_{\text{rms}} I_{\text{rms}}$$

Its units are volt-amperes (VA).

Using Equations 60 and 63, we can write

$$P^2 + Q^2 = (V_{\text{rms}} I_{\text{rms}})^2 \cos^2(\theta) + (V_{\text{rms}} I_{\text{rms}})^2 \sin^2(\theta)$$

However, $\cos^2(\theta) + \sin^2(\theta) = 1$, so we have

$$P^2 + Q^2 = (V_{rms}I_{rms})^2 \tag{64}$$

Units

Often, the units given for a quantity indicate whether the quantity is power (W), reactive power (VAR), or apparent power (VA). For example, if we say that we have a 5-kW load, this means that $P = 5$ kW. On the other hand, if we have a 5-kVA load, $V_{rms}I_{rms} = 5$ kVA. If we say that a load absorbs 5 kVAR, then $Q = 5$ kVAR.

Power Triangle

The relationships between real power P, reactive power Q, apparent power $V_{rms}I_{rms}$, and the power angle θ can be represented by the **power triangle**. The power triangle is shown in Figure 23(a) for an inductive load, in which case θ and Q are positive. The power triangle for a capacitive load is shown in Figure 23(b), in which case θ and Q are negative.

The power triangle is a compact way to represent ac power relationships.

Additional Power Relationships

The impedance Z is

$$Z = |Z| \; \angle\theta = R + jX$$

in which R is the resistance of the load and X is the reactance. This is illustrated in Figure 24. We can write

$$\cos(\theta) = \frac{R}{|Z|} \tag{65}$$

and

$$\sin(\theta) = \frac{X}{|Z|} \tag{66}$$

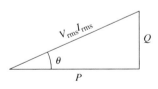
(a) Inductive load (θ positive)

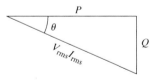
(b) Capacitive load (θ negative)

Figure 23 Power triangles for inductive and capacitive loads.

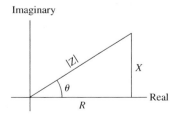

Figure 24 The load impedance in the complex plane.

249

Substituting Equation 65 into Equation 59, we find that

$$P = \frac{V_m I_m}{2} \times \frac{R}{|Z|} \qquad (67)$$

However, Equation 53 states that $I_m = V_m/|Z|$, so we have

$$P = \frac{I_m^2}{2} R \qquad (68)$$

In Equation 69, *R* is the real part of the impedance through which the current flows.

Using the fact that $I_{rms} = I_m/\sqrt{2}$, we get

$$P = I_{rms}^2 R \qquad (69)$$

In Equation 70, *X* is the imaginary part (including the algebraic sign) of the impedance through which the current flows.

In a similar fashion, we can show that

$$Q = I_{rms}^2 X \qquad (70)$$

Reactive power *Q* is positive for inductive loads and negative for capacitive loads.

In applying Equation 70, we retain the algebraic sign of X. For an inductive load, X is positive, whereas for a capacitive load, X is negative. This is not hard to remember if we keep in mind that Q is positive for inductive loads and negative for capacitive loads.

Furthermore, in Section 1, we showed that the average power delivered to a resistance is

In Equation 71, V_{Rrms} is the rms voltage across the resistance.

$$P = \frac{V_{Rrms}^2}{R} \qquad (71)$$

where V_{Rrms} is the rms value of the voltage *across the resistance*. (Notice in Figure 20 that the source voltage does not appear across the resistance, because the reactance is in series with the resistance.)

Similarly, we have

In Equation 72, V_{Xrms} is the rms voltage across the reactance.

$$Q = \frac{V_{Xrms}^2}{X} \qquad (72)$$

where V_{Xrms} is the rms value of the voltage *across the reactance*. Here again, X is positive for an inductance and negative for a capacitance.

Complex Power

Consider the portion of a circuit shown in Figure 25. The **complex power**, denoted as **S**, delivered to this circuit is defined as one half the product of the phasor voltage **V** and the complex conjugate of the phasor current **I***.

$$\mathbf{S} = \frac{1}{2}\mathbf{VI}^* \qquad (73)$$

The phasor voltage is $\mathbf{V} = V_m \angle \theta_v$ in which V_m is the peak value of the voltage and θ_v is the phase angle of the voltage. Furthermore, the phasor current is $\mathbf{I} = I_m \angle \theta_i$

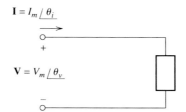

Figure 25 The complex power delivered to this circuit element is $\mathbf{S} = \frac{1}{2}\mathbf{VI}^*$.

where I_m is the peak value and θ_i is the phase angle of the current. Substituting into Equation 73, we have

$$\mathbf{S} = \frac{1}{2}\mathbf{VI}^* = \frac{1}{2}(V_m \angle \theta_v) \times (I_m \angle -\theta_i) = \frac{V_m I_m}{2} \angle \theta_v - \theta_i = \frac{V_m I_m}{2} \angle \theta \qquad (74)$$

where, as before, $\theta = \theta_v - \theta_i$ is the power angle. Expanding the right-hand term of Equation 74 into real and imaginary parts, we have

$$\mathbf{S} = \frac{V_m I_m}{2} \cos(\theta) + j\frac{V_m I_m}{2} \sin(\theta)$$

However, the first term on the right-hand side is the average power P delivered to the circuit and the second term is j times the reactive power. Thus, we can write:

$$\mathbf{S} = \frac{1}{2}\mathbf{VI}^* = P + jQ \qquad (75)$$

If we know the complex power $\mathbf{S}$, then we can find the power, reactive power, and apparent power:

$$P = \text{Re}(\mathbf{S}) = \text{Re}\left(\frac{1}{2}\mathbf{VI}^*\right) \qquad (76)$$

$$Q = \text{Im}(\mathbf{S}) = \text{Im}\left(\frac{1}{2}\mathbf{VI}^*\right) \qquad (77)$$

$$\text{apparent power} = |\mathbf{S}| = \left|\frac{1}{2}\mathbf{VI}^*\right| \qquad (78)$$

where $\text{Re}(\mathbf{S})$ denotes the real part of $\mathbf{S}$ and $\text{Im}(\mathbf{S})$ denotes the imaginary part of $\mathbf{S}$.

Example 7	AC Power Calculations

Compute the power and reactive power taken from the source for the circuit of Example 5. Also, compute the power and reactive power delivered to each element in the circuit. For convenience, the circuit and the currents that were computed in Example 5 are shown in Figure 26.

Solution To find the power and reactive power for the source, we must first find the power angle which is given by Equation 62:

$$\theta = \theta_v - \theta_i$$

The angle of the source voltage is $\theta_v = -90°$, and the angle of the current delivered by the source is $\theta_i = -135°$. Therefore, we have

$$\theta = -90° - (-135°) = 45°$$

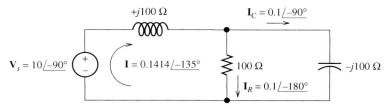

Figure 26 Circuit and currents for Example 7.

The rms source voltage and current are

$$V_{srms} = \frac{|\mathbf{V}_s|}{\sqrt{2}} = \frac{10}{\sqrt{2}} = 7.071 \text{ V}$$

$$I_{rms} = \frac{|\mathbf{I}|}{\sqrt{2}} = \frac{0.1414}{\sqrt{2}} = 0.1 \text{ A}$$

Now, we use Equations 60 and 63 to compute the power and reactive power delivered by the source:

$$P = V_{srms}I_{rms} \cos(\theta)$$
$$= 7.071 \times 0.1 \cos(45°) = 0.5 \text{ W}$$
$$Q = V_{srms}I_{rms} \sin(\theta)$$
$$= 7.071 \times 0.1 \sin(45°) = 0.5 \text{ VAR}$$

An alternative and more compact method for computing P and Q is to first find the complex power and then take the real and imaginary parts:

$$\mathbf{S} = \frac{1}{2}\mathbf{V}_s\mathbf{I}^* = \frac{1}{2}(10 \angle{-90°})(0.1414 \angle{135°}) = 0.707 \angle{45°} = 0.5 + j0.5$$
$$P = \text{Re}(\mathbf{S}) = 0.5 \text{ W}$$
$$Q = \text{Im}(\mathbf{S}) = 0.5 \text{ VAR}$$

We can use Equation 70 to compute the reactive power delivered to the inductor, yielding

$$Q_L = I_{rms}^2 X_L = (0.1)^2(100) = 1.0 \text{ VAR}$$

For the capacitor, we have

$$Q_C = I_{Crms}^2 X_C = \left(\frac{0.1}{\sqrt{2}}\right)^2 (-100) = -0.5 \text{ VAR}$$

Notice that we have used the rms value of the current through the capacitor in this calculation. Furthermore, notice that the reactance X_C of the capacitance is negative. As expected, the reactive power is negative for a capacitance. The reactive power for the resistance is zero. As a check, we can verify that the reactive power delivered by the source is equal to the sum of the reactive powers absorbed by the inductance and capacitance. This is demonstrated by

$$Q = Q_L + Q_C$$

The power delivered to the resistance is

$$P_R = I_{Rrms}^2 R = \left(\frac{|\mathbf{I}_R|}{\sqrt{2}}\right)^2 R = \left(\frac{0.1}{\sqrt{2}}\right)^2 100$$

$$= 0.5 \text{ W}$$

The power absorbed by the capacitance and inductance is given by

$$P_L = 0$$

$$P_C = 0$$

Thus, all of the power delivered by the source is absorbed by the resistance. ■

In power distribution systems, we typically encounter much larger values of power, reactive power, and apparent power than the small values of the preceding example. For example, a large power plant may generate 1000 MW. A 100-hp motor used in an industrial application absorbs approximately 85 kW of electrical power under full load.

A typical residence absorbs a *peak* power in the range of 10 to 40 kW. The *average* power for my home (which is of average size, has two residents, and does not use electrical heating) is approximately 600 W. It is interesting to keep your average power consumption and the power used by various appliances in mind because it gives you a clear picture of the economic and environmental impact of turning off lights, computers, and so on, that are not being used.

Example 8   Using Power Triangles

Consider the situation shown in Figure 27. Here, a voltage source delivers power to two loads connected in parallel. Find the power, reactive power, and power factor for the source. Also, find the phasor current $\mathbf{I}$.

Solution   By the units given in the figure, we see that load A has an *apparent power* of 10 kVA. On the other hand, the *power* for load B is specified as 5 kW.

Furthermore, load A has a power factor of 0.5 leading, which means that the current leads the voltage in load A. Another way to say this is that load A is capacitive. Similarly, load B has a power factor of 0.7 lagging (or inductive).

Our approach is to find the power and reactive power for each load. Then, we add these values to find the power and reactive power for the source. Finally, we compute the power factor for the source and then find the current.

Because load A has a leading (capacitive) power factor, we know that the reactive power Q_A and power angle θ_A are negative. The power triangle for load A is shown

Calculations for load A

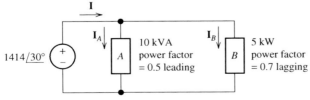

Figure 27 Circuit for Example 8.

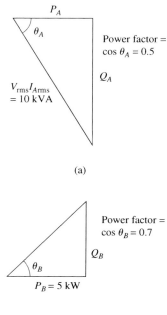

Figure 28 Power triangles for loads
A and *B* of Example 8.   (b)

in Figure 28(a). The power factor is

$$\cos(\theta_A) = 0.5$$

The power is

$$P_A = V_{\text{rms}} I_{A\text{rms}} \cos(\theta_A) = 10^4(0.5) = 5 \text{ kW}$$

Solving Equation 64 for reactive power, we have

$$Q_A = \sqrt{(V_{\text{rms}} I_{A\text{rms}})^2 - P_A^2}$$
$$= \sqrt{(10^4)^2 - (5000)^2}$$
$$= -8.660 \text{ kVAR}$$

Notice that we have selected the negative value for Q_A, because we know that reactive power is negative for a capacitive (leading) load.

Calculations for load *B*

The power triangle for load *B* is shown in Figure 28(b). Since load *B* has a lagging (inductive) power factor, we know that the reactive power Q_B and power angle θ_B are positive. Thus,

$$\theta_B = \arccos(0.7) = 45.57°$$

Applying trigonometry, we can write

$$Q_B = P_B \tan(\theta_B) = 5000 \tan(45.57°)$$
$$Q_B = 5.101 \text{ kVAR}$$

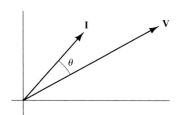

Figure 29 Phasor diagram for
Example 8.

At this point, as shown here we can find the power and reactive power delivered by the source:

$$P = P_A + P_B = 5 + 5 = 10 \text{ kW}$$

$$Q = Q_A + Q_B = -8.660 + 5.101 = -3.559 \text{ kVAR}$$

Total power is obtained by adding the powers for the various loads. Similarly, the reactive powers are added.

Because Q is negative, we know that the power angle is negative. Thus, we have

Power calculations for the source

$$\theta = \arctan\left(\frac{Q}{P}\right) = \arctan\left(\frac{-3.559}{10}\right) = -19.59°$$

The power factor is

$$\cos(\theta) = 0.9421$$

Power-system engineers frequently express power factors as percentages and would state this power factor as 94.21 percent leading.

The complex power delivered by the source is

$$\mathbf{S} = P + jQ = 10 - j3.559 = 10.61 \; \underline{/-19.59°} \text{ kVA}$$

Thus, we have

$$\mathbf{S} = \frac{1}{2}\mathbf{V}_s\mathbf{I}^* = \frac{1}{2}(1414 \; \underline{/30°})\mathbf{I}^* = 10.61 \times 10^3 \; \underline{/-19.59°} \text{ kVA}$$

Solving for the phasor current, we obtain:

$$\mathbf{I} = 15.0 \; \underline{/49.59°} \text{ A}$$

The phasor diagram for the current and voltage is shown in Figure 29. Notice that the current is leading the voltage. ∎

Power-Factor Correction

We have seen that large currents can flow in energy-storage devices (inductance and capacitance) without average power being delivered. In heavy industry, many loads are partly inductive, and large amounts of reactive power flow. This reactive power causes higher currents in the power distribution system. Consequently, the lines and transformers must have higher ratings than would be necessary to deliver the same average power to a resistive (100 percent power factor) load.

Power-factor correction can provide a significant economic advantage for large consumers of electrical energy.

Energy rates charged to industry depend on the power factor, with higher charges for energy delivered at lower power factors. (Power factor is not taken into account for residential customers.) Therefore, it is advantageous to choose loads that operate at near unity power factor. A common approach is to place capacitors in parallel with an inductive load to increase the power factor.

Example 9   Power-Factor Correction

A 50-kW load operates from a 60-Hz 10-kV-rms line with a power factor of 60 percent lagging. Compute the capacitance that must be placed in parallel with the load to achieve a 90 percent lagging power factor.

Solution   First, we find the load power angle:

$$\theta_L = \arccos(0.6) = 53.13°$$

Then, we use the power-triangle concept to find the reactive power of the load. Hence,

$$Q_L = P_L \tan(\theta_L) = 66.67 \text{ kVAR}$$

After adding the capacitor, the power will still be 50 kW and the power angle will become

$$\theta_{new} = \arccos(0.9) = 25.84°$$

The new value of the reactive power will be

$$Q_{new} = P_L \tan(\theta_{new}) = 24.22 \text{ kVAR}$$

Thus, the reactive power of the capacitance must be

$$Q_C = Q_{new} - Q_L = -42.45 \text{ kVAR}$$

Now, we find that the reactance of the capacitor is

$$X_C = -\frac{V_{rms}^2}{Q_C} = \frac{(10^4)^2}{42,450} = -2356 \ \Omega$$

Finally, the angular frequency is

$$\omega = 2\pi 60 = 377.0$$

and the required capacitance is

$$C = \frac{1}{\omega |X_C|} = \frac{1}{377 \times 2356} = 1.126 \ \mu\text{F}$$

     ■

Exercise 12   **a.** A voltage source $\mathbf{V} = 707.1 \ \underline{/40°}$ delivers 5 kW to a load with a power factor of 100 percent. Find the reactive power and the phasor current. **b.** Repeat if the power factor is 20 percent lagging. **c.** For which power factor would the current ratings of the conductors connecting the source to the load be higher? In which case could the wiring be a lower cost?

Answer   **a.** $Q = 0$, $\mathbf{I} = 14.14\ \underline{/40°}$; **b.** $Q = 24.49$ kVAR, $\mathbf{I} = 70.7\ \underline{/-38.46°}$; **c.** The current ratings for the conductors would need to be five times higher for part (b) than for part (a). Clearly, the wiring could be a lower cost for 100 percent power factor. □

Exercise 13   A 1-kV-rms 60-Hz voltage source delivers power to two loads in parallel. The first load is a 10-μF capacitor, and the second load absorbs an apparent power of 10 kVA with an 80 percent lagging power factor. Find the total power, the total reactive power, the power factor for the source, and the rms source current.

Answer $P = 8$ kW, $Q = 2.23$ kVAR, PF $= 96.33$ percent lagging, $I_{rms} = 8.305$ A. □

6   THÉVENIN AND NORTON EQUIVALENT CIRCUITS

Thévenin Equivalent Circuits

A two-terminal network composed of sources and resistances has a Thévenin equivalent circuit consisting of a voltage source in series with a resistance. We can apply this concept to circuits composed of sinusoidal sources (all having a common frequency), resistances, inductances, and capacitances. Here, the Thévenin equivalent consists of a phasor voltage source in series with a complex impedance as shown in Figure 30. Recall that phasors and complex impedances apply only for steady-state operation; therefore, these Thévenin equivalents are valid for only steady-state operation of the circuit.

As in resistive circuits, the Thévenin voltage is equal to the open-circuit voltage of the two-terminal circuit. In ac circuits, we use phasors, so we can write

> The Thévenin voltage is equal to the open-circuit phasor voltage of the original circuit.

$$\mathbf{V}_t = \mathbf{V}_{oc} \tag{79}$$

The Thévenin impedance Z_t can be found by zeroing the *independent* sources and looking back into the terminals to find the equivalent impedance. (Recall that in zeroing a voltage source, we reduce its voltage to zero, and it becomes a short circuit. On the other hand, in zeroing a current source, we reduce its current to zero, and it becomes an open circuit.) Also, keep in mind that we must not zero the *dependent* sources.

> We can find the Thévenin impedance by zeroing the independent sources and determining the impedance looking into the circuit terminals.

Another approach to determining the Thévenin impedance is first to find the short-circuit phasor current $\mathbf{I}_{sc}$ and the open-circuit voltage $\mathbf{V}_{oc}$. Then, the Thévenin impedance is given by

> The Thévenin impedance equals the open-circuit voltage divided by the short-circuit current.

$$Z_t = \frac{\mathbf{V}_{oc}}{\mathbf{I}_{sc}} = \frac{\mathbf{V}_t}{\mathbf{I}_{sc}} \tag{80}$$

Thus, except for the use of phasors and complex impedances, the concepts and procedures for Thévenin equivalents of steady-state ac circuits are the same as for resistive circuits.

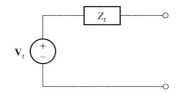

Figure 30 The Thévenin equivalent for an ac circuit consists of a phasor voltage source $\mathbf{V}_t$ in series with a complex impedance Z_t.

Figure 31 The Norton equivalent circuit consists of a phasor current source $\mathbf{I}_n$ in parallel with the complex impedance Z_t.

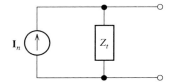

Norton Equivalent Circuits

Another equivalent for a two-terminal steady-state ac circuit is the Norton equivalent, which consists of a phasor current source $\mathbf{I}_n$ in parallel with the Thévenin impedance. This is shown in Figure 31. The Norton current is equal to the short-circuit current of the original circuit:

$$\mathbf{I}_n = \mathbf{I}_{\text{sc}} \tag{81}$$

Thévenin and Norton Equivalents

Find the Thévenin and Norton equivalent circuits for the circuit shown in Figure 32(a).

Solution We must find two of the three quantities: $\mathbf{V}_{\text{oc}}$, $\mathbf{I}_{\text{sc}}$, or Z_t. Often, it pays to look for the two that can be found with the least amount of work. In this case, we elect to start by zeroing the sources to find Z_t. After that part of the problem is finished, we will find the short-circuit current.

If we zero the sources, we obtain the circuit shown in Figure 32(b). The Thévenin impedance is the impedance seen looking back into terminals a–b. This is the parallel

First, look to see which two of the three quantities $\mathbf{V}_{\text{oc}}$, $\mathbf{I}_{\text{sc}}$, or Z_t are easiest to determine.

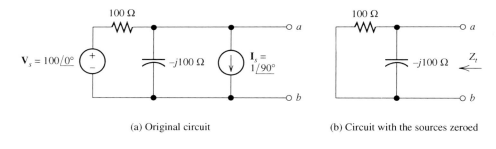

(a) Original circuit   (b) Circuit with the sources zeroed

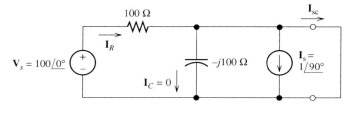

(c) Circuit with a short circuit

Figure 32 Circuit of Example 10.

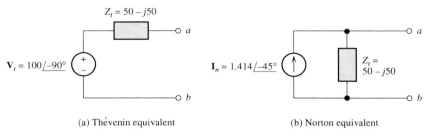

(a) Thévenin equivalent   (b) Norton equivalent

Figure 33 Thévenin and Norton equivalents for the circuit of Figure 32(a).

combination of the resistance and the impedance of the capacitance. Thus, we have

$$Z_t = \frac{1}{1/100 + 1/(-j100)}$$

$$= \frac{1}{0.01 + j0.01}$$

$$= \frac{1}{0.01414 \;\angle 45°}$$

$$= 70.71 \;\angle{-45°}$$

$$= 50 - j50 \;\Omega$$

Now, we apply a short circuit to terminals a–b and find the current, which is shown in Figure 32(c). With a short circuit, the voltage across the capacitance is zero. Therefore, $\mathbf{I}_C = 0$. Furthermore, the source voltage $\mathbf{V}_s$ appears across the resistance, so we have

$$\mathbf{I}_R = \frac{\mathbf{V}_s}{100} = \frac{100}{100} = 1 \;\angle 0° \text{ A}$$

Then applying KCL, we can write

$$\mathbf{I}_{sc} = \mathbf{I}_R - \mathbf{I}_s = 1 - 1 \;\angle 90° = 1 - j = 1.414 \;\angle{-45°} \text{ A}$$

Next, we can solve Equation 80 for the Thévenin voltage:

$$\mathbf{V}_t = \mathbf{I}_{sc}Z_t = 1.414 \;\angle{-45°} \times 70.71 \;\angle{-45°} = 100 \;\angle{-90°} \text{ V}$$

Finally, we can draw the Thévenin and Norton equivalent circuits, which are shown in Figure 33. ∎

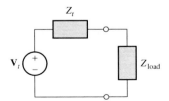

Figure 34 The Thévenin equivalent of a two-terminal circuit delivering power to a load impedance.

Maximum Average Power Transfer

Sometimes, we are faced with the problem of adjusting a load impedance to extract the maximum average power from a two-terminal circuit. This situation is shown in Figure 34, in which we have represented the two-terminal circuit by its

Thévenin equivalent. Of course, the power delivered to the load depends on the load impedance. A short-circuit load receives no power because the voltage across it is zero. Similarly, an open-circuit load receives no power because the current through it is zero. Furthermore, a pure reactive load (inductance or capacitance) receives no power because the load power factor is zero.

Two situations are of interest. First, suppose that the load impedance can take any complex value. Then, it turns out that the load impedance for maximum-power transfer is the complex conjugate of the Thévenin impedance:

$$Z_{\text{load}} = Z_t^*$$

Let us consider why this is true. Suppose that the Thévenin impedance is

$$Z_t = R_t + jX_t$$

Then, the load impedance for maximum-power transfer is

$$Z_{\text{load}} = Z_t^* = R_t - jX_t$$

Of course, the total impedance seen by the Thévenin source is the sum of the Thévenin impedance and the load impedance:

$$
\begin{aligned}
Z_{\text{total}} &= Z_t + Z_{\text{load}} \\
&= R_t + jX_t + R_t - jX_t \\
&= 2R_t
\end{aligned}
$$

Thus, the reactance of the load cancels the internal reactance of the two-terminal circuit. Maximum power is transferred to a given load resistance by maximizing the current. For given resistances, maximum current is achieved by choosing the reactance to minimize the total impedance magnitude. Of course, for fixed resistances, the minimum impedance magnitude occurs for zero total reactance.

Having established the fact that the total reactance should be zero, we have a resistive circuit.

The second case of interest is a load that is constrained to be a pure resistance. In this case, it can be shown that the load resistance for maximum-power transfer is equal to the magnitude of the Thévenin impedance:

$$Z_{\text{load}} = R_{\text{load}} = |Z_t|$$

Example 11   Maximum Power Transfer

Determine the maximum power that can be delivered to a load by the two-terminal circuit of Figure 32(a) if **a.** the load can have any complex value and **b.** the load must be a pure resistance.

Solution   In Example 10, we found that the circuit has the Thévenin equivalent shown in Figure 33(a). The Thévenin impedance is

$$Z_t = 50 - j50 \ \Omega$$

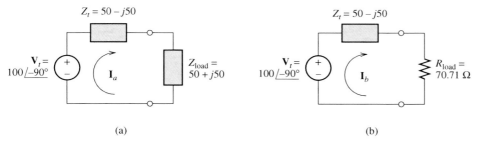

$Z_t = 50 - j50$

$V_t = 100\underline{/-90°}$

$Z_{load} = 50 + j50$

I_a

$Z_t = 50 - j50$

$V_t = 100\underline{/-90°}$

$R_{load} = 70.71\ \Omega$

I_b

(a)

(b)

Figure 35 Thévenin equivalent circuit and loads of Example 11.

a. The complex load impedance that maximizes power transfer is

$$Z_{load} = Z_t^* = 50 + j50$$

The Thévenin equivalent with this load attached is shown in Figure 35(a). The current is

$$\mathbf{I}_a = \frac{\mathbf{V}_t}{Z_t + Z_{load}}$$

$$= \frac{100\ \underline{/-90°}}{50 - j50 + 50 + j50}$$

$$= 1\ \underline{/-90°}\ \text{A}$$

The rms load current is $I_{arms} = 1/\sqrt{2}$. Finally, the power delivered to the load is

$$P = I_{arms}^2 R_{load} = \left(\frac{1}{\sqrt{2}}\right)^2 (50) = 25\ \text{W}$$

b. The purely resistive load for maximum power transfer is

$$R_{load} = |Z_t|$$
$$= |50 - j50|$$
$$= \sqrt{50^2 + (-50)^2}$$
$$= 70.71\ \Omega$$

The Thévenin equivalent with this load attached is shown in Figure 35(b). The current is

$$\mathbf{I}_b = \frac{\mathbf{V}_t}{Z_t + Z_{load}}$$

$$= \frac{100\ \underline{/-90°}}{50 - j50 + 70.71}$$

$$= \frac{100\ \underline{/-90°}}{130.66\ \underline{/-22.50°}}$$

$$= 0.7654\ \underline{/-67.50°}\ \text{A}$$

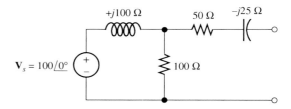

Figure 36 Circuit of Exercises 14 and 15.

The power delivered to this load is

$$P = I_{brms}^2 R_{load}$$
$$= \left(\frac{0.7653}{\sqrt{2}}\right)^2 70.71$$
$$= 20.71 \text{ W}$$

Notice that the power available to a purely resistive load is less than that for a complex load. ∎

Exercise 14 Find the Thévenin impedance, the Thévenin voltage, and the Norton current for the circuit shown in Figure 36.
Answer $Z_t = 100 + j25 \ \Omega$, $\mathbf{V}_t = 70.71 \ \underline{/-45°}$, $\mathbf{I}_n = 0.686 \ \underline{/-59.0°}$. ☐

Exercise 15 Determine the maximum power that can be delivered to a load by the two-terminal circuit of Figure 36 if **a.** the load can have any complex value and **b.** the load must be a pure resistance.
Answer **a.** 6.25 W; **b.** 6.16 W. ☐

7 BALANCED THREE-PHASE CIRCUITS

Much of the power used by business and industry is supplied by three-phase distribution systems. Plant engineers need to be familiar with three-phase power.

We will see that there are important advantages in generating and distributing power with multiple ac voltages having different phases. We consider the most common case: three equal-amplitude ac voltages having phases that are 120° apart. This is known as a **balanced three-phase source**, an example of which is illustrated in Figure 37. [Recall that in double-subscript notation for voltages the first subscript is the positive reference. Thus, $v_{an}(t)$ is the voltage between nodes a and n with the positive reference at node a.]

The source shown in Figure 37(a) is said to be **wye connected (Y connected)**. Later in this chapter, we consider another configuration, known as the delta (Δ) connection.

The three voltages shown in Figure 37(b) are given by

$$v_{an}(t) = V_Y \cos(\omega t) \tag{82}$$
$$v_{bn}(t) = V_Y \cos(\omega t - 120°) \tag{83}$$
$$v_{cn}(t) = V_Y \cos(\omega t + 120°) \tag{84}$$

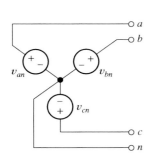

(a) Three-phase source

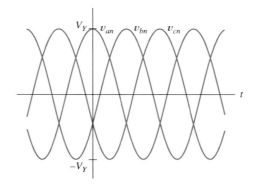

(b) Voltages versus time

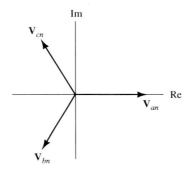

(c) Phasor diagram

Figure 37 A balanced three-phase voltage source.

where V_Y is the magnitude of each source in the wye-connected configuration. The corresponding phasors are

$$\mathbf{V}_{an} = V_Y \angle 0° \qquad (85)$$

$$\mathbf{V}_{bn} = V_Y \angle{-120°} \qquad (86)$$

$$\mathbf{V}_{cn} = V_Y \angle 120° \qquad (87)$$

The phasor diagram is shown in Figure 37(c).

Phase Sequence

This set of voltages is said to have a **positive phase sequence** because the voltages reach their peak values in the order abc. Refer to Figure 37(c) and notice that v_{an} leads v_{bn}, which in turn leads v_{cn}. (Recall that we think of the phasors as rotating counterclockwise in determining phase relationships.) If we interchanged b and c, we would have a **negative phase sequence**, in which the order is acb.

Phase sequence can be important. For example, if we have a three-phase induction motor, the direction of rotation is opposite for the two phase sequences. To reverse the direction of rotation of such a motor, we would interchange the b and c connections. (You may find this piece of information useful if you ever work with

Three-phase sources can have either a positive or negative phase sequence.

The direction of rotation of certain three-phase motors can be reversed by changing the phase sequence.

three-phase motors, which are very common in industry.) Because circuit analysis is very similar for both phase sequences, we consider only the positive phase sequence in most of the discussion that follows.

Wye–Wye Connection

Three-phase sources and loads can be connected either in a wye configuration or in a delta configuration.

Consider the three-phase source connected to a balanced three-phase load shown in Figure 38. The wires a–A, b–B, and c–C are called **lines**, and the wire n–N is called the **neutral**. This configuration is called a wye–wye (Y–Y) connection with neutral. By the term *balanced load*, we mean that the three load impedances are equal. (In this book, we consider only balanced loads.)

Later, we will see that other configurations are useful. For example, the neutral wire n–N can be omitted. Furthermore, the source and load can be connected in the form of a delta. We will see that currents, voltages, and power can be computed for these other configurations by finding an equivalent wye–wye circuit. Thus, the key to understanding three-phase circuits is a careful examination of the wye–wye circuit.

The key to understanding the various three-phase configurations is a careful examination of the wye–wye circuit.

Often, we use the term *phase* to refer to part of the source or the load. Thus, phase A of the source is $v_{an}(t)$, and phase A of the load is the impedance connected between A and N. We refer to V_Y as the **phase voltage** or as the **line-to-neutral voltage** of the wye-connected source. (Power-systems engineers usually specify rms values rather than peak magnitudes. Unless stated otherwise, we use phasors having magnitudes equal to the peak values rather than the rms values.) Furthermore, $\mathbf{I}_{aA}$, $\mathbf{I}_{bB}$, and $\mathbf{I}_{cC}$ are called **line currents**. (Recall that in the double-subscript notation for currents, the reference direction is from the first subscript to the second. Thus, $\mathbf{I}_{aA}$ is the current referenced from node a to node A, as illustrated in Figure 38.)

In this chapter, we take the magnitude of a phasor to be the peak value. Power-systems engineers often use the rms value as the magnitude for phasors.

The current in phase A of the load is given by

$$\mathbf{I}_{aA} = \frac{\mathbf{V}_{an}}{Z \angle \theta} = \frac{V_Y \angle 0°}{Z \angle \theta} = I_L \angle{-\theta}$$

where $I_L = V_Y/Z$ is the magnitude of the line current. Because the load impedances are equal, all of the line currents are the same, except for phase. Thus, the currents are given by

$$i_{aA}(t) = I_L \cos(\omega t - \theta) \tag{88}$$

$$i_{bB}(t) = I_L \cos(\omega t - 120° - \theta) \tag{89}$$

$$i_{cC}(t) = I_L \cos(\omega t + 120° - \theta) \tag{90}$$

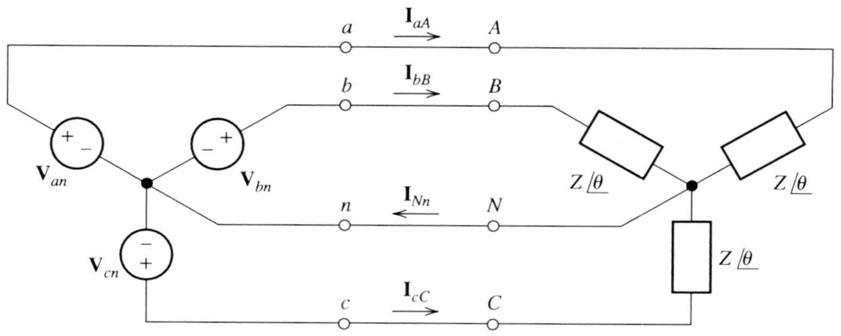

Figure 38 A three-phase wye–wye connection with neutral.

The neutral current in Figure 38 is given by

$$i_{Nn}(t) = i_{aA}(t) + i_{bB}(t) + i_{cC}(t)$$

In terms of phasors, this is

$$\mathbf{I}_{Nn} = \mathbf{I}_{aA} + \mathbf{I}_{bB} + \mathbf{I}_{cC}$$

$$= I_L \underline{/-\theta} + I_L \underline{/-120° - \theta} + I_L \underline{/120° - \theta}$$

$$= I_L \underline{/-\theta} \times (1 + 1 \underline{/-120°} + 1 \underline{/120°})$$

$$= I_L \underline{/-\theta} \times (1 - 0.5 - j0.866 - 0.5 + j0.866)$$

$$= 0$$

Thus, the sum of three phasors with equal magnitudes and 120° apart in phase is zero. (We make use of this fact again later in this section.)

We have shown that the neutral current is zero in a balanced three-phase system. Consequently, the neutral wire can be eliminated without changing any of the voltages or currents. Then, the three source voltages are delivered to the three load impedances with three wires.

An important advantage of three-phase systems compared with single phase is that the wiring for connecting the sources to the loads is less expensive. As shown in Figure 39, it would take six wires to connect three single-phase sources to three loads separately, whereas only three wires (four if the neutral wire is used) are needed for the three-phase connection to achieve the same power transfer.

> The sum of three equal magnitude phasors 120° apart in phase is zero.

> The neutral current is zero in a balanced wye–wye system. Thus in theory, the neutral wire can be inserted or removed without affecting load currents or voltages. This is *not* true if the load is unbalanced, which is often the case in real power distribution systems.

Power

Another advantage of balanced three-phase systems, compared with single-phase systems, is that the total power is constant (as a function of time) rather than pulsating. (Refer to Figure 2 to see that power pulsates in the single-phase case.) To show that the power is constant for the balanced wye–wye connection shown in Figure 38, we write an expression for the total power. The power delivered to phase A of the load is $v_{an}(t)i_{aA}(t)$. Similarly, the power for each of the other phases of the load is the product of the voltage and the current. Thus, the total power is

$$p(t) = v_{an}(t)i_{aA}(t) + v_{bn}(t)i_{bB}(t) + v_{cn}(t)i_{cC}(t) \tag{91}$$

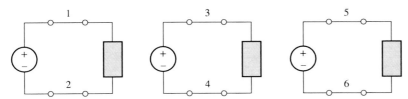

Figure 39 Six wires are needed to connect three single-phase sources to three loads. In a three-phase system, the same power transfer can be accomplished with three wires.

Using Equations 82, 83, and 84 to substitute for the voltages and Equations 88, 89, and 90 to substitute for the currents, we obtain

$$
\begin{aligned}
p(t) = V_Y \cos(\omega t) I_L \cos(\omega t - \theta) \\
+ V_Y \cos(\omega t - 120°) I_L \cos(\omega t - \theta - 120°) \\
+ V_Y \cos(\omega t + 120°) I_L \cos(\omega t - \theta + 120°)
\end{aligned}
\tag{92}
$$

Using the trigonometric identity

$$
\cos(x)\cos(y) = \frac{1}{2}\cos(x-y) + \frac{1}{2}\cos(x+y)
$$

we find that Equation 92 can be written as

$$
\begin{aligned}
p(t) = 3\frac{V_Y I_L}{2}\cos(\theta) + \frac{V_Y I_L}{2}[\cos(2\omega t - \theta) \\
+ \cos(2\omega t - \theta - 240°) + \cos(2\omega t - \theta + 480°)]
\end{aligned}
\tag{93}
$$

However, the term in brackets is

$$
\begin{aligned}
\cos(2\omega t - \theta) + \cos(2\omega t - \theta - 240°) + \cos(2\omega t - \theta + 480°) \\
= \cos(2\omega t - \theta) + \cos(2\omega t - \theta + 120°) + \cos(2\omega t - \theta - 120°) \\
= 0
\end{aligned}
$$

(Here, we have used the fact, established earlier, that the sum is zero for three sine waves of equal amplitude and 120° apart in phase.) Thus, the expression for power becomes

$$
p(t) = 3\frac{V_Y I_L}{2}\cos(\theta)
\tag{94}
$$

Notice that the total power is constant with respect to time. A consequence of this fact is that the torque required to drive a three-phase generator connected to a balanced load is constant, and vibration is lessened. Similarly, the torque produced by a three-phase motor is constant rather than pulsating as it is for a single-phase motor.

The rms voltage from each line to neutral is

$$
V_{Y\text{rms}} = \frac{V_Y}{\sqrt{2}}
\tag{95}
$$

Similarly, the rms value of the line current is

$$
I_{L\text{rms}} = \frac{I_L}{\sqrt{2}}
\tag{96}
$$

Using Equations 95 and 96 to substitute into Equation 94, we find that

$$
P_{\text{avg}} = p(t) = 3 V_{Y\text{rms}} I_{L\text{rms}} \cos(\theta)
\tag{97}
$$

Reactive Power

As in single-phase circuits, power flows back and forth between the sources and energy-storage elements contained in a three-phase load. This power is called *reactive power*. The higher currents that result because of the presence of reactive power require wiring and other power-distribution components having higher ratings. The reactive power delivered to a balanced three-phase load is given by

$$Q = 3\frac{V_Y I_L}{2}\sin(\theta) = 3V_{Y\text{rms}}I_{L\text{rms}}\sin(\theta) \qquad (98)$$

Line-to-Line Voltages

As we have mentioned earlier, the voltages between terminals a, b, or c and the neutral point n are called **line-to-neutral voltages**. On the other hand, voltages between a and b, b and c, or a and c are called **line-to-line voltages** or, more simply, **line voltages**. Thus $\mathbf{V}_{an}$, $\mathbf{V}_{bn}$, and $\mathbf{V}_{cn}$ are line-to-neutral voltages, whereas $\mathbf{V}_{ab}$, $\mathbf{V}_{bc}$, and $\mathbf{V}_{ca}$ are line-to-line voltages. (For consistency, we choose the subscripts cyclically in the order $abcabc$.) Let us consider the relationships between line-to-line voltages and line-to-neutral voltages.

We can obtain the following relationship by applying KVL to Figure 38:

$$\mathbf{V}_{ab} = \mathbf{V}_{an} - \mathbf{V}_{bn}$$

Using Equations 85 and 86 to substitute for $\mathbf{V}_{an}$ and $\mathbf{V}_{bn}$, we obtain

$$\mathbf{V}_{ab} = V_Y\ \angle 0° - V_Y\ \angle{-120°} \qquad (99)$$

which is equivalent to

$$\mathbf{V}_{ab} = V_Y\ \angle 0° + V_Y\ \angle 60° \qquad (100)$$

This relationship is illustrated in Figure 40. It can be shown that Equation 100 reduces to

$$\mathbf{V}_{ab} = \sqrt{3}V_Y\ \angle 30° \qquad (101)$$

We denote the magnitude of the line-to-line voltage as V_L. The magnitude of the line-to-line voltage is $\sqrt{3}$ times the magnitude of the line-to-neutral voltage:

$$V_L = \sqrt{3}V_Y \qquad (102)$$

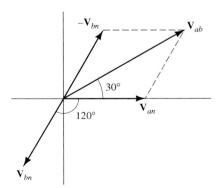

Figure 40 Phasor diagram showing the relationship between the line-to-line voltage $\mathbf{V}_{ab}$ and the line-to-neutral voltages $\mathbf{V}_{an}$ and $\mathbf{V}_{bn}$.

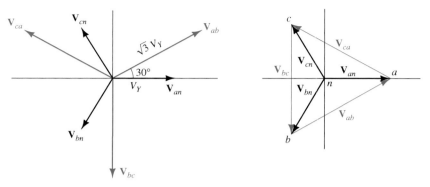

Figure 41(b) provides a convenient way to remember the phase relationships between line-to-line and line-to-neutral voltages.

(a) All phasors starting from the origin

(b) A more intuitive way to draw the phasor diagram

Figure 41 Phasor diagram showing line-to-line voltages and line-to-neutral voltages.

Thus, the relationship between the line-to-line voltage $\mathbf{V}_{ab}$ and the line-to-neutral voltage $\mathbf{V}_{an}$ is

$$\mathbf{V}_{ab} = \mathbf{V}_{an} \times \sqrt{3} \ \underline{/30°} \tag{103}$$

Similarly, it can be shown that

$$\mathbf{V}_{bc} = \mathbf{V}_{bn} \times \sqrt{3} \ \underline{/30°} \tag{104}$$

and

$$\mathbf{V}_{ca} = \mathbf{V}_{cn} \times \sqrt{3} \ \underline{/30°} \tag{105}$$

These voltages are shown in Figure 41.

Example 12   Analysis of a Wye–Wye System

A balanced positive-sequence wye-connected 60-Hz three-phase source has line-to-neutral voltages of $V_Y = 1000$ V. This source is connected to a balanced wye-connected load. Each phase of the load consists of a 0.1-H inductance in series with a 50-Ω resistance. Find the line currents, the line-to-line voltages, the power, and the reactive power delivered to the load. Draw a phasor diagram showing the line-to-neutral voltages, the line-to-line voltages, and the line currents. Assume that the phase angle of $\mathbf{V}_{an}$ is zero.

Solution   First, by computing the complex impedance of each phase of the load, we find that

$$Z = R + j\omega L = 50 + j2\pi(60)(0.1) = 50 + j37.70$$
$$= 62.62 \ \underline{/37.02°}$$

Next, we draw the circuit as shown in Figure 42(a). In balanced wye–wye calculations, we can assume that n and N are connected. (The currents and voltages are the same whether or not the neutral connection actually exists.) Thus, $\mathbf{V}_{an}$ appears across phase A of the load, and we can write

$$\mathbf{I}_{aA} = \frac{\mathbf{V}_{an}}{Z} = \frac{1000 \ \underline{/0°}}{62.62 \ \underline{/37.02°}} = 15.97 \ \underline{/-37.02°}$$

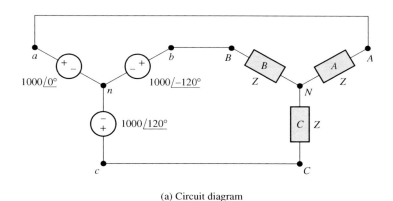

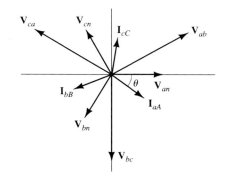

(a) Circuit diagram   (b) Phasor diagram

Figure 42 Circuit and phasor diagram for Example 12.

Similarly,

$$\mathbf{I}_{bB} = \frac{\mathbf{V}_{bn}}{Z} = \frac{1000\ \angle{-120°}}{62.62\ \angle{37.02°}} = 15.97\ \angle{-157.02°}$$

$$\mathbf{I}_{cC} = \frac{\mathbf{V}_{cn}}{Z} = \frac{1000\ \angle{120°}}{62.62\ \angle{37.02°}} = 15.97\ \angle{82.98°}$$

We use Equations 103, 104, and 105 to find the line-to-line phasors:

$$\mathbf{V}_{ab} = \mathbf{V}_{an} \times \sqrt{3}\ \angle{30°} = 1732\ \angle{30°}$$

$$\mathbf{V}_{bc} = \mathbf{V}_{bn} \times \sqrt{3}\ \angle{30°} = 1732\ \angle{-90°}$$

$$\mathbf{V}_{ca} = \mathbf{V}_{cn} \times \sqrt{3}\ \angle{30°} = 1732\ \angle{150°}$$

The power delivered to the load is given by Equation 94:

$$P = 3\frac{V_Y I_L}{2}\cos(\theta) = 3\left(\frac{1000 \times 15.97}{2}\right)\cos(37.02°) = 19.13\ \text{kW}$$

The reactive power is given by Equation 98:

$$Q = 3\frac{V_Y I_L}{2}\sin(\theta) = 3\left(\frac{1000 \times 15.97}{2}\right)\sin(37.02°) = 14.42\ \text{kVAR}$$

The phasor diagram is shown in Figure 42(b). As usual, we have chosen a different scale for the currents than for the voltages. ∎

Exercise 16 A balanced positive-sequence wye-connected 60-Hz three-phase source has line-to-line voltages of $V_L = 1000$ V. This source is connected to a balanced wye-connected load. Each phase of the load consists of a 0.2-H inductance in series with a 100-Ω resistance. Find the line-to-neutral voltages, the line currents, the power, and the reactive power delivered to the load. Assume that the phase of $\mathbf{V}_{an}$ is zero.

Answer $\mathbf{V}_{an} = 577.4 \; \underline{/0°}, \mathbf{V}_{bn} = 577.4 \; \underline{/-120°}, \mathbf{V}_{cn} = 577.4 \; \underline{/120°};$
$\mathbf{I}_{aA} = 4.61 \; \underline{/-37°}, \mathbf{I}_{bB} = 4.61 \; \underline{/-157°}, \mathbf{I}_{cC} = 4.61 \; \underline{/83°}; P = 3.19 \, \text{kW};$
$Q = 2.40 \, \text{kVAR}.$ □

Delta-Connected Sources

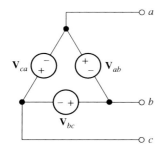

Figure 43
Delta-connected
three-phase source.

A set of balanced three-phase voltage sources can be connected in the form of a delta, as shown in Figure 43. Ordinarily, we avoid connecting voltage sources in closed loops. However, in this case, it turns out that the sum of the voltages is zero:

$$\mathbf{V}_{ab} + \mathbf{V}_{bc} + \mathbf{V}_{ca} = 0$$

Thus, the current circulating in the delta is zero. (Actually, this is a first approximation. There are many subtleties of power distribution systems that are beyond the scope of our discussion. For example, the voltages in actual power distribution systems are not exactly sinusoidal; instead, they are the sum of several harmonic components. The behavior of harmonic components is an important factor in making a choice between wye- and delta-connected sources or loads.)

For a given delta-connected source, we can find an equivalent wye-connected source (or vice versa) by using Equations 103 through 105. Clearly, a delta-connected source has no neutral point, so a four-wire connection is possible for only a wye-connected source.

Wye- and Delta-Connected Loads

Load impedances can be either wye connected or delta connected, as shown in Figure 44. It can be shown that the two loads are equivalent if

$$Z_\Delta = 3Z_Y \tag{106}$$

Thus, we can convert a delta-connected load to an equivalent wye-connected load, or vice versa.

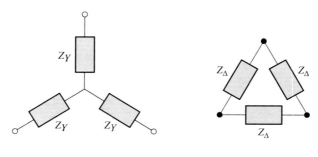

(a) Wye-connected load   (b) Delta-connected load

Figure 44 Loads can be either wye connected or delta connected.

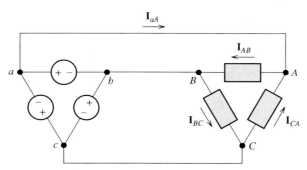

Figure 45 A delta-connected source delivering power to a delta-connected load.

Delta–Delta Connection

Figure 45 shows a delta-connected source delivering power to a delta-connected load. We assume that the source voltages are given by

$$\mathbf{V}_{ab} = V_L \ \angle 30° \tag{107}$$

$$\mathbf{V}_{bc} = V_L \ \angle{-90°} \tag{108}$$

$$\mathbf{V}_{ca} = V_L \ \angle 150° \tag{109}$$

These phasors are shown in Figure 41. (We have chosen the phase angles of the delta-connected source to be consistent with our earlier discussion.)

If the impedances of the connecting wires are zero, the line-to-line voltages at the load are equal to those at the source. Thus $\mathbf{V}_{AB} = \mathbf{V}_{ab}$, $\mathbf{V}_{BC} = \mathbf{V}_{bc}$, and $\mathbf{V}_{CA} = \mathbf{V}_{ca}$.

We assume that the impedance of each phase of the load is $Z_\Delta \ \angle\theta$. Then, the load current for phase AB is

$$\mathbf{I}_{AB} = \frac{\mathbf{V}_{AB}}{Z_\Delta \ \angle\theta} = \frac{\mathbf{V}_{ab}}{Z_\Delta \ \angle\theta} = \frac{V_L \ \angle 30°}{Z_\Delta \ \angle\theta} = \frac{V_L}{Z_\Delta} \ \angle 30° - \theta$$

We define the magnitude of the current as

$$I_\Delta = \frac{V_L}{Z_\Delta} \tag{110}$$

Hence,

$$\mathbf{I}_{AB} = I_\Delta \ \angle 30° - \theta \tag{111}$$

Similarly,

$$\mathbf{I}_{BC} = I_\Delta \ \angle{-90°} - \theta \tag{112}$$

$$\mathbf{I}_{CA} = I_\Delta \ \angle 150° - \theta \tag{113}$$

The current in line a–A is

$$\mathbf{I}_{aA} = \mathbf{I}_{AB} - \mathbf{I}_{CA}$$
$$= I_\Delta \ \angle 30° - \theta \ - I_\Delta \ \angle 150° - \theta$$
$$= (I_\Delta \ \angle 30° - \theta \ ) \times (1 - 1 \ \angle 120° \ )$$

$$= (I_\Delta \ \underline{/30° - \theta}) \times (1.5 - j0.8660)$$

$$= (I_\Delta \ \underline{/30° - \theta}) \times (\sqrt{3} \ \underline{/-30°})$$

$$= \mathbf{I}_{AB} \times \sqrt{3} \ \underline{/-30°}$$

The magnitude of the line current is

For a balanced delta-connected load, the line-current magnitude is equal to the square root of three times the current magnitude in any arm of the delta.

$$I_L = \sqrt{3}I_\Delta \qquad (114)$$

Analysis of a Balanced Delta–Delta System

Consider the circuit shown in Figure 46(a). A delta-connected source supplies power to a delta-connected load through wires having impedances of $Z_{\text{line}} = 0.3 + j0.4 \ \Omega$. The load impedances are $Z_\Delta = 30 + j6$. The source voltages are

$$\mathbf{V}_{ab} = 1000 \ \underline{/30°}$$

$$\mathbf{V}_{bc} = 1000 \ \underline{/-90°}$$

$$\mathbf{V}_{ca} = 1000 \ \underline{/150°}$$

Find the line current, the line-to-line voltage at the load, the current in each phase of the load, the power delivered to the load, and the power dissipated in the line.

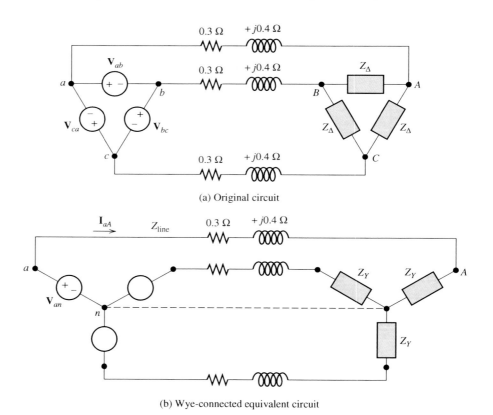

(a) Original circuit

(b) Wye-connected equivalent circuit

Figure 46 Circuit of Example 13.

Solution First, we find the wye-connected equivalents for the source and the load. (Actually, we only need to work with one third of the circuit because the other two thirds are the same except for phase angles.) We choose to work with the A phase of the wye-equivalent circuit. Solving Equation 103 for $\mathbf{V}_{an}$, we find that

Often, it is convenient to start an analysis by finding the wye–wye equivalent of a system.

$$\mathbf{V}_{an} = \frac{\mathbf{V}_{ab}}{\sqrt{3} \ \angle 30°} = \frac{1000 \ \angle 30°}{\sqrt{3} \ \angle 30°} = 577.4 \ \angle 0°$$

Using Equation 106, we have

$$Z_Y = \frac{Z_\Delta}{3} = \frac{30 + j6}{3} = 10 + j2$$

Now, we can draw the wye-equivalent circuit, which is shown in Figure 46(b).

In a balanced wye–wye system, we can consider the neutral points to be connected together as shown by the dashed line in Figure 46(b). This reduces the three-phase circuit to three single-phase circuits. For phase A of Figure 46(b), we can write

$$\mathbf{V}_{an} = (Z_{\text{line}} + Z_Y)\mathbf{I}_{aA}$$

Therefore,

$$\begin{aligned} \mathbf{I}_{aA} &= \frac{\mathbf{V}_{an}}{Z_{\text{line}} + Z_Y} = \frac{577.4 \ \angle 0°}{0.3 + j0.4 + 10 + j2} \\ &= \frac{577.4 \ \angle 0°}{10.3 + j2.4} = \frac{577.4 \ \angle 0°}{10.58 \ \angle 13.12°} \\ &= 54.60 \ \angle -13.12° \end{aligned}$$

To find the line-to-neutral voltage at the load, we write

$$\begin{aligned} \mathbf{V}_{An} &= \mathbf{I}_{Aa}Z_Y = 54.60 \ \angle -13.12° \times (10 + j2) \\ &= 54.60 \ \angle -13.12° \times 10.20 \ \angle 11.31° \\ &= 556.9 \ \angle -1.81° \end{aligned}$$

Now, we compute the line-to-line voltage at the load:

$$\begin{aligned} \mathbf{V}_{AB} &= \mathbf{V}_{An} \times \sqrt{3} \ \angle 30° = 556.9 \ \angle -1.81° \times \sqrt{3} \ \angle 30° \\ &= 964.6 \ \angle 28.19° \end{aligned}$$

The current through phase AB of the load is

$$\mathbf{I}_{AB} = \frac{\mathbf{V}_{AB}}{Z_\Delta} = \frac{964.6 \ \angle 28.19°}{30 + j6} = \frac{964.6 \ \angle 28.19°}{30.59 \ \angle 11.31°}$$
$$= 31.53 \ \angle 16.88°$$

The power delivered to phase AB of the load is the rms current squared times the resistance:

$$P_{AB} = I_{AB\text{rms}}^2 R = \left(\frac{31.53}{\sqrt{2}}\right)^2 (30) = 14.91 \text{ kW}$$

The powers delivered to the other two phases of the load are the same, so the total power is

$$P = 3P_{AB} = 44.73 \text{ kW}$$

The power lost in line A is

$$P_{\text{line}A} = I^2_{aA\text{rms}}R_{\text{line}} = \left(\frac{54.60}{\sqrt{2}}\right)^2 (0.3) = 0.447 \text{ kW}$$

The power lost in the other two lines is the same, so the total line loss is

$$P_{\text{line}} = 3 \times P_{\text{line}A} = 1.341 \text{ kW}$$ ∎

Exercise 17 A delta-connected source has voltages given by

$$\mathbf{V}_{ab} = 1000 \ \angle 30°$$

$$\mathbf{V}_{bc} = 1000 \ \angle{-90°}$$

$$\mathbf{V}_{ca} = 1000 \ \angle 150°$$

This source is connected to a delta-connected load consisting of 50-Ω resistances. Find the line currents and the power delivered to the load.

Answer $\mathbf{I}_{aA} = 34.6 \ \angle 0°$, $\mathbf{I}_{bB} = 34.6 \ \angle{-120°}$, $\mathbf{I}_{cC} = 34.6 \ \angle 120°$; $P = 30$ kW. ☐

8 AC ANALYSIS USING MATLAB

In this section, we will illustrate how MATLAB can greatly facilitate the analysis of complicated ac circuits. In fact, a practicing engineer working at a computer might have little use for a calculator, as it is easy to keep a MATLAB window open for all sorts of engineering calculations. Of course, you will probably need to use calculators for course exams and when you take the Professional Engineer (PE) exams. The PE exams allow only fairly simple scientific calculators, and you should practice with one of those allowed before attempting the exams.

Complex Data in MATLAB

By default, MATLAB assumes that $i = j = \sqrt{-1}$. However, I have encountered at least one bug in the software attributable to using j instead of i, and therefore I recommend using i in MATLAB and the Symbolic Toolbox. We need to be careful to avoid using i for other purposes when using MATLAB to analyze ac circuits. For example, if we were to use i as the name of a current or other variable, we would later experience errors if we also used i for the imaginary unit without reassigning its value.

Complex numbers are represented in rectangular form (such as 3 + 4i or alternatively 3 + i*4) in MATLAB.

We can use the fact that $M \ \angle \theta = M \exp(j\theta)$ to enter polar data. In MATLAB, angles are assumed to be in radians, so we need to multiply angles that are expressed in degrees by $\pi/180$ to convert to radians before entering them. For example, we use the following command to enter the voltage $V_s = 5\sqrt{2} \ \angle 45°$:

```
>> Vs = 5*sqrt(2)*exp(i*45*pi/180)
Vs =
   5.0000 + 5.0000i
```

We can readily verify that MATLAB has correctly computed the rectangular form of $5\sqrt{2}\ \angle 45°$.

Alternatively, we could use Euler's formula

$$M\ \angle \theta = M\exp(j\theta) = M\cos(\theta) + jM\sin(\theta)$$

to enter polar data, again with angles in radians. For example, $V_s = 5\sqrt{2}\ \angle 45°$ can be entered as:

```
>> Vs = 5*sqrt(2)*cos(45*pi/180) + i*5*sqrt(2)*sin(45*pi/180)
Vs =
   5.0000 + 5.0000i
```

Values that are already in rectangular form can be entered directly. For example, to enter $Z = 3 + j4$, we use the command:

```
>> Z = 3 + i*4
Z =
   3.0000 + 4.0000i
```

Then, if we enter

```
>> Ix = Vs/Z
Ix =
   1.4000 - 0.2000i
```

MATLAB performs the complex arithmetic and gives the answer in rectangular form.

Finding the Polar Form of MATLAB Results

Frequently, we need the polar form of a complex value calculated by MATLAB. We can find the magnitude using the abs command and the angle in radians using the angle command. To obtain the angle in degrees, we must convert the angle from radians by multiplying by $180/\pi$. Thus, to obtain the magnitude and angle in degrees for Vs, we would enter the following commands:

```
>> abs(Vs) % Find the magnitude of Vs.
ans =
    7.0711
>> (180/pi)*angle(Vs) % Find the angle of Vs in degrees.
ans =
    45.0000
```

Adding New Functions to MATLAB

Because we often want to enter values or see results in polar form with the angles in degrees, it is convenient to add two new functions to MATLAB. Thus, we write an m-file, named pin.m, containing the commands to convert from polar to rectangular form, and store it in our working MATLAB folder. The commands in the m-file are:

```
function z = pin(magnitude, angleindegrees)
z = magnitude*exp(i*angleindegrees*pi/180)
```

275

Then, we can enter $Vs = 5\sqrt{2}\ \angle 45°$ simply by typing the command:

```
>> Vs = pin(5*sqrt(2),45)
Vs =
   5.0000 + 5.0000i
```

We have chosen pin as the name of this new function to suggest "polar input." This file is included in the MATLAB folder.

Similarly, to obtain the polar form of an answer, we create a new function, named pout (to suggest "polar out"), with the commands:

```
function [y] = pout(x);
magnitude = abs(x);
angleindegrees = (180/pi)*angle(x);
y = [magnitude angleindegrees];
```

which are stored in the m-file named pout.m. Then, to find the polar form of a result, we can use the new function. For example,

```
>> pout(Vs)
ans =
    7.0711   45.0000
```

Here is another simple example:

```
>> pout(i*200)
ans =
   200   90
```

Solving Network Equations with MATLAB

We can readily solve node voltage or mesh equations and perform other calculations for ac circuits in MATLAB. The steps are:

1. Write the mesh current or node voltage equations.
2. Put the equations into matrix form, which is $\mathbf{ZI} = \mathbf{V}$ for mesh currents, in which $\mathbf{Z}$ is the coefficient matrix, $\mathbf{I}$ is the column vector of mesh current variables to be found, and $\mathbf{V}$ is the column vector of constant terms. For node voltages, the matrix equations take the form $\mathbf{YV} = \mathbf{I}$ in which $\mathbf{Y}$ is the coefficient matrix, $\mathbf{V}$ is the column vector of node voltage variables to be determined, and $\mathbf{I}$ is the column vector of constants.
3. Enter the matrices into MATLAB and compute the mesh currents or node voltages using the inverse matrix approach. $\mathbf{I} = \text{inv}(\mathbf{Z}) \times \mathbf{V}$ for mesh currents or $\mathbf{V} = \text{inv}(\mathbf{Y}) \times \mathbf{I}$ for node voltages, where inv denotes the matrix inverse.
4. Use the results to compute any other quantities of interest.

Example 14   Phasor Mesh-Current Analysis with MATLAB

Determine the values for the mesh currents, the real power supplied by $\mathbf{V}_1$, and the reactive power supplied by $\mathbf{V}_1$ in the circuit of Figure 47.

Solution   First, we apply KVL to each loop obtaining the mesh-current equations:

$$(5 + j3)\mathbf{I}_1 + (50\ \angle{-10°})(\mathbf{I}_1 - \mathbf{I}_2) = 2200\sqrt{2}$$

$$(50\ \angle{-10°})(\mathbf{I}_2 - \mathbf{I}_1) + (4 + j)\mathbf{I}_2 + 2000\sqrt{2}\ \angle{30} = 0$$

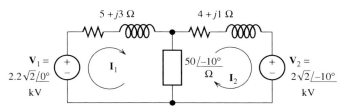

Figure 47 Cirucit for Example 14.

In matrix form, these equations become

$$
\begin{bmatrix} (5 + j3 + 50\ \angle{-10°}) & -50\ \angle{-10°} \\ -50\ \angle{-10°} & (4 + j + 50\ \angle{-10°}) \end{bmatrix} \begin{bmatrix} \mathbf{I}_1 \\ \mathbf{I}_2 \end{bmatrix} = \begin{bmatrix} 2200\sqrt{2} \\ -2000\sqrt{2}\ \angle{-10°} \end{bmatrix}
$$

We will solve these equations for $\mathbf{I}_1$ and $\mathbf{I}_2$. Then, we will compute the complex power delivered by $\mathbf{V}_1$

$$
\mathbf{S}_1 = \frac{1}{2}\mathbf{V}_1\mathbf{I}_1^*
$$

Finally, the power is the real part of $\mathbf{S}_1$ and the reactive power is the imaginary part.

We enter the coefficient matrix $\mathbf{Z}$ and the voltage matrix $\mathbf{V}$ into MATLAB, making use of our new pin function to enter polar values. Then, we calculate the current matrix.

```
>> Z = [(5 + i*3 + pin(50,-10)) (-pin(50,-10));...
    (-pin(50,-10)) (4 + i + pin(50,-10))];
>> V = [2200*sqrt(2); -pin(2000*sqrt(2),-10)];
>> I = inv(Z)*V
I =
  74.1634 + 29.0852i
  17.1906 + 26.5112i
```

This has given us the values of the mesh currents in rectangular form. Next, we obtain the polar form for the mesh currents, making use of our new pout function:

```
>> pout(I(1))
ans =
  79.6628  21.4140
>> pout(I(2))
ans =
  31.5968  57.0394
```

Thus, the currents are $\mathbf{I}_1 = 79.66\ \angle{21.41°}$ A and $\mathbf{I}_2 = 31.60\ \angle{57.04°}$ A, rounded to two decimal places. Next, we compute the complex power, real power, and reactive power for the first source.

$$
\mathbf{S}_1 = \frac{1}{2}\mathbf{V}_1\mathbf{I}_1^*
$$

```
>> S1 = (1/2)*(2200*sqrt(2))*conj(I(1));
>> P1 = real(S1)
P1 =
  1.1537e + 005
>> Q1 = imag(S1)
Q1 =
 -4.5246e + 004
```

Thus, the power supplied by $\mathbf{V}_1$ is 115.37 kW and the reactive power is -45.25 kVAR. The commands for this example appear in the m-file named Example_5_14. ∎

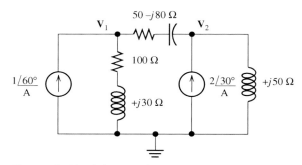

Figure 48 Circuit for Exercise 18.

Exercise 18 Use MATLAB to solve for the phasor node voltages in polar form for the circuit of Figure 48.

Answer The MATLAB commands are:

```
clear
Y = [(1/(100+i*30)+1/(50-i*80)) (-1/(50-i*80));...
     (-1/(50-i*80)) (1/(i*50)+1/(50-i*80))];
I = [pin(1,60); pin(2,30)];
V = inv(Y)*I;
pout(V(1))
pout(V(2))
```

and the results are $\mathbf{V}_1 = 79.98\;\underline{/106.21°}$ and $\mathbf{V}_2 = 124.13\;\underline{/116.30°}$. ☐

Summary

1. A sinusoidal voltage is given by $v(t) = V_m \cos(\omega t + \theta)$, where V_m is the peak value of the voltage, ω is the angular frequency in radians per second, and θ is the phase angle. The frequency in hertz is $f = 1/T$, where T is the period. Furthermore, $\omega = 2\pi f$.

2. For uniformity, we express sinusoidal voltages in terms of the cosine function. A sine function can be converted to a cosine function by use of the identity $\sin(z) = \cos(z - 90°)$.

3. The root-mean-square (rms) value (or effective value) of a periodic voltage $v(t)$ is

$$V_{\mathrm{rms}} = \sqrt{\frac{1}{T} \int_0^T v^2(t)\, dt}$$

The average power delivered to a resistance by $v(t)$ is

$$P_{\mathrm{avg}} = \frac{V_{\mathrm{rms}}^2}{R}$$

Similarly, for a current $i(t)$, we have

$$I_{\mathrm{rms}} = \sqrt{\frac{1}{T} \int_0^T i^2(t)\, dt}$$

and the average power delivered if $i(t)$ flows through a resistance is

$$P_{\mathrm{avg}} = I_{\mathrm{rms}}^2 R$$

For a sinusoid, the rms value is the peak value divided by $\sqrt{2}$.

4. We can represent sinusoids with phasors. The magnitude of the phasor is the peak value of the sinusoid. The phase angle of the phasor is the phase angle of the sinusoid (assuming that we have written the sinusoid in terms of a cosine function).

5. We can add (or subtract) sinusoids by adding (or subtracting) their phasors.

6. The phasor voltage for a passive circuit is the phasor current times the complex impedance of the circuit. For a resistance, $\mathbf{V}_R = R\mathbf{I}_R$, and the voltage is in phase with the current. For an

inductance, $\mathbf{V}_L = j\omega L \mathbf{I}_L$, and the voltage leads the current by 90°. For a capacitance, $\mathbf{V}_C = -j(1/\omega C)\mathbf{I}_C$, and the voltage lags the current by 90°.

7. Many techniques for resistive circuits can be applied directly to sinusoidal circuits if the currents and voltages are replaced by phasors and the passive circuit elements are replaced by their complex impedances. For example, complex impedances can be combined in series or parallel in the same way as resistances (except that complex arithmetic must be used). Node voltages, the current-division principle, and the voltage-division principle also apply to ac circuits.

8. When a sinusoidal current flows through a sinusoidal voltage, the average power delivered is $P = V_{rms}I_{rms}\cos(\theta)$, where θ is the power angle, which is found by subtracting the phase angle of the current from the phase angle of the voltage (i.e., $\theta = \theta_v - \theta_i$). The power factor is $\cos(\theta)$.

9. Reactive power is the flow of energy back and forth between the source and energy-storage elements (L and C). We define reactive power to be positive for an inductance and negative for a capacitance. The net energy transferred per cycle by reactive power flow is zero. Reactive power is important because a power distribution system must have higher current ratings if

reactive power flows than would be required for zero reactive power.

10. Apparent power is the product of rms voltage and rms current. Many useful relationships between power, reactive power, apparent power, and the power angle can be obtained from the power triangle shown in Figure 23.

11. In steady state, a network composed of resistances, inductances, capacitances, and sinusoidal sources (all of the same frequency) has a Thévenin equivalent consisting of a phasor voltage source in series with a complex impedance. The Norton equivalent consists of a phasor current source in parallel with the Thévenin impedance.

12. For maximum-power transfer from a two-terminal ac circuit to a load, the load impedance is selected to be the complex conjugate of the Thévenin impedance. If the load is constrained to be a pure resistance, the value for maximum power transfer is equal to the magnitude of the Thévenin impedance.

13. Because of savings in wiring, three-phase power distribution is more economical than single phase. The power flow in balanced three-phase systems is smooth, whereas power pulsates in single-phase systems. Thus, three-phase motors generally have the advantage of producing less vibration than single-phase motors.

Problems

Section 1: Sinusoidal Currents and Voltages

P1. What are the units for angular frequency ω? For frequency f? What is the relationship between them?

P2. Consider the plot of the sinusoidal voltage $v(t) = V_m\cos(\omega t + \theta)$ shown in Figure 1 on page 216. Which of the numbered statements below best describes: **a.** decreasing the peak amplitude V_m? **b.** increasing the frequency f? **c.** increasing θ? **d.** decreasing the angular frequency ω? **e.** increasing the period?

1. Stretches the sinusoidal curve vertically.
2. Compresses the sinusoidal curve vertically.
3. Stretches the sinusoidal curve horizontally.
4. Compresses the sinusoidal curve horizontally.
5. Translates the sinusoidal curve to the right.
6. Translates the sinusoidal curve to the left.

---

* Denotes that answers are contained in the Student Solutions files.

P3. In terms of physical units, such as m, kg, C and s, what are the units of radians? What are the *physical* units for angular frequency?

*P4. A voltage is given by $v(t) = 10\sin(1000\pi t + 30°)$. First, use a cosine function to express $v(t)$. Then, find the angular frequency, the frequency in hertz, the phase angle, the period, and the rms value. Find the power that this voltage delivers to a 50-Ω resistance. Find the first value of time after $t = 0$ that $v(t)$ reaches its peak value. Sketch $v(t)$ to scale versus time.

P5. Repeat Problem P4 for $v(t) = 12\sin(400\pi t - 120°)$.

*P6. A sinusoidal voltage $v(t)$ has an rms value of 20 V, a period of 100 μs, and reaches a positive peak at $t = 20\,\mu$s. Write an expression for $v(t)$.

P7. Given a sinusoidal current $i(t)$ that has an rms value of 10 A, a period of 5 ms, and reaches a positive peak at $t = 1$ ms. Write an expression for $i(t)$.

P8. A sinusoidal voltage has a peak value of 50 V, a frequency of 1000 Hz, and crosses zero with positive slope at $t = 0.1$ ms. Write an expression for the voltage.

P9. A current $i(t) = 10\cos(2000\pi t)$ flows through a 100-Ω resistance. Sketch $i(t)$ and $p(t)$ to scale versus time. Find the average power delivered to the resistance.

P10. We have a voltage $v(t) = 1000\sin(500\pi t)$ across a 500-Ω resistance. Sketch $v(t)$ and $p(t)$ to scale versus time. Find the average power delivered to the resistance.

P11. A **Lissajous figure** results if one sinusoid is plotted versus another. Consider $x(t) = \cos(\omega_x t)$ and $y(t) = \cos(\omega_y t + \theta)$. Use MATLAB to generate values of x and y for 20 seconds at 100 points per second and obtain a plot of y versus x for: **a.** $\omega_x = \omega_y = 2\pi$ and $\theta = 90°$; **b.** $\omega_x = \omega_y = 2\pi$ and $\theta = 45°$; **c.** $\omega_x = \omega_y = 2\pi$ and $\theta = 0°$; **d.** $\omega_x = 2\pi$, $\omega_y = 4\pi$, and $\theta = 0°$.

*P12. Find the rms value of the voltage waveform shown in Figure P12.

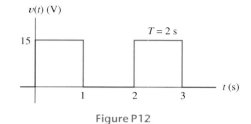

Figure P12

*P13. Find the rms value of the current waveform shown in Figure P13.

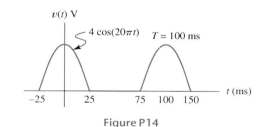

Figure P13

P14. Calculate the rms value of the half-wave rectified sinusoidal wave shown in Figure P14.

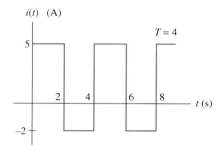

Figure P14

P15. Use MATLAB to determine the rms value of $v(t) = A\cos(2\pi t) + B\sin(2\pi t)$.

P16. Find the rms value of the voltage waveform shown in Figure P16.

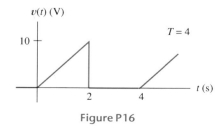

Figure P16

P17. Determine the rms value of $v(t) = 15 + 10\cos(20\pi t)$.

P18. Compute the rms value of the periodic waveform shown in Figure P18.

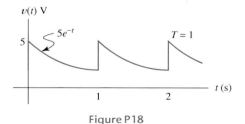

Figure P18

P19. Is the rms value of a periodic waveform always equal to the peak value divided by the square root of two? When is it?

P20. Use MATLAB to determine the rms value of $v(t)$ which has a period of 1 s and is given by $v(t) = 10\exp(-5t)\sin(20\pi t)$ V for $0 \le t \le 1$ s.

Section 2: Phasors

P21. Explain two methods to determine the phase relationship between two sinusoids of the same frequency.

P22. List the steps we follow in adding sinusoidal currents or voltages. What must be true of the sinusoids?

*P23. Reduce $5\cos(\omega t + 75°) - 3\cos(\omega t - 75°) + 4\sin(\omega t)$ to the form $V_m\cos(\omega t + \theta)$.

*P24. Suppose that $v_1(t) = 100\cos(\omega t)$ and $v_2(t) = 100\sin(\omega t)$. Use phasors to reduce the sum $v_s(t) = v_1(t) + v_2(t)$ to a single term of the form $V_m\cos(\omega t + \theta)$. Draw a phasor diagram, showing $\mathbf{V}_1, \mathbf{V}_2$, and $\mathbf{V}_s$. State the phase relationships between each pair of these phasors.

*P25. Consider the phasors shown in Figure P25. The frequency of each signal is $f = 200$ Hz. Write a time-domain expression for each voltage in the form $V_m\cos(\omega t + \theta)$. State the phase relationships between pairs of these phasors.

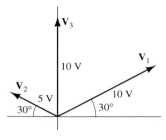

Figure P25

P26. Write an expression for the sinusoid shown in Figure P26 of the form $v(t) = V_m\cos(\omega t + \theta)$, giving the numerical values of V_m, ω, and θ. Also, determine the phasor and the rms value of $v(t)$.

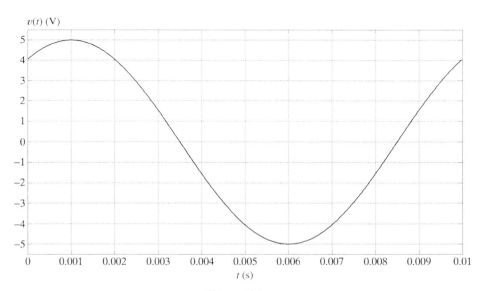

Figure P26

P27. Suppose we have two sinusoidal voltages of the same frequency with rms values of 10 V and 7 V, respectively. The phase angles are unknown. What is the smallest rms value that the sum of these voltages could have? The largest? Justify your answers.

P28. A sinusoidal current $i(t)$ has a phase angle of $60°$. Furthermore, $i_1(t)$ attains its positive peak 0.25 ms earlier than current $i_2(t)$ does. Both currents have a frequency of 500 Hz. Determine the phase angle of $i_2(t)$.

P29. Reduce the expression

$$15 \sin(\omega t - 45°) + 5 \cos(\omega t - 30°)$$
$$+ 10 \cos(\omega t - 120°)$$

to the form $V_m \cos(\omega t + \theta)$.

P30. Suppose that $v_1(t) = 90 \cos(\omega t - 15°)$ and $v_2(t) = 50 \sin(\omega t - 60°)$. Use phasors to reduce the sum $v_s(t) = v_1(t) + v_2(t)$ to a single term of the form $V_m \cos(\omega t + \theta)$. State the phase relationships between each pair of these phasors. (*Hint*: Sketch a phasor diagram showing $\mathbf{V}_1$, $\mathbf{V}_2$, and $\mathbf{V}_s$.)

P31. Suppose we have a circuit in which the voltage is $v_1(t) = 10 \cos(\omega t - 30°)$ V. Furthermore, the current $i_1(t)$ has an rms value of 10 A and lags $v_1(t)$ by $40°$. (The current and the voltage have the same frequency.) Draw a phasor diagram and write an expression for $i_1(t)$ of the form $I_m \cos(\omega t + \theta)$.

P32. Use MATLAB to obtain a plot of $v(t) = \cos(19\pi t) + \cos(21\pi t)$ for t ranging from 0 to 2 s. Explain why the terms in this expression cannot be combined by using phasors. Then, considering that the two terms can be represented as the real projection of the sum of two vectors rotating at different speeds in the complex plane, comment on the plot.

Section 3: Complex Impedances

P33. Write the relationship between the phasor voltage and phasor current for an inductance. Repeat for capacitance.

P34. What is the phase relationship between current and voltage for a pure resistance? For an inductance? For a capacitance?

*P35. A voltage $v_L(t) = 10 \cos(2000\pi t)$ is applied to a 100-mH inductance. Find the complex impedance of the inductance. Find the phasor voltage and current, and construct a phasor diagram. Write the current as a function of time. Sketch the voltage and current to scale versus time. State the phase relationship between the current and voltage.

P36. A certain circuit element is known to be a pure resistance, a pure inductance, or a pure capacitance. Determine the type and value (in ohms, henrys, or farads) of the element if the voltage and current for the element are given by: **a.** $v(t) = 100 \cos(100t + 30°)$ V, $i(t) = 2 \cos(100t + 30°)$ A; **b.** $v(t) = 100 \cos(400t + 30°)$ V, $i(t) = 3 \sin(400t + 30°)$ A; **c.** $v(t) = 100 \sin(200t + 30°)$ V, $i(t) = 2 \cos(200t + 30°)$ A.

*P37. A voltage $v_C(t) = 10 \cos(2000\pi t)$ is applied to a 10-μF capacitance. Find the complex impedance of the capacitance. Find the phasor voltage and current, and construct a phasor diagram. Write the current as a function of time. Sketch the voltage and current to scale versus time. State the phase relationship between the current and voltage.

P38. **a.** The current and voltage for a certain circuit element are shown in Figure P38(a). Determine the nature and value of the element. **b.** Repeat for Figure P38(b).

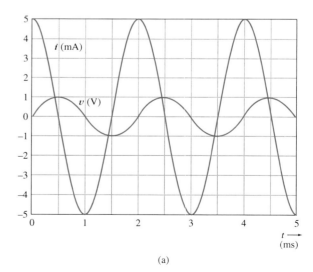

(a)

Figure P38

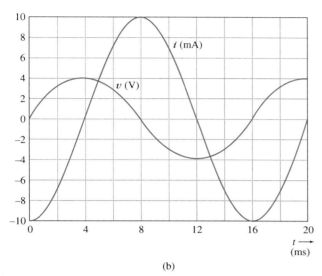

(b)

Figure P38 (*Cont.*)

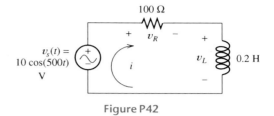

Figure P42

P39. Use MATLAB or manually produce plots of the magnitudes of the impedances of a 10-mH inductance, a 10-μF capacitance, and a 50-Ω resistance to scale versus frequency for the range from zero to 1000 Hz.

P40. **a.** A certain element has a phasor voltage of $\mathbf{V} = 50 \angle 45° \,\mathrm{V}$ and current of $\mathbf{I} = 10 \angle 45° \,\mathrm{A}$. The angular frequency is 1000 rad/s. Determine the nature and value of the element. **b.** Repeat for $\mathbf{V} = 20 \angle -45° \,\mathrm{V}$ and current of $\mathbf{I} = 5 \angle -135° \,\mathrm{A}$. **c.** Repeat for $\mathbf{V} = 100 \angle 30° \,\mathrm{V}$ and current of $\mathbf{I} = 5 \angle 120° \,\mathrm{A}$.

Section 4: Circuit Analysis with Phasors and Complex Impedances

P41. Describe the step-by-step procedure for steady-state analysis of circuits with sinusoidal sources. What condition must be true of the sources?

*P42. Find the phasors for the current and for the voltages of the circuit shown in Figure P42. Construct a phasor diagram showing $\mathbf{V}_S$, $\mathbf{I}$, $\mathbf{V}_R$, and $\mathbf{V}_L$. What is the phase relationship between $\mathbf{V}_S$ and $\mathbf{I}$?

P43. Change the inductance to 0.3 H, and repeat Problem P42.

*P44. Find the phasors for the current and the voltages for the circuit shown in Figure P44. Construct a phasor diagram showing $\mathbf{V}_S$, $\mathbf{I}$, $\mathbf{V}_R$, and $\mathbf{V}_C$. What is the phase relationship between $\mathbf{V}_S$ and $\mathbf{I}$?

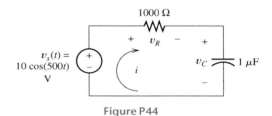

Figure P44

P45. Repeat Problem P44, changing the capacitance value to 4 μF.

*P46. Find the complex impedance in polar form of the network shown in Figure P46 for $\omega = 500$. Repeat for $\omega = 1000$ and $\omega = 2000$.

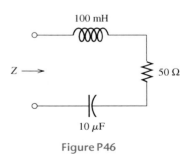

Figure P46

283

P47. Compute the complex impedance of the network shown in Figure P47 for $\omega = 500$. Repeat for $\omega = 1000$ and $\omega = 2000$. Give the answers in both polar and rectangular forms.

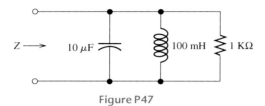

Figure P47

P48. A 100-μF capacitance is connected in parallel with the series combination of a 10-mH inductance and a 1-Ω resistance. Calculate the impedance of the combination in polar form for angular frequencies of 500, 1000, and 2000 radians per second.

*P49. Consider the circuit shown in Figure P49. Find the phasors $\mathbf{I}_s$, $\mathbf{V}$, $\mathbf{I}_R$, $\mathbf{I}_L$, and $\mathbf{I}_C$. Compare the peak value of $i_L(t)$ with the peak value of $i_s(t)$. Do you find the answer surprising? Explain.

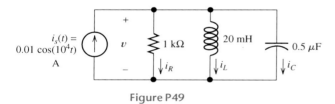

Figure P49

P50. Find the phasors for the voltage and the currents of the circuit shown in Figure P50. Construct a phasor diagram showing $\mathbf{I}_s$, $\mathbf{V}$, $\mathbf{I}_R$, and $\mathbf{I}_L$. What is the phase relationship between $\mathbf{V}$ and $\mathbf{I}_s$?

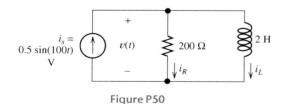

Figure P50

P51. Consider the circuit shown in Figure P51. Find the phasors $\mathbf{V}_s$, $\mathbf{I}$, $\mathbf{V}_L$, $\mathbf{V}_R$, and $\mathbf{V}_C$.

Compare the peak value of $v_L(t)$ with the peak value of $v_s(t)$. Do you find the answer surprising? Explain.

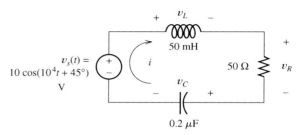

Figure P51

*P52. Find the phasors for the voltage and the currents for the circuit shown in Figure P52. Construct a phasor diagram showing $\mathbf{I}_s$, $\mathbf{V}$, $\mathbf{I}_R$, and $\mathbf{I}_C$. What is the phase relationship between $\mathbf{V}$ and $\mathbf{I}_s$?

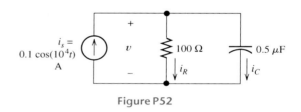

Figure P52

P53. Find the phasors $\mathbf{I}$, $\mathbf{I}_R$, and $\mathbf{I}_C$ for the circuit shown in Figure P53.

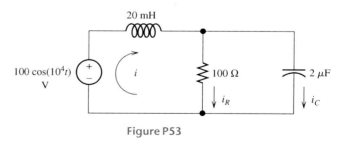

Figure P53

P54. Consider the circuit shown in Figure P54. Find the phasors $\mathbf{V}_1$, $\mathbf{V}_2$, $\mathbf{V}_R$, $\mathbf{V}_L$, and $\mathbf{I}$. Draw the phasor diagram to scale. What is the phase relationship between $\mathbf{I}$ and $\mathbf{V}_1$? Between $\mathbf{I}$ and $\mathbf{V}_L$?

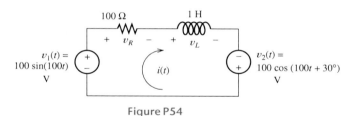

Figure P54

P55. **a.** Sketch or use the computer program of your choice to produce a plot of the impedance magnitude versus angular frequency for a 20-mH inductance in series with a 50-μF capacitance. Allow ω to range from zero to 2000 rad/s and the vertical axis to range from 0 to 100 Ω. **b.** Repeat with the inductance and capacitance in parallel.

P56. **a.** Sketch or use the computer program of your choice to produce a plot of the impedance magnitude versus angular frequency for a 20-mH inductance in series with a 50-Ω resistance. Allow ω to range from zero to 5000 rad/s. **b.** Repeat with the inductance and resistance in parallel.

P57. Solve for the node voltage shown in Figure P57.

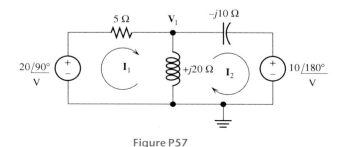

Figure P57

P58. Solve for the node voltage shown in Figure P58.

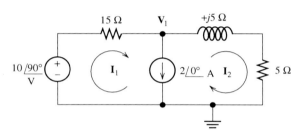

Figure P58

Section 5: Power in AC Circuits

P59. How are power factor and power angle related?

P60. What are the customary units for real power? For reactive power? For apparent power?

P61. How do we compute the complex power delivered to a circuit component? How are average power and reactive power related to complex power?

P62. A load is said to have a leading power factor. Is it capacitive or inductive? Is the reactive power positive or negative? Repeat for a load with lagging power factor.

P63. Assuming that a nonzero ac source is applied, state whether the power and reactive power are positive, negative, or zero for: **a.** a pure resistance; **b.** a pure inductance; **c.** a pure capacitance.

P64. Define what we mean by "power-factor correction." For power-factor correction of an inductive load, what type of element should we place in parallel with the load?

P65. **a.** Sketch a power triangle for an inductive load, label the sides, and show the power angle. **b.** Repeat for a capacitive load.

P66. Discuss why power plant and distribution system engineers are concerned with **a.** the real power absorbed by a load; **b.** with the reactive power.

*P67. Consider the circuit shown in Figure P67. Find the phasor current **I**. Find the power, reactive power, and apparent power delivered by the source. Find the power factor and state whether it is lagging or leading.

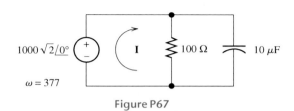

Figure P67

P68. Repeat Problem P67, replacing the capacitance by a 0.5-H inductance.

*P69. Consider a load that has an impedance given by $Z = 100 - j50\ \Omega$. The current flowing through this load is $\mathbf{I} = 15\sqrt{2}\ \underline{/30°}$ A. Is the load inductive or capacitive? Determine the power factor, power, reactive power, and apparent power delivered to the load.

P70. The phasor voltage across a certain load is $\mathbf{V} = 1500\sqrt{2}\,\underline{/-120°}$ V, and the phasor current through it is $\mathbf{I} = 15\sqrt{2}\,\underline{/75°}$ A. The current direction is referenced pointing out of the positive voltage reference. Determine the complex power, power factor, power, reactive power, and apparent power delivered to the load. Also, determine the load impedance. Is the power factor leading or lagging?

P71. The voltage across a certain load is $\mathbf{V} = 1200\sqrt{2}\,\underline{/30°}$ V, and the load impedance given by $Z = 40 - j30\ \Omega$. Is the load inductive or capacitive? Determine the power factor, complex power, real power, reactive power, and apparent power delivered to the load.

P72. The voltage across a load is $v(t) = 10^4\sqrt{2}\cos(\omega t + 75°)$ V, and the current through the load is $i(t) = 2\sqrt{2}\cos(\omega t + 30°)$ A. The reference direction for the current points into the positive reference for the voltage. Determine the complex power, the power factor, the real power, the reactive power, and the apparent power for the load. Is this load inductive or capacitive?

P73. Determine the power for each element, including the sources, shown in Figure P73. Also, state whether each element is delivering or absorbing average power.

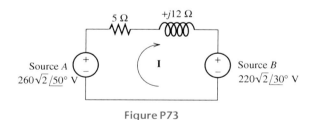

Figure P73

P74. Given that a nonzero ac voltage source is applied, state whether the power and reactive power are positive, negative, or zero for:
a. a resistance in series with an inductance;
b. a resistance in series with a capacitance;
c. a pure resistance. (Assume that the resistances, inductance, and capacitance are nonzero and finite in value.)

P75. Given that a nonzero ac voltage source is applied, what can you say about whether the power and reactive power are positive, negative, or zero for a pure capacitance in series with a pure inductance? Consider cases in which the impedance magnitude of the capacitance is greater than, equal to, or less than the impedance magnitude of the inductance.

P76. Repeat Problem P75 for the inductance and capacitance in parallel.

P77. A 60-Hz 220-V-rms source supplies power to a load consisting of a resistance in series with a capacitance. The real power is 2000 W, and the apparent power is 2500 VA. Determine the value of the resistance and the value of the capacitance.

*P78. Two loads, A and B, are connected in parallel across a 1-kV rms 60-Hz line, as shown in Figure P78. Load A consumes 10 kW with a 90 percent lagging power factor. Load B has an apparent power of 15 kVA with an 80 percent lagging power factor. Find the power, reactive power, and apparent power delivered by the source. What is the power factor seen by the source?

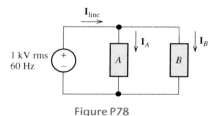

Figure P78

P79. Repeat Problem P78 given that load A consumes 50 kW with a 60 percent lagging power factor and load B consumes 75 kW with an 80 percent lagging power factor.

P80. Determine the power for each element, including the sources, shown in Figure P80. Also, state whether each element is delivering or absorbing average power.

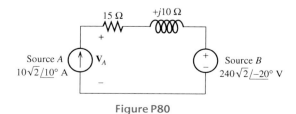

Figure P80

P81. Find the power, reactive power, and apparent power delivered by the source in Figure P81. Find the power factor and state whether it is leading or lagging.

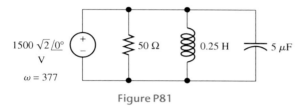

Figure P81

P82. Repeat Problem P81 with the resistance, inductance, and capacitance connected in series rather than in parallel.

*P83. Consider the situation shown in Figure P83. A 1000-V rms source delivers power to a load. The load consumes 100 kW with a power factor of 25 percent lagging. **a.** Find the phasor **I,** assuming that the capacitor is not connected to the circuit. **b.** Find the value of the capacitance that must be connected in parallel with the load to achieve a power factor of 100 percent. Usually, power-systems engineers rate capacitances used for power-factor correction in terms of their reactive power rating. What is the rating of this capacitance in kVAR? Assuming that this capacitance is connected, find the new value for the phasor **I. c.** Suppose that the source is connected to the load by a long distance. What are the potential advantages and disadvantages of connecting the capacitance across the load?

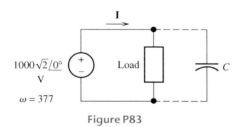

Figure P83

Section 6: Thévenin and Norton Equivalent Circuits

P84. Of what does an ac steady-state Thévenin equivalent circuit consist? A Norton equivalent circuit? How are the values of the parameters of these circuits determined?

P85. For an ac circuit consisting of a load connected to a Thévenin circuit, is it possible for the load voltage to exceed the Thévenin voltage in magnitude? If not, why not? If so, under what conditions is it possible? Explain.

P86. To attain maximum power delivered to a load, what value of load impedance is required if: **a.** the load can have any complex value; **b.** the load must be pure resistance?

*P87. **a.** Find the Thévenin and Norton equivalent circuits for the circuit shown in Figure P87. **b.** Find the maximum power that this circuit can deliver to a load if the load can have any complex impedance. **c.** Solve (b) for the condition that the load is purely resistive.

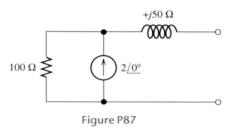

Figure P87

P88. Find the Thévenin voltage, Thévenin impedance, and Norton current for the two-terminal circuit shown in Figure P88.

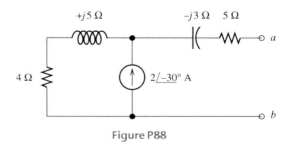

Figure P88

P89. Find the Thévenin and Norton equivalent circuits for the circuit shown in Figure P89. Find the maximum power that this circuit can deliver to a load if the load can have any complex impedance. Repeat if the load must be purely resistive.

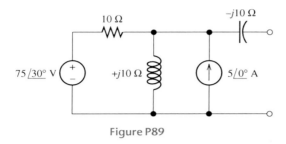

Figure P89

P90. Draw the Thévenin and Norton equivalent circuits for Figure P90, labeling the elements and terminals.

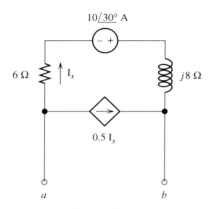

Figure P90

*P91. The Thévenin equivalent of a two-terminal network is shown in Figure P91. The frequency is $f = 60$ Hz. We wish to connect a load across terminals a–b that consists of a resistance and a capacitance in parallel such that the power delivered to the resistance is maximized. Find the value of the resistance and the value of the capacitance.

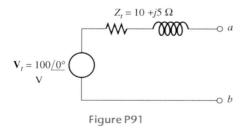

Figure P91

P92. Repeat Problem P91 with the load required to consist of a resistance and a capacitance in series.

Section 7: Balanced Three-Phase Circuits

P93. A three-phase source has

$$v_{an}(t) = 100\cos(\omega t - 60°)\text{ V}$$
$$v_{bn}(t) = 100\cos(\omega t + 60°)\text{ V}$$
$$v_{cn}(t) = -100\cos(\omega t)\text{ V}$$

Is this a positive-sequence or a negative-sequence source? Find time-domain expressions for $v_{ab}(t)$, $v_{bc}(t)$, and $v_{ca}(t)$.

P94. We have a balanced positive-sequence three-phase source for which:

$$v_{an}(t) = 120\cos(100\pi t + 75°)\text{ V}$$

a. Find the frequency of this source in Hz.
b. Give expressions for $v_{bn}(t)$ and $v_{cn}(t)$.
c. Repeat part (b) for a negative-sequence source.

*P95. Each phase of a wye-connected load consists of a 50-Ω resistance in parallel with a 100-μF capacitance. Find the impedance of each phase of an equivalent delta-connected load. The frequency of operation is 60 Hz.

*P96. A balanced wye-connected three-phase source has line-to-neutral voltages of 440 V rms. Find the rms line-to-line voltage magnitude. If this source is applied to a wye-connected load composed of three 30-Ω resistances, find the rms line-current magnitude and the total power delivered.

P97. What can you say about the flow of power as a function of time between a balanced three-phase source and a balanced load? Is this true of a single-phase source and a load? How is this a potential advantage for the three-phase system? What is another advantage of three-phase power distribution compared with single-phase?

P98. A delta-connected source delivers power to a delta-connected load, as shown in Figure P98. The rms line-to-line voltage at the source is $V_{ab\text{rms}} = 440$ V. The load impedance is $Z_\Delta = 12 + j3\ \Omega$. Find $\mathbf{I}_{aA}$, $\mathbf{V}_{AB}$, $\mathbf{I}_{AB}$, the total power delivered to the load, and the power lost in the line.

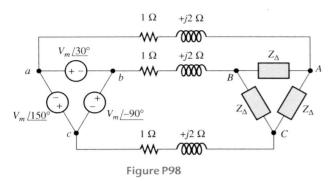

Figure P98

*P99. Repeat Problem P98, with $Z_\Delta = 15 - j6\ \Omega$.

P100. A balanced wye-connected three-phase source has line-to-neutral voltages of 277 V rms. Find the rms line-to-line voltage. This source is applied to a delta-connected load, each arm of which consists of a 15-Ω resistance in parallel with a +$j30$-Ω reactance. Determine the rms line current magnitude, the power factor, and the total power delivered.

P101. A negative-sequence wye-connected source has line-to-neutral voltages $\mathbf{V}_{an} = V_Y \angle 0°$, $\mathbf{V}_{bn} = V_Y \angle 120°$, and $\mathbf{V}_{cn} = V_Y \angle -120°$. Find the line-to-line voltages $\mathbf{V}_{ab}$, $\mathbf{V}_{bc}$, and $\mathbf{V}_{ca}$. Construct a phasor diagram showing both sets of voltages and compare with Figure 41.

P102. A balanced positive-sequence wye-connected 60-Hz three-phase source has line-to-line voltages of $V_L = 208$ V rms. This source is connected to a balanced wye-connected load. Each phase of the load consists of an impedance of $30 + j40\ \Omega$. Find the line-to-neutral voltage phasors, the line-to-line voltage phasors, the line-current phasors, the power, and the reactive power delivered to the load. Assume that the phase of $\mathbf{V}_{an}$ is zero.

P103. In this chapter, we have considered balanced loads only. However, it is possible to determine an equivalent wye for an unbalanced delta, and vice versa. Consider the equivalent circuits shown in Figure P103. Derive formulas for the impedances of the wye in terms of the impedances of the delta. (*Hint:* Equate the impedances between corresponding pairs of terminals of the two circuits with

the third terminal open. Then, solve the equations for Z_a, Z_b, and Z_c in terms of Z_A, Z_B, and Z_C. Take care in distinguishing between upper- and lowercase subscripts.)

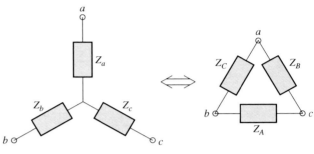

Figure P103

P104. Repeat Problem P103, but solve for the impedances of the delta in terms of those of the wye. [*Hint:* Start by working in terms of the admittances of the delta (Y_A, Y_B, and Y_C) and the impedances of the wye (Z_a, Z_b, and Z_c). Short terminals b and c for each circuit. Then equate the admittances between terminal a and the shorted terminals for the two circuits. Repeat this twice more with shorts between the remaining two pairs of terminals. Solve the equations to determine Y_A, Y_B, and Y_C in terms of Z_a, Z_b, and Z_c. Finally, invert the equations for Y_A, Y_B, and Y_C to obtain equations relating the impedances. Take care in distinguishing between upper- and lowercase subscripts.]

Section 8: AC Analysis Using MATLAB

*P105. Use MATLAB to solve for the node voltages shown in Figure P105.

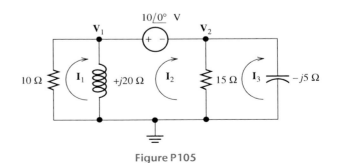

Figure P105

P106. Use MATLAB to solve for the mesh currents shown in Figure P105.

*P107. Use MATLAB to solve for the mesh currents shown in Figure P57.

P108. Use MATLAB to solve for the mesh currents shown in Figure P58.

P109. Use MATLAB to solve for the node voltages shown in Figure P109.

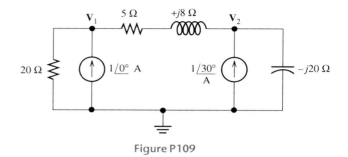

Figure P109

Practice Test

Here is a practice test you can use to check your comprehension of the most important concepts in this chapter. Answers can be found at the end of this chapter and complete solutions are included in the Student Solutions files.

T1. Determine the rms value of the current shown in Figure T1 and the average power delivered to the 50-Ω resistance.

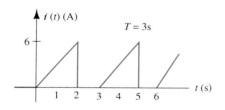

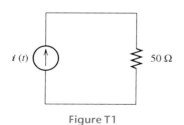

Figure T1

T2. Reduce the expression

$$v(t) = 5\sin(\omega t + 45°) + 5\cos(\omega t - 30°)$$

to the form $V_m \cos(\omega t + \theta)$.

T3. We have two voltages $v_1(t) = 15\sin(400\pi t + 45°)$ V and $v_2(t) = 5\cos(400\pi t - 30°)$ V.

Determine (including units): **a.** the rms value of $v_1(t)$; **b.** the frequency of the voltages; **c.** the angular frequency of the voltages; **d.** the period of the voltages; **e.** the phase relationship between $v_1(t)$ and $v_2(t)$.

T4. Find the phasor values of $\mathbf{V}_R$, $\mathbf{V}_L$, and $\mathbf{V}_C$ in polar form for the circuit of Figure T4.

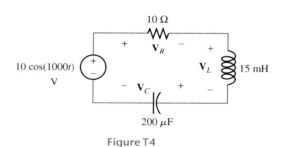

Figure T4

T5. Determine the complex power, power, reactive power, and apparent power absorbed by the load in Figure T5. Also, determine the power factor for the load.

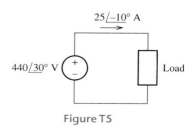

Figure T5

290

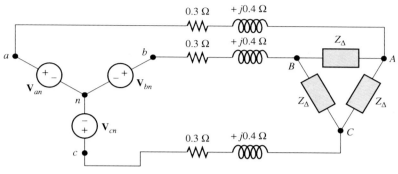

Figure T6

T6. Determine the line current $\mathbf{I}_{aA}$ in polar form for the circuit of Figure T6. This is a positive-sequence, balanced, three-phase system with $\mathbf{V}_{an} = 208 \underline{/30°}$ V and $Z_{\Delta} = 6 + j8$ Ω.

T7. Write the MATLAB commands to obtain the values of the mesh currents of Figure T7 in polar form. You may use the pin and pout functions defined in this chapter if you wish.

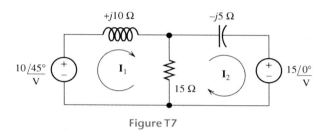

Figure T7

Answers for the Practice Test

T1. $I_{rms} = \sqrt{8} = 2.828$ A; $P = 400$ W.

T2. $v(t) = 9.914 \cos(\omega t - 37.50°)$

T3. **a.** $V_{1rms} = 10.61$ V; **b.** $f = 200$ Hz; **c.** $\omega = 400\pi$ radians/s; **d.** $T = 5$ ms; **e.** $\mathbf{V}_1$ lags $\mathbf{V}_2$ by 15° or $\mathbf{V}_2$ leads $\mathbf{V}_1$ by 15°.

T4. $\mathbf{V}_R = 7.071 \underline{/-45°}$ V; $\mathbf{V}_L = 10.606 \underline{/45°}$ V; $\mathbf{V}_C = 5.303 \underline{/-135°}$ V.

T5. $\mathbf{S} = 5500 \underline{/40°} = 4213 + j3535$ VA;
$P = 4213$ W; $Q = 3535$ VAR; apparent power $= 5500$ VA;
Power factor $= 76.6$ percent lagging.

T6. $\mathbf{I}_{aA} = 54.26 \underline{/-23.13°}$ A.

T7. The commands are:

```
Z = [(15+i*10) -15; -15 (15-i*5)]
V = [pin(10,45); -15]
I = inv(Z)*V
pout(I(1))
pout(I(2))
```

Frequency Response, Bode Plots, and Resonance

From Chapter 6 of *Electrical Engineering: Principles and Applications*, Fifth Edition, Allan R. Hambley. Copyright © 2011 by Pearson Education, Inc. Published by Pearson Prentice Hall. All rights reserved.

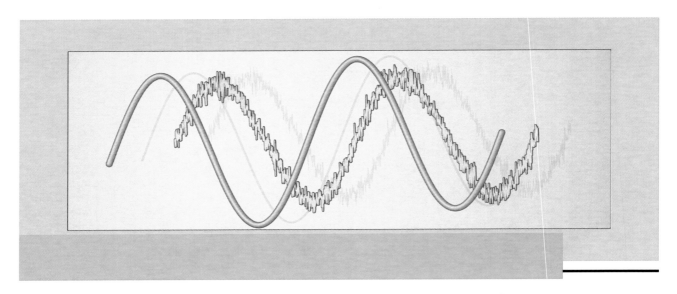

Frequency Response, Bode Plots, and Resonance

Study of this chapter will enable you to:

- State the fundamental concepts of Fourier analysis.

- Use a filter's transfer function to determine its output for a given input consisting of sinusoidal components.

- Use circuit analysis to determine the transfer functions of simple circuits.

- Draw first-order lowpass or highpass filter circuits and sketch their transfer functions.

- Understand decibels, logarithmic frequency scales, and Bode plots.

- Draw the Bode plots for transfer functions of first-order filters.

- Calculate parameters for series- and parallel-resonant circuits.

- Select and design simple filter circuits.

- Use MATALAB to derive and plot network functions.

- Design simple digital signal-processing systems.

Introduction to this chapter:

Much of electrical engineering is concerned with information-bearing currents and voltages that we call **signals**. For example, transducers on an internal combustion engine provide electrical signals that represent temperature, speed, throttle position, and the rotational position of the crankshaft. These signals are **processed** (by electrical circuits) to determine the optimum firing instant for each cylinder. Finally, electrical pulses are generated for each spark plug.

Surveyors can measure distances by using an instrument that emits a pulse of light that is reflected by a mirror at the point of interest. The return light pulse is converted to an electrical signal that is processed by circuits to determine the round-trip time delay between the instrument and the mirror. Finally, the delay is converted to distance and displayed.

Another example of signal processing is the electrocardiogram, which is a plot of the electrical signal generated by the human heart. In a cardiac-care unit, circuits and computers are employed to extract information concerning the behavior of a patient's heart. A physician or nurse is alerted when the patient needs attention.

In general, **signal processing** is concerned with manipulating signals to extract information and using that information to generate other useful electrical signals. It is an important and far-reaching subject. In this chapter, we consider several simple but, nevertheless, useful circuits from a signal-processing point of view.

You should already know how to analyze circuits containing sinusoidal sources, all of which have a common frequency. An important application is electrical power systems. However, most real-world information-bearing electrical signals are not sinusoidal. Nevertheless, we will see that phasor concepts can be very useful in understanding how circuits respond to nonsinusoidal signals. This is true because nonsinusoidal signals can be considered to be the sum of sinusoidal components having various frequencies, amplitudes, and phases.

1 FOURIER ANALYSIS, FILTERS, AND TRANSFER FUNCTIONS

Fourier Analysis

As mentioned in the introduction to this chapter, most information-bearing signals are not sinusoidal. For example, the waveform produced by a microphone for speech or music is a complex nonsinusoidal waveform that is not predictable in advance. Figure 1(a) shows a (very) short segment of a music signal.

Even though many interesting signals are not sinusoidal, it turns out that we can construct any waveform by adding sinusoids that have the proper amplitudes, frequencies, and phases. For illustration, the waveform shown in Figure 1(a) is the sum of the sinusoids shown in Figure 1(b). The waveform shown in Figure 1 is relatively simple because it is composed of only three components. Most natural

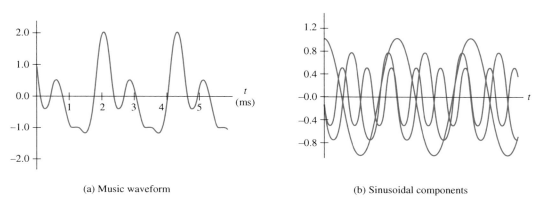

(a) Music waveform

(b) Sinusoidal components

Figure 1 The short segment of a music waveform shown in (a) is the sum of the sinusoidal components shown in (b).

signals contain thousands of components. (In theory, the number is infinite in many cases.)

When we listen to music, our ears respond differently to the various frequency components. Some combinations of amplitudes and frequencies are pleasing, whereas other combinations are not. Thus, in the design of signal-processing circuits (such as amplifiers) for audio signals, we must consider how the circuits respond to components having different frequencies.

Fourier analysis is a mathematical technique for finding the amplitudes, frequencies, and phases of the components of a given waveform. Aside from mentioning some of the results of Fourier analysis, we will not develop the theory in detail. *The important point is that all real-world signals are sums of sinusoidal components.*

All real-world signals are sums of sinusoidal components having various frequencies, amplitudes, and phases.

The range of the frequencies of the components depends on the type of signal under consideration. The frequency ranges for several types of signals are given in Table 1. Thus, electrocardiograms are created from signals that are composed of numerous sinusoidal components with frequencies ranging from 0.05 Hz to 100 Hz.

Fourier Series of a Square Wave. As another example, consider the signal shown in Figure 2(a), which is called a **square wave**. Fourier analysis shows that the square wave can be written as an infinite series of sinusoidal components,

$$v_{sq}(t) = \frac{4A}{\pi} \sin(\omega_0 t) + \frac{4A}{3\pi} \sin(3\omega_0 t) + \frac{4A}{5\pi} \sin(5\omega_0 t) + \cdots \qquad (1)$$

in which $\omega_0 = 2\pi/T$ is the called the **fundamental angular frequency** of the square wave.

Figure 2(b) shows several of the terms in this series and the result of summing the first five terms. Clearly, even the sum of the first five terms is a fairly good approximation to the square wave, and the approximation becomes better as more components are added. Thus, the square wave is composed of an infinite number of sinusoidal components. The frequencies of the components are odd integer multiples of the fundamental frequency, the amplitudes decline with increasing frequency, and the phases of all components are $-90°$. Unlike the square wave, the components of real-world signals are confined to finite ranges of frequency, and their amplitudes are not given by simple mathematical expressions.

The components of real-world signals are confined to finite ranges of frequency.

Zero frequency corresponds to dc.

Sometimes a signal contains a component that has a frequency of zero. For zero frequency, a general sinusoid of the form $A\cos(\omega t + \theta)$ becomes simply $A\cos(\theta)$, which is constant for all time. Recall that we refer to constant voltages as dc, so zero frequency corresponds to dc. The transfer function for $f = 0$ is the constant (dc) output divided by the dc input.

Table 1. Frequency Ranges of Selected Signals

Electrocardiogram	0.05 to 100 Hz
Audible sounds	20 Hz to 15 kHz
AM radio broadcasting	540 to 1600 kHz
Analog video signals (U.S. standards)	Dc to 4.2 MHz
FM radio broadcasting	88 to 108 MHz
Cellular phone	824 to 894 MHz and 1850 to 1990 MHz
Satellite television downlinks (C-band)	3.7 to 4.2 GHz
Digital satellite television	12.2 to 12.7 GHz

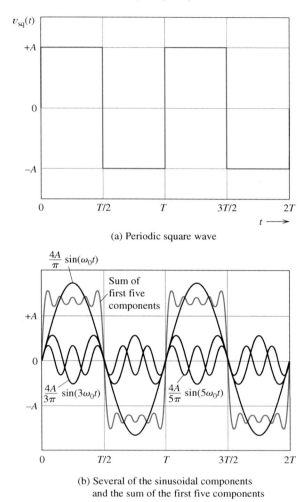

Figure 2 A square wave and some of its components.

In sum, the fact that all signals are composed of sinusoidal components is a fundamental idea in electrical engineering. The frequencies of the components, as well as their amplitudes and phases, for a given signal can be determined by theoretical analysis or by laboratory measurements (using an instrument called a *spectrum analyzer*). Very often, the design of a system for processing information-bearing signals is based on considerations of how the system should respond to components of various frequencies.

> ... the fact that all signals are composed of sinusoidal components is a fundamental idea in electrical engineering.

Filters

There are many applications in which we want to retain components in a given range of frequencies and discard the components in another range. This can be accomplished by the use of electrical circuits called **filters**. (Actually, filters can take many forms, but we limit our discussion to a few relatively simple *RLC* circuits.)

Usually, filter circuits are **two-port networks**, an example of which is illustrated in Figure 3. The signal to be filtered is applied to the input port and (ideally) only

Figure 3 When an input signal $v_{in}(t)$ is applied to the input port of a filter, some components are passed to the output port, while others are not, depending on their frequencies. Thus, $v_{out}(t)$ contains some of the components of $v_{in}(t)$, but not others. Usually, the amplitudes and phases of the components are altered in passing through the filter.

Figure 3 When an input signal $v_{in}(t)$ is applied to the input port of a filter, some components are passed to the output port, while others are not, depending on their frequencies. Thus, $v_{out}(t)$ contains some of the components of $v_{in}(t)$, but not others. Usually, the amplitudes and phases of the components are altered in passing through the filter.

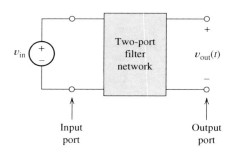

Input port   Output port

Filters process the sinusoid components of an input signal differently depending on the frequency of each component. Often, the goal of the filter is to retain the components in certain frequency ranges and to reject components in other ranges.

RLC circuits provide one way to realize filters.

the components in the frequency range of interest appear at the output port. For example, an FM radio antenna produces a voltage composed of signals from many transmitters. By using a filter that retains the components in the frequency range from 88 to 108 MHz and discards everything else, we can select the FM radio signals and reject other signals that could interfere with the process of extracting audio information.

The impedances of inductances and capacitances change with frequency. For example, the impedance of an inductance is $Z_L = \omega L \angle 90° = 2\pi f L \angle 90°$. Thus, the high-frequency components of a voltage signal applied to an inductance experience a higher impedance magnitude than do the low-frequency components. Consequently, electrical circuits can respond selectively to signal components, depending on their frequencies. Thus, *RLC* circuits provide one way to realize electrical filters. We consider several specific examples later in this chapter.

Transfer Functions

Consider the two-port network shown in Figure 3. Suppose that we apply a sinusoidal input signal having a frequency denoted as f and having a phasor $\mathbf{V}_{in}$. In steady state, the output signal is sinusoidal and has the same frequency as the input. The output phasor is denoted as $\mathbf{V}_{out}$.

The **transfer function** $H(f)$ of the two-port filter is defined to be the ratio of the phasor output voltage to the phasor input voltage as a function of frequency:

The transfer function $H(f)$ of the two-port filter is defined to be the ratio of the phasor output voltage to the phasor input voltage as a function of frequency.

$$H(f) = \frac{\mathbf{V}_{out}}{\mathbf{V}_{in}} \qquad (2)$$

Because phasors are complex, the transfer function is a complex quantity having both magnitude and phase. Furthermore, both the magnitude and the phase can be functions of frequency.

The transfer-function magnitude is the ratio of the output amplitude to the input amplitude. The phase of the transfer function is the output phase minus the input phase. Thus, the magnitude of the transfer function shows how the amplitude of each frequency component is affected by the filter. Similarly, the phase of the transfer function shows how the phase of each frequency component is affected by the filter.

The magnitude of the transfer function shows how the amplitude of each frequency component is affected by the filter. Similarly, the phase of the transfer function shows how the phase of each frequency component is affected by the filter.

Using the Transfer Function to Determine the Output

The transfer function $H(f)$ of a filter is shown in Figure 4. [Notice that the magnitude $|H(f)|$ and phase $\angle H(f)$ are shown separately in the figure.] If the input signal is given by

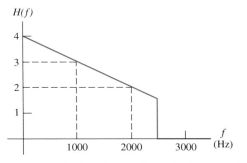
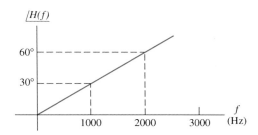

Figure 4 The transfer function of a filter. See Examples 1 and 2.

$$v_{in}(t) = 2 \, \cos(2000\pi t + 40°)$$

find an expression (as a function of time) for the output of the filter.

Solution By inspection, the frequency of the input signal is $f = 1000$ Hz. Referring to Figure 4, we see that the magnitude and phase of the transfer function are $|H(1000)| = 3$ and $\underline{/H(1000)} = 30°$, respectively. Thus, we have

$$H(1000) = 3\underline{/30°} = \frac{\mathbf{V}_{out}}{\mathbf{V}_{in}}$$

The phasor for the input signal is $\mathbf{V}_{in} = 2\underline{/40°}$, and we get

$$\mathbf{V}_{out} = H(1000) \times \mathbf{V}_{in} = 3\underline{/30°} \times 2\underline{/40°} = 6\underline{/70°}$$

Thus, the output signal is

$$v_{out}(t) = 6 \, \cos(2000\pi t + 70°)$$

In this case, the amplitude of the input is tripled by the filter. Furthermore, the signal is phase shifted by 30°. Of course, this is evident from the values shown in the plots of the transfer function at $f = 1000$. ■

Exercise 1 Repeat Example 1 if the input signal is given by **a.** $v_{in}(t) = 2 \cos(4000\pi t)$ and **b.** $v_{in}(t) = 1 \, \cos(6000\pi t - 20°)$.
Answer   **a.** $v_{out}(t) = 4 \, \cos(4000\pi t + 60°)$; **b.** $v_{out}(t) = 0$.   ▫
Notice that the effect of the filter on the magnitude and phase of the signal depends on signal frequency.

Example: Graphic Equalizer. You may own a stereo audio system that has a *graphic equalizer*, which is a filter that has an adjustable transfer function. Usually, the controls of the equalizer are arranged so their positions give an approximate representation of the transfer-function magnitude versus frequency. (Actually, the equalizer in a stereo system contains two filters—one for the left channel and one for the right channel—and the controls are ganged together.) Users can adjust the transfer function to achieve the mix of amplitudes versus frequency that is most pleasing to them.

Input Signals with Multiple Components. If the input signal to a filter contains several frequency components, we can find the output for each input component separately and then add the output components. This is an application of the superposition principle.

A step-by-step procedure for determining the output of a filter for an input with multiple components is as follows:

1. Determine the frequency and phasor representation for each input component.
2. Determine the (complex) value of the transfer function for each component.
3. Obtain the phasor for each output component by multiplying the phasor for each input component by the corresponding transfer-function value.
4. Convert the phasors for the output components into time functions of various frequencies. Add these time functions to produce the output.

Example 2   Using the Transfer Function with Several Input Components

Suppose that the input signal for the filter of Figure 4 is given by

$$v_{in}(t) = 3 + 2\,\cos(2000\pi t) + \cos(4000\pi t - 70°)$$

Find an expression for the output signal.

Solution   We start by breaking the input signal into its components. The first component is

Step 1.

$$v_{in1}(t) = 3$$

and the second component is

$$v_{in2}(t) = 2\cos(2000\pi t)$$

and the third component is

$$v_{in3}(t) = \cos(4000\pi t - 70°)$$

Step 2.

By inspection, we see that the frequencies of the components are 0, 1000, and 2000 Hz, respectively. Referring to the transfer function shown in Figure 4, we find that

$$H(0) = 4$$
$$H(1000) = 3\angle 30°$$

and

$$H(2000) = 2\angle 60°$$

The constant (dc) output term is simply $H(0)$ times the dc input:

$$v_{out1} = H(0)v_{in1} = 4 \times 3 = 12$$

Step 3.

The phasor outputs for the two input sinusoids are

$$\mathbf{V}_{out2} = H(1000) \times \mathbf{V}_{in2} = 3\angle 30° \times 2\angle 0° = 6\angle 30°$$
$$\mathbf{V}_{out3} = H(2000) \times \mathbf{V}_{in3} = 2\angle 60° \times 1\angle -70° = 2\angle -10°$$

Next, we can write the output components as functions of time: Step 4.

$$v_{out1}(t) = 12$$
$$v_{out2}(t) = 6\ \cos(2000\pi t + 30°)$$

and

$$v_{out3}(t) = 2\ \cos(4000\pi t - 10°)$$

Finally, we add the output components to find the output voltage:

$$v_{out}(t) = v_{out1}(t) + v_{out2}(t) + v_{out3}(t)$$

and

$$v_{out}(t) = 12 + 6\ \cos(2000\pi t + 30°) + 2\ \cos(4000\pi t - 10°) \quad\blacksquare$$

Notice that we did not add the phasors $\mathbf{V}_{out2}$ and $\mathbf{V}_{out3}$ in Example 2. The phasor concept was developed for sinusoids, all of which have the same frequency. *Hence, convert the phasors back into time-dependent signals before adding the components.*

We must convert the phasors back into time-dependent signals before adding the components.

Real-world information-bearing signals contain thousands of components. In principle, the output of a given filter for any input signal could be found by using the procedure of Example 2. However, it would usually be much too tedious to carry out. Fortunately, we will not need to do this. *It is the principle that is most important.* In summary, we can say that linear circuits (or any other systems for which the relationship between input and output can be described by linear time-invariant differential equations) behave as if they

1. Separate the input signal into components having various frequencies.
2. Alter the amplitude and phase of each component depending on its frequency.
3. Add the altered components to produce the output signal.

This process is illustrated in Figure 5.

The transfer function of a filter is important because it shows how the components are altered in amplitude and phase.

Experimental Determination of the Transfer Function. To determine the transfer function of a filter experimentally, we connect a sinusoidal source to the input port, measure the amplitudes and phases of both the input signal and the resulting output signal, and divide the output phasor by the input phasor. This is repeated for each frequency of interest. The experimental setup is illustrated in Figure 6. Various instruments, such as voltmeters and oscilloscopes, can be employed to measure the amplitudes and phases.

In the next few sections of this chapter, we use mathematical analysis to investigate the transfer functions of several relatively simple electrical circuits.

Exercise 2 Consider the transfer function shown in Figure 4. The input signal is given by
$$v_{in}(t) = 2\ \cos(1000\pi t + 20°) + 3\ \cos(3000\pi t)$$

Find an expression for the output signal.

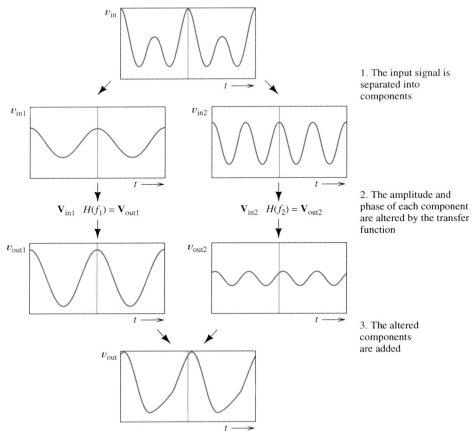

Figure 5 Filters behave as if they separate the input into components, modify the amplitudes and phases of the components, and add the altered components to produce the output.

Figure 6 To measure the transfer function, we apply a sinusoidal input signal, measure the amplitudes and phases of input and output in steady state, and then divide the phasor output by the phasor input. The procedure is repeated for each frequency of interest.

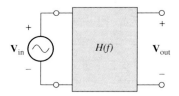

Answer $v_{out}(t) = 7 \cos(1000\pi t + 35°) + 7.5 \cos(3000\pi t + 45°)$. □

Exercise 3 Consider the transfer function shown in Figure 4. The input signal is given by

$$v_{in}(t) = 1 + 2 \cos(2000\pi t) + 3 \cos(6000\pi t)$$

Find an expression for the output signal.

Answer $v_{out}(t) = 4 + 6 \cos(2000\pi t + 30°)$. Notice that the 3-kHz component is totally eliminated (rejected) by the filter. □

PRACTICAL APPLICATION 1

Active Noise Cancellation

Noise and vibration are annoying to passengers in helicopters and other aircraft. Traditional sound-absorbing materials can be very effective in reducing noise levels, but are too bulky and massive for application in aircraft. An alternative approach is an electronic system that cancels noise. The diagram of such a system is shown in Figure PA1. A microphone near the sources of the noise, such as the engines, samples the noise before it enters the passenger area. The resulting electrical signal passes through a filter whose transfer function is continuously adjusted by a special-purpose computer to match the transfer function of the sound path. Finally, an inverted version of the signal is applied to loudspeakers. The sound waves from the speaker are out of phase with those from the noise source, resulting in partial cancellation. Another set of microphones on the headrest monitors the sound experienced by the passenger so that the computer can determine the filter adjustments needed to best cancel the sound.

Recently, noise-canceling systems based on these principles have appeared that contain all of the system elements in a lightweight headset. Many passengers on commercial aircraft wear these headsets to provide themselves with a quieter, more restful trip.

For more information, you may wish to read "Noise and Vibration Control" in the September 1994 issue of *Aerospace Engineering*. According to the article, systems such as this, weighing 50 to 100 lb, achieve results comparable to that of up to 1000 lb of sound-absorbing materials.

Sources: "Anti-noise system," *Aerospace Engineering*, December 1993, pp. 15–16; L. E. Trego, "Noise and vibration control," *Aerospace Engineering*, September 1994, pp. 10–12.

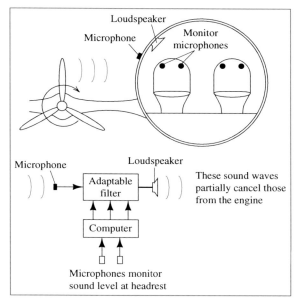

Figure PA1

2 FIRST-ORDER LOWPASS FILTERS

Consider the circuit shown in Figure 7. We will see that this circuit tends to pass low-frequency components and reject high-frequency components. (In other words, for low frequencies, the output amplitude is nearly the same as the input. For high frequencies, the output amplitude is much less than the input.) A first-order differential equation describes this circuit. Because of these facts, the circuit is called a **first-order lowpass filter**.

To determine the transfer function, we apply a sinusoidal input signal having a phasor $\mathbf{V}_{in}$, and then we analyze the behavior of the circuit as a function of the source frequency f.

We can determine the transfer functions of *RLC* circuits by using steady-state analysis with complex impedances as a function of frequency.

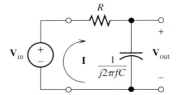

Figure 7 A first-order lowpass filter.

The phasor current is the input voltage divided by the complex impedance of the circuit. This is given by

$$I = \frac{\mathbf{V}_{in}}{R + 1/j2\pi fC} \tag{3}$$

The phasor for the output voltage is the product of the phasor current and the impedance of the capacitance, illustrated by

$$\mathbf{V}_{out} = \frac{1}{j2\pi fC}I \tag{4}$$

Using Equation 3 to substitute for $\mathbf{I}$, we have

$$\mathbf{V}_{out} = \frac{1}{j2\pi fC} \times \frac{\mathbf{V}_{in}}{R + 1/j2\pi fC} \tag{5}$$

Recall that the transfer function $H(f)$ is defined to be the ratio of the output phasor to the input phasor:

$$H(f) = \frac{\mathbf{V}_{out}}{\mathbf{V}_{in}} \tag{6}$$

Rearranging Equation 5, we have

$$H(f) = \frac{\mathbf{V}_{out}}{\mathbf{V}_{in}} = \frac{1}{1 + j2\pi fRC} \tag{7}$$

Next, we define the parameter:

$$f_B = \frac{1}{2\pi RC} \tag{8}$$

Then, the transfer function can be written as

$$H(f) = \frac{1}{1 + j(f/f_B)} \tag{9}$$

Magnitude and Phase Plots of the Transfer Function

As expected, the transfer function $H(f)$ is a complex quantity having a magnitude and phase angle. Referring to the expression on the right-hand side of Equation 9, the magnitude of $H(f)$ is the magnitude of the numerator (which is unity) over the magnitude of the denominator. Recall that the magnitude of a complex quantity is

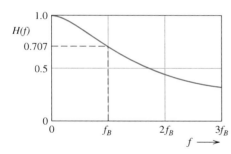 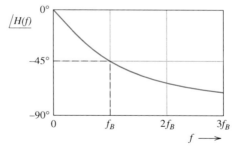

Figure 8 Magnitude and phase of the first-order lowpass transfer function versus frequency.

the square root of the sum of the real part squared and the imaginary part squared. Thus, the magnitude is given by

$$|H(f)| = \frac{1}{\sqrt{1 + (f/f_B)^2}} \tag{10}$$

Referring to the expression on the right-hand side of Equation 9, the phase angle of the transfer function is the phase of the numerator (which is zero) minus the phase of the denominator. This is given by

$$\angle H(f) = -\arctan\left(\frac{f}{f_B}\right) \tag{11}$$

Plots of the magnitude and phase of the transfer function are shown in Figure 8. For low frequencies (f approaching zero), the magnitude is approximately unity and the phase is nearly zero, which means that the amplitudes and phases of low-frequency components are affected very little by this filter. The low-frequency components are passed to the output almost unchanged in amplitude or phase.

On the other hand, for high frequencies ($f \gg f_B$), the magnitude of the transfer function approaches zero. Thus, the amplitude of the output is much smaller than the amplitude of the input for the high-frequency components. We say that the high-frequency components are rejected by the filter. Furthermore, at high frequencies, the phase of the transfer function approaches $-90°$. Thus, as well as being reduced in amplitude, the high-frequency components are phase shifted.

Notice that for $f = f_B$, the magnitude of the output is $1/\sqrt{2} \cong 0.707$ times the magnitude of the input signal. When the amplitude of a voltage is multiplied by a factor of $1/\sqrt{2}$, the power that the voltage can deliver to a given resistance is multiplied by a factor of one-half (because power is proportional to voltage squared). Thus, f_B is called the **half-power frequency**.

At the half-power frequency, the transfer-function magnitude is $1/\sqrt{2} \cong 0.707$ times its maximum value.

Applying the Transfer Function

As we saw in Section 1, if an input signal to a filter consists of several components of different frequencies, we can use the transfer function to compute the output for each component separately. Then, we can find the complete output by adding the separate components.

| **Example 3** | Calculation of *RC* Lowpass Output |

Suppose that an input signal given by

$$v_{in}(t) = 5\,\cos(20\pi t) + 5\,\cos(200\pi t) + 5\,\cos(2000\pi t)$$

is applied to the lowpass *RC* filter shown in Figure 9. Find an expression for the output signal.

Solution The filter has the form of the lowpass filter analyzed in this section. The half-power frequency is given by

$$f_B = \frac{1}{2\pi RC} = \frac{1}{2\pi \times (1000/2\pi) \times 10 \times 10^{-6}} = 100\ \text{Hz}$$

The first component of the input signal is

$$v_{in1}(t) = 5\,\cos(20\pi t)$$

For this component, the phasor is $\mathbf{V}_{in1} = 5\angle 0°$, and the angular frequency is $\omega = 20\pi$. Therefore, $f = \omega/2\pi = 10$. The transfer function of the circuit is given by Equation 9, which is repeated here for convenience:

$$H(f) = \frac{1}{1 + j(f/f_B)}$$

Evaluating the transfer function for the frequency of the first component ($f = 10$), we have

$$H(10) = \frac{1}{1 + j(10/100)} = 0.9950\angle{-5.71°}$$

The output phasor for the $f = 10$ component is simply the input phasor times the transfer function. Thus, we obtain

$$\mathbf{V}_{out1} = H(10) \times \mathbf{V}_{in1}$$
$$= (0.9950\angle{-5.71°}) \times (5\angle 0°) = 4.975\angle{-5.71°}$$

Hence, the output for the first component of the input signal is

$$v_{out1}(t) = 4.975\,\cos(20\pi t - 5.71°)$$

Similarly, the second component of the input signal is

$$v_{in2}(t) = 5\,\cos(200\pi t)$$

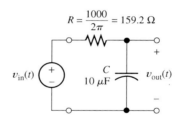

$$R = \frac{1000}{2\pi} = 159.2\ \Omega$$

Figure 9 Circuit of Example 3. The resistance has been picked so the break frequency turns out to be a convenient value.

and we have

$$\mathbf{V}_{in2} = 5\angle 0°$$

The frequency of the second component is $f = 100$:

$$H(100) = \frac{1}{1 + j(100/100)} = 0.7071\angle{-45°}$$

$$\mathbf{V}_{out2} = H(100) \times \mathbf{V}_{in2}$$

$$= (0.7071\angle{-45°}) \times (5\angle 0°) = 3.535\angle{-45°}$$

Therefore, the output for the second component of the input signal is

$$v_{out2}(t) = 3.535 \cos(200\pi t - 45°)$$

Finally, for the third and last component, we have

$$v_{in3}(t) = 5 \cos(2000\pi t)$$

$$\mathbf{V}_{in3} = 5\angle 0°$$

$$H(1000) = \frac{1}{1 + j(1000/100)} = 0.0995\angle{-84.29°}$$

$$\mathbf{V}_{out3} = H(1000) \times \mathbf{V}_{in3}$$

$$= (0.0995\angle{-84.29°}) \times (5\angle 0°) = 0.4975\angle{-84.29°}$$

Consequently, the output for the third component of the input signal is

$$v_{out3}(t) = 0.4975 \cos(2000\pi t - 84.29°)$$

Now, we can write an expression for the output signal by adding the output components:

$$v_{out}(t) = 4.975 \cos(20\pi t - 5.71°) + 3.535 \cos(200\pi t - 45°)$$

$$+ 0.4975 \cos(2000\pi t - 84.29°)$$

Notice that each component of the input signal $v_{in}(t)$ is treated differently by this filter. The $f = 10$ component is nearly unaffected in amplitude and phase. The $f = 100$ component is reduced in amplitude by a factor of 0.7071 and phase shifted by $-45°$. The amplitude of the $f = 1000$ component is reduced by approximately an order of magnitude. Thus, the filter discriminates against the high-frequency components. ■

Application of the First-Order Lowpass Filter

A simple application of the first-order lowpass filter is the tone control on a simple AM radio. The tone control adjusts the resistance and, therefore, the break frequency of the filter. Suppose that we are listening to an interesting news item from a distant radio station with an AM radio and lightning storms are causing electrical noise. It turns out that the components of voice signals are concentrated in the low end of the audible-frequency range. On the other hand, the noise caused by lightning has roughly equal-amplitude components at all frequencies. In this situation, we could adjust the tone control to lower the break frequency. Then, the high-frequency noise components would be rejected, while most of the voice components would be passed. In this way, we can improve the ratio of desired signal power to noise power produced by the loudspeaker and make the news more intelligible.

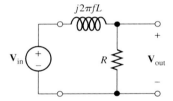

Figure 10 Another first-order
lowpass filter; see Exercise 4.

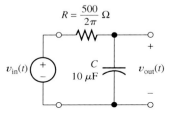

Figure 11 Circuit for Exercise 5.

Using Phasors with Components of Different Frequencies

We should not add the
phasors for components with
different frequencies.

Recall that phasors can be combined only for sinusoids with the same frequency. It is important to understand that *we should not add the phasors for components with different frequencies*. Thus, in the preceding example, we used phasors to find the output components as functions of time, which we then added.

Exercise 4 Derive an expression for the transfer function $H(f) = \mathbf{V}_{out}/\mathbf{V}_{in}$ of the filter shown in Figure 10. Show that $H(f)$ takes the same form as Equation 9 if we define $f_B = R/2\pi L$. ◻

Exercise 5 Suppose that the input signal for the circuit shown in Figure 11 is given by

$$v_{in}(t) = 10 \, \cos(40\pi t) + 5 \, \cos(1000\pi t) + 5 \, \cos(2\pi 10^4 t)$$

Find an expression for the output signal $v_{out}(t)$.
Answer

$$v_{out}(t) = 9.95 \, \cos(40\pi t - 5.71°) + 1.86 \, \cos(1000\pi t - 68.2°)$$

$$+ 0.100 \, \cos(2\pi 10^4 t - 88.9°)$$

◻

3 DECIBELS, THE CASCADE CONNECTION, AND LOGARITHMIC FREQUENCY SCALES

In comparing the performance of various filters, it is helpful to express the magnitudes of the transfer functions in **decibels**. To convert a transfer-function magnitude to decibels, we multiply the common logarithm (base 10) of the transfer-function magnitude by 20:

$$|H(f)|_{dB} = 20 \log |H(f)| \qquad (12)$$

(A transfer function is a ratio of voltages and is converted to decibels as 20 times the logarithm of the ratio. On the other hand, ratios of powers are converted to decibels by taking 10 times the logarithm of the ratio.)

Table 2. Transfer-Function Magnitudes and Their Decibel Equivalents

$|H(f)|$	$|H(f)|_{dB}$
100	40
10	20
2	6
$\sqrt{2}$	3
1	0
$1/\sqrt{2}$	−3
1/2	−6
0.1	−20
0.01	−40

Table 2 shows the decibel equivalents for selected values of transfer-function magnitude. Notice that the decibel equivalents are positive for magnitudes greater than unity, whereas the decibel equivalents are negative for magnitudes less than unity.

In many applications, the ability of a filter to strongly reject signals in a given frequency band is of primary importance. For example, a common problem associated with audio signals is that a small amount of the ac power line voltage can inadvertently be added to the signal. When applied to a loudspeaker, this 60-Hz component produces a disagreeable hum. (Actually, this problem is rapidly becoming a thing of the past as digital technologies replace analog.)

Usually, we approach this problem by trying to eliminate the electrical path by which the power line voltage is added to the desired audio signal. However, this is sometimes not possible. Then, we could try to design a filter that rejects the 60-Hz component and passes components at other frequencies. The magnitude of a filter transfer function to accomplish this is shown in Figure 12(a). A filter such as this, designed to eliminate components in a narrow range of frequencies, is called a **notch filter**.

It turns out that to reduce a loud hum (as loud as a heated conversation) to be barely audible, the transfer function must be −80 dB or less for the 60-Hz component, which corresponds to $|H(f)| = 10^{-4}$ or smaller. On the other hand, the transfer-function magnitude should be close to unity for the components to be passed by the filter. We refer to the range of frequencies to be passed as the **passband**.

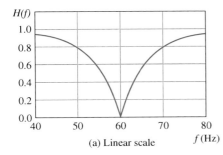
(a) Linear scale

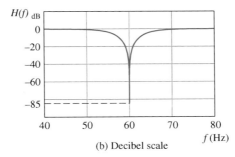
(b) Decibel scale

Figure 12 Transfer-function magnitude of a notch filter used to reduce hum in audio signals.

When we plot $|H(f)|$ without converting to decibels, it is difficult to show both values clearly on the same plot. If we choose a scale that shows the passband magnitude, we cannot see whether the magnitude is sufficiently small at 60 Hz. This is the case for the plot shown in Figure 12(a). On the other hand, if we choose a linear scale that clearly shows the magnitude at 60 Hz, the magnitude would be way off scale at other frequencies of interest.

However, when the magnitude is converted to decibels, both parts of the magnitude are readily seen. For example, Figure 12(b) shows the decibel equivalent for the magnitude plot shown in Figure 12(a). On this plot, we can see that the passband magnitude is approximately unity (0 dB) and that at 60 Hz, the magnitude is sufficiently small (less than −80 dB).

Thus, one of the advantages of converting transfer-function magnitudes to decibels before plotting is that very small and very large magnitudes can be displayed clearly on a single plot. We will see that another advantage is that decibel plots for many filter circuits can be approximated by straight lines (provided that a logarithmic scale is used for frequency). Furthermore, to understand some of the jargon used by electrical engineers, we must be familiar with decibels.

One of the advantages of converting transfer-function magnitudes to decibels before plotting is that very small and very large magnitudes can be displayed clearly on a single plot.

Cascaded Two-Port Networks

In the cascade connection, the output of one filter is connected to the input of a second filter.

When we connect the output terminals of one two-port circuit to the input terminals of another two-port circuit, we say that we have a **cascade** connection. This is illustrated in Figure 13. Notice that the output voltage of the first two-port network is the input voltage of the second two-port. The overall transfer function is

$$H(f) = \frac{\mathbf{V}_{\text{out}}}{\mathbf{V}_{\text{in}}}$$

However, the output voltage of the cascade is the output of the second two port (i.e., $\mathbf{V}_{\text{out}} = \mathbf{V}_{\text{out2}}$). Furthermore, the input to the cascade is the input to the first two port (i.e., $\mathbf{V}_{\text{in}} = \mathbf{V}_{\text{in1}}$). Thus,

$$H(f) = \frac{\mathbf{V}_{\text{out2}}}{\mathbf{V}_{\text{in1}}}$$

Multiplying and dividing by $\mathbf{V}_{\text{out1}}$, we have

$$H(f) = \frac{\mathbf{V}_{\text{out1}}}{\mathbf{V}_{\text{in1}}} \times \frac{\mathbf{V}_{\text{out2}}}{\mathbf{V}_{\text{out1}}}$$

Now, the output voltage of the first two port is the input to the second two port (i.e., $\mathbf{V}_{\text{out1}} = \mathbf{V}_{\text{in2}}$). Hence,

$$H(f) = \frac{\mathbf{V}_{\text{out1}}}{\mathbf{V}_{\text{in1}}} \times \frac{\mathbf{V}_{\text{out2}}}{\mathbf{V}_{\text{in2}}}$$

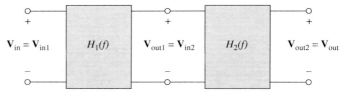

Figure 13 Cascade connection of two two-port circuits.

Finally, we can write

$$H(f) = H_1(f) \times H_2(f) \tag{13}$$

Thus, the transfer function of the cascade connection is the product of the transfer functions of the individual two-port networks. This fact can be extended to three or more two ports connected in cascade.

A potential source of difficulty in applying Equation 13 is that the transfer function of a two port usually depends on what is attached to its output terminals. *Thus, in applying Equation 13, we must find $H_1(f)$ with the second two port attached.*

In applying Equation 13, we must find $H_1(f)$ with the second two port attached.

Taking the magnitudes of the terms on both sides of Equation 13 and expressing in decibels, we have

$$20 \log |H(f)| = 20 \log \left[|H_1(f)| \times |H_2(f)| \right] \tag{14}$$

Using the fact that the logarithm of a product is equal to the sum of the logarithms of the terms in the product, we have

$$20 \log |H(f)| = 20 \log |H_1(f)| + 20 \log |H_2(f)| \tag{15}$$

which can be written as

$$|H(f)|_{dB} = |H_1(f)|_{dB} + |H_2(f)|_{dB} \tag{16}$$

Thus, in decibels, the individual transfer-function magnitudes are added to find the overall transfer-function magnitude for a cascade connection.

In decibels, the individual transfer-function magnitudes are added to find the overall transfer-function magnitude for a cascade connection.

Logarithmic Frequency Scales

We often use a **logarithmic scale** for frequency when plotting transfer functions. On a logarithmic scale, the variable is *multiplied* by a given factor for equal increments of length along the axis. (On a linear scale, equal lengths on the scale correspond to *adding* a given amount to the variable.) For example, a logarithmic frequency scale is shown in Figure 14.

On a logarithmic scale, the variable is multiplied by a given factor for equal increments of length along the axis.

A **decade** is a range of frequencies for which the ratio of the highest frequency to the lowest is 10. The frequency range from 2 to 20 Hz is one decade. Similarly, the range from 50 to 5000 Hz is two decades. (50 to 500 Hz is one decade, and 500 to 5000 Hz is another decade.)

An **octave** is a two-to-one change in frequency. For example, the range 10 to 20 Hz is one octave. The range 2 to 16 kHz is three octaves.

Suppose that we have two frequencies f_1 and f_2 for which $f_2 > f_1$. The number of decades between f_1 and f_2 is given by

$$\text{number of decades} = \log\left(\frac{f_2}{f_1}\right) \tag{17}$$

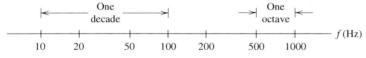

Figure 14 Logarithmic frequency scale.

in which we assume that the logarithm is base 10. The number of octaves between the two frequencies is

$$\text{number of octaves} = \log_2\left(\frac{f_2}{f_1}\right) = \frac{\log(f_2/f_1)}{\log(2)} \tag{18}$$

The advantage of a logarithmic frequency scale compared with a linear scale is that the variations in the magnitude or phase of a transfer function for a low range of frequency such as 10 to 20 Hz, as well as the variations in a high range such as 10 to 20 MHz, can be clearly shown on a single plot. With a linear scale, either the low range would be severely compressed or the high range would be off scale.

Exercise 6 Suppose that $|H(f)| = 50$. Find the decibel equivalent.
Answer $|H(f)|_{dB} = 34$ dB. □

Exercise 7 a. Suppose that $|H(f)|_{dB} = 15$ dB. Find $|H(f)|$. **b.** Repeat for $|H(f)|_{dB} = 30$ dB.
Answer **a.** $|H(f)| = 5.62$; **b.** $|H(f)| = 31.6$. □

Exercise 8 a. What frequency is two octaves higher than 1000 Hz? **b.** Three octaves lower? **c.** Two decades higher? **d.** One decade lower?
Answer **a.** 4000 Hz is two octaves higher than 1000 Hz; **b.** 125 Hz is three octaves lower than 1000 Hz; **c.** 100 kHz is two decades higher than 1000 Hz; **d.** 100 Hz is one decade lower than 1000 Hz. □

Exercise 9 a. What frequency is halfway between 100 and 1000 Hz on a logarithmic frequency scale? **b.** On a linear frequency scale?
Answer **a.** 316.2 Hz is halfway between 100 and 1000 Hz on a logarithmic scale; **b.** 550 Hz is halfway between 100 and 1000 Hz on a linear frequency scale. □

Exercise 10 a. How many decades are between $f_1 = 20$ Hz and $f_2 = 15$ kHz? (This is the approximate range of audible frequencies.) **b.** How many octaves?
Answer

a. Number of decades $= \log\left(\frac{15\text{ kHz}}{20\text{ Hz}}\right) = 2.87$

b. Number of octaves $= \frac{\log(15000/20)}{\log(2)} = 9.55$ □

4 BODE PLOTS

A Bode plot is a plot of the decibel magnitude of a network function versus frequency using a logarithmic scale for frequency.

A **Bode plot** is a plot of the decibel magnitude of a network function versus frequency using a logarithmic scale for frequency. Because it can clearly illustrate very large and very small magnitudes for a wide range of frequencies on one plot, the Bode plot is particularly useful for displaying transfer functions. Furthermore, it turns out that Bode plots of network functions can often be closely approximated by straight-line segments, so they are relatively easy to draw. (Actually, we now use computers to plot functions, so this advantage is not as important as it once was.) Terminology related to these plots is frequently encountered in signal-processing literature. Finally, an understanding of Bode plots enables us to make estimates quickly when dealing with transfer functions.

To illustrate Bode plot concepts, we consider the first-order lowpass transfer function of Equation 9, repeated here for convenience:

$$H(f) = \frac{1}{1 + j(f/f_B)}$$

The magnitude of this transfer function is given by Equation 10, which is

$$|H(f)| = \frac{1}{\sqrt{1 + (f/f_B)^2}}$$

To convert the magnitude to decibels, we take 20 times the logarithm of the magnitude:

$$|H(f)|_{dB} = 20 \log |H(f)|$$

Substituting the expression for the transfer-function magnitude, we get

$$|H(f)|_{dB} = 20 \log \frac{1}{\sqrt{1 + (f/f_B)^2}}$$

Using the properties of the logarithm, we obtain

$$|H(f)|_{dB} = 20 \log(1) - 20 \log \sqrt{1 + \left(\frac{f}{f_B}\right)^2}$$

Of course, the logarithm of unity is zero. Therefore,

$$|H(f)|_{dB} = -20 \log \sqrt{1 + \left(\frac{f}{f_B}\right)^2}$$

Finally, since $\log(\sqrt{x}) = \frac{1}{2} \log(x)$, we have

$$|H(f)|_{dB} = -10 \log[1 + \left(\frac{f}{f_B}\right)^2] \tag{19}$$

Notice that the value given by Equation 19 is approximately 0 dB for $f \ll f_B$. Thus, for low frequencies, the transfer-function magnitude is approximated by the horizontal straight line shown in Figure 15, labeled as the **low-frequency asymptote**.

On the other hand, for $f \gg f_B$, Equation 19 is approximately

$$|H(f)|_{dB} \cong -20 \log \left(\frac{f}{f_B}\right) \tag{20}$$

Evaluating for various values of f, we obtain the results shown in Table 3. Plotting these values results in the straight line shown sloping downward on the right-hand side of Figure 15, labeled as the **high-frequency asymptote**. Notice that the two straight-line asymptotes intersect at the half-power frequency f_B. For this reason, f_B is also known as the **corner frequency** or as the **break frequency**.

Also, notice that the slope of the high-frequency asymptote is -20 dB per decade of frequency. (This slope can also be stated as -6 dB per octave.)

If we evaluate Equation 19 at $f = f_B$, we find that

$$|H(f_B)|_{dB} = -3 \text{ dB}$$

Thus, the asymptotes are in error by only 3 dB at the corner frequency. The actual curve for $|H(f)|_{dB}$ is also shown in Figure 15.

The low-frequency asymptote is constant at 0 dB.

The high-frequency asymptote slopes downward at 20 dB/decade, starting from 0 dB at f_B.

Notice that the two straight-line asymptotes intersect at the half-power frequency f_B.

The asymptotes are in error by only 3 dB at the corner frequency f_B.

Table 3. Values of the Approximate Expression (Equation 20) for Selected Frequencies

f	$|H(f)|_{dB}$
f_B	0
$2f_B$	−6
$10f_B$	−20
$100f_B$	−40
$1000f_B$	−60

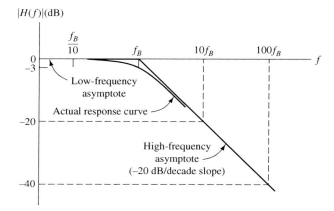

Figure 15 Magnitude Bode plot for the first-order lowpass filter.

Phase Plot

The phase of the first-order lowpass transfer function is given by Equation 11, which is repeated here for convenience:

$$\angle H(f) = -\arctan\left(\frac{f}{f_B}\right)$$

Evaluating, we find that the phase approaches zero at very low frequencies, equals −45° at the break frequency, and approaches −90° at high frequencies.

Figure 16 shows a plot of phase versus frequency. Notice that the curve can be approximated by the following straight-line segments:

1. A horizontal line at zero for $f < f_B/10$.

2. A sloping line from zero phase at $f_B/10$ to −90° at $10f_B$.

3. A horizontal line at −90° for $f > 10f_B$.

The actual phase curve departs from these straight-line approximations by less than 6°. Hence, working by hand, we could easily construct an approximate plot of phase.

Many circuit functions can be plotted by the methods we have demonstrated for the simple lowpass *RC* circuit; however, we will not try to develop your skill at this to a high degree. Bode plots of amplitude and phase for *RLC* circuits are easily produced by computer programs. We have shown the manual approach to analyzing and drawing the Bode plot for the *RC* lowpass filter mainly to present the concepts and terminology.

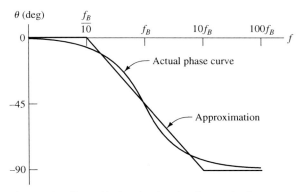

Figure 16 Phase Bode plot for the first-order lowpass filter.

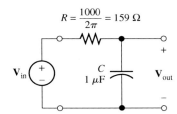

Figure 17 Circuit for Exercise 11.

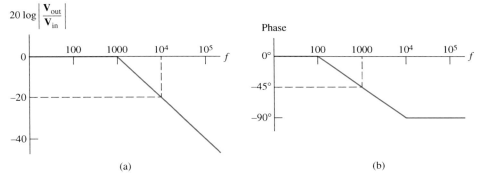

(a)   (b)

Figure 18 Answers for Exercise 11.

Exercise 11 Sketch the approximate straight-line Bode magnitude and phase plots to scale for the circuit shown in Figure 17.

Answer See Figure 18. □

5 FIRST-ORDER HIGHPASS FILTERS

The circuit shown in Figure 19 is called a **first-order highpass filter**. It can be analyzed in much the same manner as the lowpass circuit considered earlier in this chapter. The resulting transfer function is given by

$$H(f) = \frac{\mathbf{V}_{out}}{\mathbf{V}_{in}} = \frac{j(f/f_B)}{1 + j(f/f_B)} \tag{21}$$

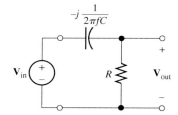

Figure 19 First-order highpass filter.

in which

$$f_B = \frac{1}{2\pi RC} \tag{22}$$

Exercise 12 Use circuit analysis to derive the transfer function for the circuit of Figure 19, and show that it can be put into the form of Equations 21 and 22. □

Magnitude and Phase of the Transfer Function

The magnitude of the transfer function is given by

$$|H(f)| = \frac{f/f_B}{\sqrt{1 + (f/f_B)^2}} \tag{23}$$

This is plotted in Figure 20(a). Notice that the transfer-function magnitude goes to zero for dc ($f = 0$). For high frequencies ($f >> f_B$), the transfer-function magnitude approaches unity. Thus, this filter passes high-frequency components and tends to reject low-frequency components. That is why the circuit is called a highpass filter.

Highpass filters are useful whenever we want to retain high-frequency components and reject low-frequency components. For example, suppose that we want to record warbler songs in a noisy environment. It turns out that bird calls fall in the high-frequency portion of the audible range. The audible range of frequencies is from 20 Hz to 15 kHz (approximately), and the calls of warblers fall (mainly) in the range above 2 kHz. On the other hand, the noise may be concentrated at lower frequencies. For example, heavy trucks rumbling down a bumpy road would produce strong noise components lower in frequency than 2 kHz. To record singing warblers in the vicinity of such a noise source, a highpass filter would be helpful. We would select R and C

Highpass filters are useful whenever we want to retain high-frequency components and reject low-frequency components.

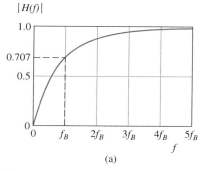

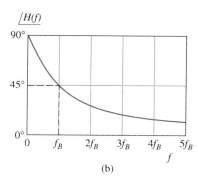

(a) (b)

Figure 20 Magnitude and phase for the first-order highpass transfer function.

to achieve a half-power frequency f_B of approximately 2 kHz. Then, the filter would pass the songs and reject some of the noise.

Recall that if the amplitude of a component is multiplied by a factor of $1/\sqrt{2}$, the power that the component can deliver to a resistance is multiplied by a factor of $1/2$. For $f = f_B, |H(f)| = 1/\sqrt{2} \cong 0.707$, so that, as in the case of the lowpass filter, f_B is called the *half-power frequency*. (Here again, several alternative names are *corner frequency*, *3-dB frequency*, and *break frequency*.)

The phase of the highpass transfer function (Equation 21) is given by

$$\angle H(f) = 90° - \arctan\left(\frac{f}{f_B}\right) \tag{24}$$

A plot of the phase shift of the highpass filter is shown in Figure 20(b).

Bode Plots for the First-Order Highpass Filter

As we have seen, a convenient way to plot transfer functions is to use the Bode plot, in which the magnitude is converted to decibels and a logarithmic frequency scale is used. In decibels, the magnitude of the highpass transfer function is

$$|H(f)|_{dB} = 20\log\frac{f/f_B}{\sqrt{1 + (f/f_B)^2}}$$

This can be written as

$$|H(f)|_{dB} = 20\log\left(\frac{f}{f_B}\right) - 10\log[1 + \left(\frac{f}{f_B}\right)^2] \tag{25}$$

For $f \ll f_B$, the second term on the right-hand side of Equation 25 is approximately zero. Thus, for $f \ll f_B$, we have

$$|H(f)|_{dB} \cong 20\log\left(\frac{f}{f_B}\right) \qquad \text{for } f \ll f_B \tag{26}$$

Evaluating this for selected values of f, we find the values given in Table 4. Plotting these values, we obtain the low-frequency asymptote shown on the left-hand side of Figure 21(a). Notice that the low-frequency asymptote slopes downward to the left at a rate of 20 dB per decade.

For $f \gg f_B$, the magnitude given by Equation 25 is approximately 0 dB. Hence,

$$|H(f)|_{dB} \cong 0 \qquad \text{for } f \gg f_B \tag{27}$$

Table 4. Values of the Approximate Expression Given in Equation 26 for Selected Frequencies

f	$|H(f)|_{dB}$
f_B	0
$f_B/2$	-6
$f_B/10$	-20
$f_B/100$	-40

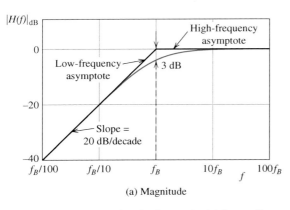

(a) Magnitude

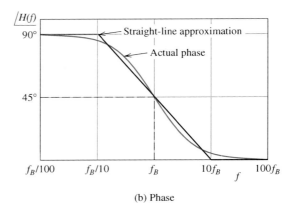

(b) Phase

Figure 21 Bode plots for the first-order highpass filter.

This is plotted as the high-frequency asymptote in Figure 21(a). Notice that the high-frequency asymptote and the low-frequency asymptote meet at $f = f_B$. (That is why f_B is sometimes called the *break frequency*.)

The actual values of $|H(f)|_{dB}$ are also plotted in Figure 21(a). Notice that the actual value at $f = f_B$ is $|H(f_B)|_{dB} = -3$ dB. Thus, the actual curve is only 3 dB from the asymptotes at $f = f_B$. For other frequencies, the actual curve is closer to the asymptotes. The Bode phase plot is shown in Figure 21(b) along with straight-line approximations.

Example 4 **Determination of the Break Frequency for a Highpass Filter**

Suppose that we want a first-order highpass filter that has a transfer-function magnitude of -30 dB at $f = 60$ Hz. Find the break frequency for this filter.

Solution   Recall that the low-frequency asymptote slopes at a rate of 20 dB/decade. Thus, we must select f_B to be

$$\frac{30 \text{ dB}}{20 \text{ dB/decade}} = 1.5 \text{ decades}$$

higher than 60 Hz. Employing Equation 17, we have

$$\log\left(\frac{f_B}{60}\right) = 1.5$$

This is equivalent to

$$\frac{f_B}{60} = 10^{1.5} = 31.6$$

which yields

$$f_B \cong 1900 \text{ Hz} \qquad \blacksquare$$

We often need a filter that greatly reduces the amplitude of a component at a given frequency, but has a negligible effect on components at nearby frequencies.

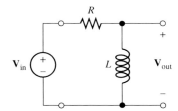

Figure 22 Circuit for Exercise 13.

The preceding example shows that to reduce the amplitude of a given component by a large factor by using a first-order filter, we must place the break frequency far from the component to be rejected. Then, components at other frequencies are also affected. This is a problem that can only be solved by using more complex (higher order) filter circuits. We consider second-order filters later in the chapter.

Exercise 13 Consider the circuit shown in Figure 22. Show that the transfer function of this filter is given by Equation 21 if the half-power frequency is defined to be $f_B = R/2\pi L$. □

Exercise 14 Suppose that we need a first-order RC highpass filter that reduces the amplitude of a component at a frequency of 1 kHz by 50 dB. The resistance is to be 1 kΩ. Find the half-power frequency and the capacitance.
Answer $f_B = 316$ kHz, $C = 503$ pF. □

6 SERIES RESONANCE

In this section and the next, we consider resonant circuits. These circuits form the basis for filters that have better performance (in passing desired signals and rejecting undesired signals that are relatively close in frequency) than first-order filters. Such filters are useful in radio receivers, for example. Another application is a notch filter to remove 60-Hz interference from audio signals. Resonance is a phenomenon that can be observed in mechanical systems as well as in electrical circuits. For example, a guitar string is a resonant mechanical system.

> Resonance is a phenomenon that can be observed in mechanical systems and electrical circuits.

We will see that when a sinusoidal source of the proper frequency is applied to a resonant circuit, voltages much larger than the source voltage can appear in the circuit. The familiar story of opera singers using their voices to break wine goblets is an example of a mechanically resonant structure (the goblet) driven by an approximately sinusoidal source (the sound), resulting in vibrations in the glass of sufficient magnitude to cause fracture. Another example is the Tacoma Narrows Bridge collapse in 1940. Driven by wind forces, a resonance of the bridge structure resulted in oscillations that tore the bridge apart. Some other examples of mechanical resonant systems are the strings of musical instruments, bells, the air column in an organ pipe, and a mass suspended by a spring.

> You can find a short video clip of the bridge in motion on the internet.

Consider the series circuit shown in Figure 23. The impedance seen by the source in this circuit is given by

$$Z_s(f) = j2\pi fL + R - j\frac{1}{2\pi fC} \qquad (28)$$

> The resonant frequency f_0 is defined to be the frequency at which the impedance is purely resistive (i.e., the total reactance is zero).

The **resonant frequency** f_0 is defined to be the frequency at which the impedance is purely resistive (i.e., the total reactance is zero). For the reactance to equal zero,

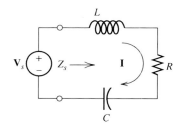

Figure 23 The series resonant circuit.

the impedance of the inductance must equal the impedance of the capacitance in magnitude. Thus, we have

$$2\pi f_0 L = \frac{1}{2\pi f_0 C} \tag{29}$$

Solving for the resonant frequency, we get

$$f_0 = \frac{1}{2\pi \sqrt{LC}} \tag{30}$$

The quality factor Q_s of a series circuit is defined to be the ratio of the reactance of the inductance at the resonant frequency to the resistance.

The **quality factor** Q_s is defined to be the ratio of the reactance of the inductance at the resonant frequency to the resistance:

$$Q_s = \frac{2\pi f_0 L}{R} \tag{31}$$

Solving Equation 29 for L and substituting into Equation 31, we obtain

$$Q_s = \frac{1}{2\pi f_0 C R} \tag{32}$$

Using Equations 30 and 31 to substitute into Equation 28, we can eventually reduce the equation for the impedance to

$$Z_s(f) = R\left[1 + jQ_s\left(\frac{f}{f_0} - \frac{f_0}{f}\right)\right] \tag{33}$$

Thus, the series resonant circuit is characterized by its quality factor Q_s and resonant frequency f_0.

Plots of the normalized magnitude and the phase of the impedance versus normalized frequency f/f_0 are shown in Figure 24. Notice that the impedance magnitude is minimum at the resonant frequency. As the quality factor becomes larger, the minimum becomes sharper.

Series Resonant Circuit as a Bandpass Filter

Referring to Figure 23, the current is given by

$$I = \frac{V_s}{Z_s(f)}$$

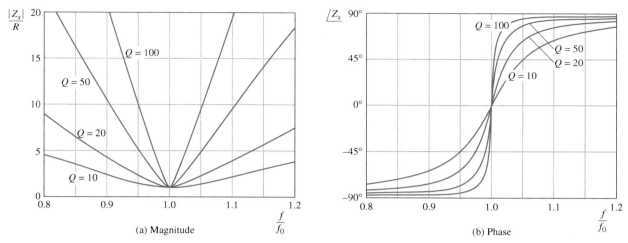

Figure 24 Plots of normalized magnitude and phase for the impedance of the series resonant circuit versus frequency.

Using Equation 33 to substitute for the impedance, we have

$$\mathbf{I} = \frac{\mathbf{V}_s/R}{1 + jQ_s(f/f_0 - f_0/f)}$$

The voltage across the resistance is

$$\mathbf{V}_R = R\mathbf{I} = \frac{\mathbf{V}_s}{1 + jQ_s(f/f_0 - f_0/f)}$$

Dividing by $\mathbf{V}_s$, we obtain the transfer function

$$\frac{\mathbf{V}_R}{\mathbf{V}_s} = \frac{1}{1 + jQ_s(f/f_0 - f_0/f)}$$

Plots of the magnitude of $\mathbf{V}_R/\mathbf{V}_s$ versus f are shown in Figure 25 for various values of Q_s.

Consider a (sinusoidal) source of constant amplitude and variable frequency. At low frequencies, the impedance magnitude of the capacitance is large, the current $\mathbf{I}$ is small in magnitude, and $\mathbf{V}_R$ is small in magnitude (compared with $\mathbf{V}_s$). At resonance, the total impedance magnitude reaches a minimum (because the reactances of the inductance and the capacitance cancel), the current magnitude is maximum, and $\mathbf{V}_R = \mathbf{V}_s$. At high frequencies, the impedance of the inductance is large, the current magnitude is small, and $\mathbf{V}_R$ is small in magnitude.

Now, suppose that we apply a source signal having components ranging in frequency about the resonant frequency. The components of the source that are close to the resonant frequency appear across the resistance with little change in amplitude. However, components that are higher or lower in frequency are significantly reduced in amplitude. Thus, a band of components centered at the resonant frequency is passed while components farther from the resonant frequency are (partly) rejected. We say that the resonant circuit behaves as a **bandpass filter**.

Recall that the half-power frequencies of a filter are the frequencies for which the transfer-function magnitude has fallen from its maximum by a factor of $1/\sqrt{2} \cong 0.707$.

The resonant circuit behaves as a bandpass filter.

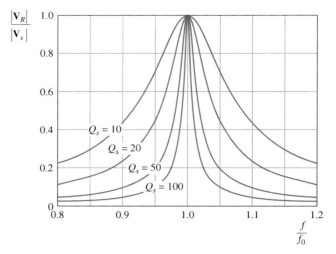

Figure 25 Plots of the transfer-function magnitude $|\mathbf{V}_R/\mathbf{V}_s|$ for the series resonant bandpass-filter circuit.

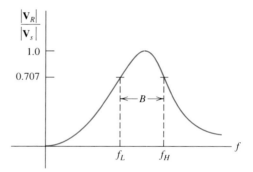

Figure 26 The bandwidth B is equal to the difference between the half-power frequencies.

For the series resonant circuit, there are two half-power frequencies f_L and f_H. This is illustrated in Figure 26.

The **bandwidth** B of this filter is the difference between the half-power frequencies:

$$B = f_H - f_L \tag{34}$$

For the series resonant circuit, it can be shown that

$$B = \frac{f_0}{Q_s} \tag{35}$$

Furthermore, for $Q_s \gg 1$, the half-power frequencies are given by the approximate expressions

$$f_H \cong f_0 + \frac{B}{2} \tag{36}$$

and

$$f_L \cong f_0 - \frac{B}{2} \tag{37}$$

Example 5	Series Resonant Circuit

Consider the series resonant circuit shown in Figure 27. Compute the resonant frequency, the bandwidth, and the half-power frequencies. Assuming that the frequency of the source is the same as the resonant frequency, find the phasor voltages across the elements and draw a phasor diagram.

Solution   First, we use Equation 30 to compute the resonant frequency:

$$f_0 = \frac{1}{2\pi \sqrt{LC}} = \frac{1}{2\pi \sqrt{0.1592 \times 0.1592 \times 10^{-6}}} = 1000 \text{ Hz}$$

The quality factor is given by Equation 31:

$$Q_s = \frac{2\pi f_0 L}{R} = \frac{2\pi \times 1000 \times 0.1592}{100} = 10$$

The bandwidth is given by Equation 35:

$$B = \frac{f_0}{Q_s} = \frac{1000}{10} = 100 \text{ Hz}$$

Next, we use Equations 36 and 37 to find the approximate half-power frequencies:

$$f_H \cong f_0 + \frac{B}{2} = 1000 + \frac{100}{2} = 1050 \text{ Hz}$$

$$f_L \cong f_0 - \frac{B}{2} = 1000 - \frac{100}{2} = 950 \text{ Hz}$$

At resonance, the impedance of the inductance and capacitance are

$$Z_L = j2\pi f_0 L = j2\pi \times 1000 \times 0.1592 = j1000 \ \Omega$$

$$Z_C = -j\frac{1}{2\pi f_0 C} = -j\frac{1}{2\pi \times 1000 \times 0.1592 \times 10^{-6}} = -j1000 \ \Omega$$

As expected, the reactances are equal in magnitude at the resonant frequency. The total impedance of the circuit is

$$Z_s = R + Z_L + Z_C = 100 + j1000 - j1000 = 100 \ \Omega$$

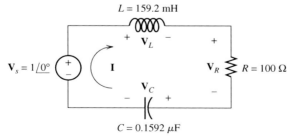

Figure 27 Series resonant circuit of Example 5. (The component values have been selected so the resonant frequency and Q_s turn out to be round numbers.)

323

The phasor current is given by

$$\mathbf{I} = \frac{\mathbf{V}_s}{Z_s} = \frac{1\angle 0°}{100} = 0.01\angle 0°$$

The voltages across the elements are

$$\mathbf{V}_R = R\mathbf{I} = 100 \times 0.01\angle 0° = 1\angle 0°$$
$$\mathbf{V}_L = Z_L\mathbf{I} = j1000 \times 0.01\angle 0° = 10\angle 90°$$
$$\mathbf{V}_C = Z_C\mathbf{I} = -j1000 \times 0.01\angle 0° = 10\angle -90°$$

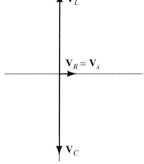

Figure 28 Phasor diagram for Example 5.

The phasor diagram is shown in Figure 28. Notice that the voltages across the inductance and capacitance are much larger than the source voltage in magnitude. Nevertheless, Kirchhoff's voltage law is satisfied because $\mathbf{V}_L$ and $\mathbf{V}_C$ are out of phase and cancel. ∎

In Example 5, we found that the voltage magnitudes across the inductance and capacitance are Q_s times higher than the source voltage. Thus, a higher quality factor leads to higher voltage magnification. This is similar to the large vibrations that can be caused in a wine goblet by an opera singer's voice.

Exercise 15 Determine the R and C values for a series resonant circuit that has $L = 10\ \mu\text{H}$, $f_0 = 1$ MHz, and $Q_s = 50$. Find the bandwidth and approximate half-power frequencies of the circuit.
Answer $C = 2533$ pF, $R = 1.257\ \Omega$, $B = 20$ kHz, $f_L \cong 990$ kHz, $f_H \cong 1010$ kHz. □

Exercise 16 Suppose that a voltage $\mathbf{V}_s = 1\angle 0°$ at a frequency of 1 MHz is applied to the circuit of Exercise 15. Find the phasor voltages across the resistance, capacitance, and inductance.
Answer $\mathbf{V}_R = 1\angle 0°$, $\mathbf{V}_C = 50\angle -90°$, $\mathbf{V}_L = 50\angle 90°$. □

Exercise 17 Find the R and L values for a series resonant circuit that has $C = 470$ pF, a resonant frequency of 5 MHz, and a bandwidth of 200 kHz.
Answer $R = 2.709\ \Omega$, $L = 2.156\ \mu\text{H}$. □

7 PARALLEL RESONANCE

Another type of resonant circuit known as a **parallel resonant circuit** is shown in Figure 29. The impedance of this circuit is given by

$$Z_p = \frac{1}{1/R + j2\pi fC - j(1/2\pi fL)} \tag{38}$$

As in the series resonant circuit, the **resonant frequency** f_0 is the frequency for which the impedance is purely resistive. This occurs when the imaginary parts of the denominator of Equation 38 cancel. Thus, we have

$$2\pi f_0 C = \frac{1}{2\pi f_0 L} \tag{39}$$

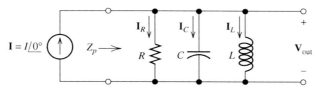

Figure 29 The parallel resonant circuit.

Solving for the resonant frequency, we get

$$f_0 = \frac{1}{2\pi\sqrt{LC}} \tag{40}$$

which is exactly the same as the expression for the resonant frequency of the series circuit discussed in Section 6.

For the parallel circuit, we define the quality factor Q_p as the ratio of the resistance to the reactance of the inductance at resonance, given by

$$Q_p = \frac{R}{2\pi f_0 L} \tag{41}$$

Notice that this is the reciprocal of the expression for the quality factor Q_s of the series resonant circuit. Solving Equation 40 for L and substituting into Equation 41, we obtain another expression for the quality factor:

> Notice that the formula for Q_p of a parallel circuit in terms of the circuit elements is the reciprocal of the formula for Q_s of a series circuit.

$$Q_p = 2\pi f_0 CR \tag{42}$$

If we solve Equations 41 and 42 for L and C, respectively, and then substitute into Equation 38, we eventually obtain

$$Z_p = \frac{R}{1 + jQ_p(f/f_0 - f_0/f)} \tag{43}$$

The voltage across the parallel resonant circuit is the product of the phasor current and the impedance:

$$\mathbf{V}_{\text{out}} = \frac{\mathbf{I}R}{1 + jQ_p(f/f_0 - f_0/f)} \tag{44}$$

Suppose that we hold the current constant in magnitude and change the frequency. Then, the magnitude of the voltage is a function of frequency. A plot of voltage magnitude for the parallel resonant circuit is shown in Figure 30. Notice that the voltage magnitude reaches its maximum $V_{o\,\text{max}} = RI$ at the resonant frequency. These curves have the same shape as the curves shown in Figures 25 and 26 for the voltage transfer function of the series resonant circuit.

The half-power frequencies f_L and f_H are defined to be the frequencies at which the voltage magnitude reaches the maximum value times $1/\sqrt{2}$. The bandwidth of the circuit is given by

$$B = f_H - f_L \tag{45}$$

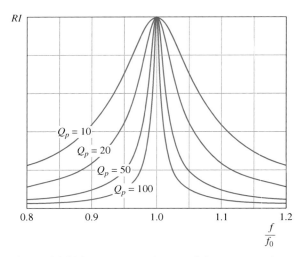

Figure 30 Voltage across the parallel resonant circuit for a constant-amplitude variable-frequency current source.

It can be shown that the bandwidth is related to the resonant frequency and quality factor by the expression

$$B = \frac{f_0}{Q_p} \tag{46}$$

Parallel Resonant Circuit

Find the L and C values for a parallel resonant circuit that has $R = 10\,k\Omega, f_0 = 1\,MHz$, and $B = 100\,kHz$. If $\mathbf{I} = 10^{-3}\underline{/0°}$, draw the phasor diagram showing the currents through each of the elements in the circuit at resonance.

Solution   First, we compute the quality factor of the circuit. Rearranging Equation 46 and substituting values, we have

$$Q_p = \frac{f_0}{B} = \frac{10^6}{10^5} = 10$$

Solving Equation 41 for the inductance and substituting values, we get

$$L = \frac{R}{2\pi f_0 Q_p} = \frac{10^4}{2\pi \times 10^6 \times 10} = 159.2\,\mu H$$

Similarly, using Equation 42, we find that

$$C = \frac{Q_p}{2\pi f_0 R} = \frac{10}{2\pi \times 10^6 \times 10^4} = 159.2\,pF$$

At resonance, the voltage is given by

$$\mathbf{V}_{out} = \mathbf{I}R = (10^{-3}\underline{/0°}) \times 10^4 = 10\underline{/0°}$$

and the currents are given by

$$\mathbf{I}_R = \frac{\mathbf{V}_{out}}{R} = \frac{10\underline{/0°}}{10^4} = 10^{-3}\underline{/0°}$$

$$\mathbf{I}_L = \frac{\mathbf{V}_{out}}{j2\pi f_0 L} = \frac{10\underline{/0°}}{j10^3} = 10^{-2}\underline{/-90°}$$

$$\mathbf{I}_C = \frac{\mathbf{V}_{out}}{-j/2\pi f_0 C} = \frac{10\underline{/0°}}{-j10^3} = 10^{-2}\underline{/90°}$$

The phasor diagram is shown in Figure 31. Notice that the currents through the inductance and capacitance are larger in magnitude than the applied source current. However, since $\mathbf{I}_C$ and $\mathbf{I}_L$ are out of phase, they cancel. ■

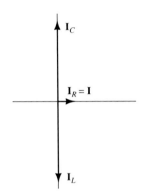

Exercise 18 A parallel resonant circuit has $R = 10\ k\Omega$, $L = 100\ \mu H$, and $C = 500$ pF. Find the resonant frequency, quality factor, and bandwidth.
Answer $f_0 = 711.8$ kHz, $Q_p = 22.36$, $B = 31.83$ kHz. □

Exercise 19 A parallel resonant circuit has $f_0 = 10$ MHz, $B = 200$ kHz, and $R = 1$ kΩ. Find L and C.
Answer $L = 0.3183\ \mu H$, $C = 795.8$ pF. □

Figure 31 Phasor diagram for Example 6.

8 IDEAL AND SECOND-ORDER FILTERS

Ideal Filters

In discussing filter performance, it is helpful to consider ideal filters. An ideal filter passes components in the desired frequency range with no change in amplitude or phase and totally rejects the components in the undesired frequency range. Depending on the locations of the frequencies to be passed and rejected, we have different types of filters: lowpass, highpass, bandpass, and band reject. The transfer functions $H(f) = \mathbf{V}_{out}/\mathbf{V}_{in}$ of the four types of ideal filters are shown in Figure 32.

- An **ideal lowpass filter** [Figure 32(a)] passes components below its cutoff frequency f_H and rejects components higher in frequency than f_H.

- An **ideal highpass filter** [Figure 32(b)] passes components above its cutoff frequency f_L and rejects components lower in frequency than f_L.

- An **ideal bandpass filter** [Figure 32(c)] passes components that lie between its cutoff frequencies (f_L and f_H) and rejects components outside that range.

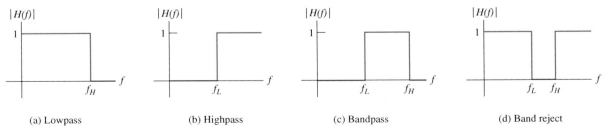

(a) Lowpass   (b) Highpass   (c) Bandpass   (d) Band reject

Figure 32 Transfer functions of ideal filters.

- An **ideal band-reject filter** [Figure 32(d)], which is also called a **notch filter**, rejects components that lie between its cutoff frequencies (f_L and f_H) and passes components outside that range.

As we have seen earlier in this chapter, filters are useful whenever a signal contains desired components in one range of frequency and undesired components in another range of frequency. For example, Figure 33(a) shows a 1-kHz sine wave that has been corrupted by high-frequency noise. By passing this noisy signal through a lowpass filter, the noise is eliminated.

Unfortunately, it is not possible to construct ideal filters—they can only be approximated by real circuits. As the circuits are allowed to increase in complexity, it is possible to design filters that do a better job of rejecting unwanted components and retaining the desired components. Thus, we will see that second-order circuits

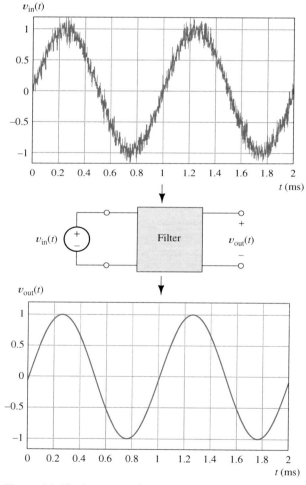

Figure 33 The input signal v_{in} consists of a 1-kHz sine wave plus high-frequency noise. By passing v_{in} through an ideal lowpass filter with the proper cutoff frequency, the sine wave is passed and the noise is rejected, resulting in a clean output signal.

perform better (i.e., closer to ideal) than the first-order circuits considered earlier in this chapter.

Second-Order Lowpass Filter

Figure 34(a) shows a second-order lowpass filter based on the series resonant circuit of Section 6. The filter is characterized by its resonant frequency f_0 and quality factor Q_s, which are given by Equations 30 and 31. It can be shown that the transfer function for this circuit is given by

$$H(f) = \frac{\mathbf{V}_{out}}{\mathbf{V}_{in}} = \frac{-jQ_s(f_0/f)}{1 + jQ_s(f/f_0 - f_0/f)} \tag{47}$$

Bode plots of the transfer-function magnitude are shown in Figure 34(c). Notice that for $Q_s \gg 1$, the transfer-function magnitude reaches a high peak in the vicinity of the resonant frequency. Usually, in designing a filter, we want the gain to be approximately constant in the passband, and we select $Q_s \cong 1$. (Actually, $Q_s = 0.707$ is the highest value for which the transfer-function magnitude does not display an increase before rolling off. The transfer function for this value of Q_s is said to be *maximally flat*, is also known as a *Butterworth function*, and is often used for lowpass filters.)

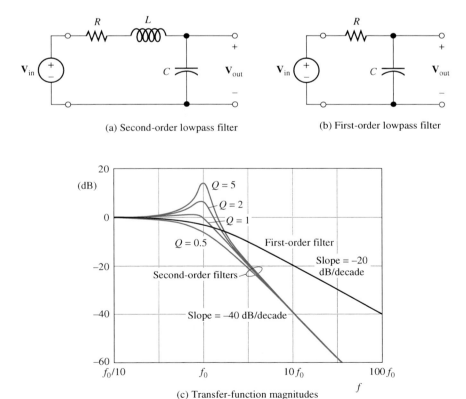

(a) Second-order lowpass filter

(b) First-order lowpass filter

(c) Transfer-function magnitudes

Figure 34 Lowpass filter circuits and their transfer-function magnitudes versus frequency.

Comparison of First- and Second-Order Filters

The transfer-function magnitude of a second-order lowpass filter declines 40 dB per decade well above the break frequency, whereas the transfer-function magnitude for the first-order filter declines at only 20 dB per decade. Thus, the second-order filter is a better approximation to an ideal lowpass filter.

For comparison, a first-order lowpass filter is shown in Figure 34(b), and the Bode plot of its transfer function is shown in Figure 34(c). The first-order circuit is characterized by its half-power frequency $f_B = 1/(2\pi RC)$. (We have selected $f_B = f_0$ in making the comparison.) Notice that above f_0 the magnitude of the transfer function falls more rapidly for the second-order filter than for the first-order filter (-40 dB/decade versus -20 dB/decade).

Second-Order Highpass Filter

A second-order highpass filter is shown in Figure 35(a), and its magnitude Bode plot is shown in Figure 35(b). Here again, we usually want the magnitude to be as nearly constant as possible in the passband, so we select $Q_s \cong 1$. (In other words, we usually want to design the filter to approximate an ideal filter as closely as possible.)

Second-Order Bandpass Filter

A second-order bandpass filter is shown in Figure 36(a), and its magnitude Bode plot is shown in Figure 36(b). The half-power bandwidth B is given by Equations 34 and 35, which state that

$$B = f_H - f_L$$

and

$$B = \frac{f_0}{Q_s}$$

Second-Order Band-Reject (Notch) Filter

A second-order band-reject filter is shown in Figure 37(a) and its magnitude Bode plot is shown in Figure 37(b). In theory, the magnitude of the transfer function is zero for $f = f_0$. [In decibels, this corresponds to $|H(f_0)| = -\infty$ dB.] However, real

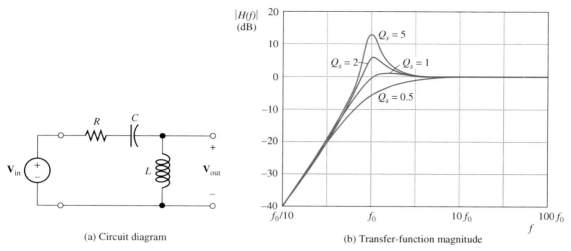

(a) Circuit diagram

(b) Transfer-function magnitude

Figure 35 Second-order highpass filter and its transfer-function magnitude versus frequency for several values of Q_s.

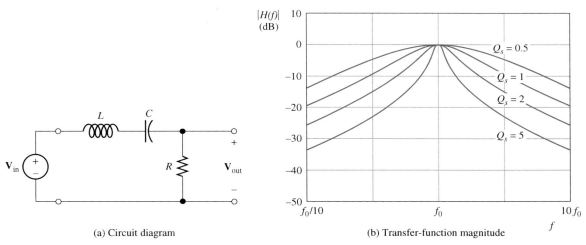

(a) Circuit diagram
(b) Transfer-function magnitude

Figure 36 Second-order bandpass filter and its transfer-function magnitude versus frequency for several values of Q_s.

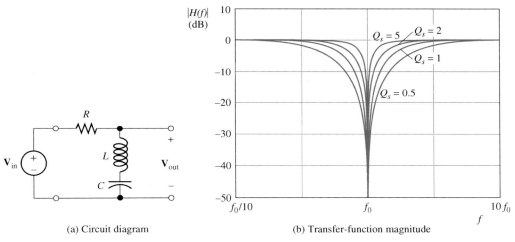

(a) Circuit diagram
(b) Transfer-function magnitude

Figure 37 Second-order band-reject filter and its transfer-function magnitude versus frequency for several values of Q_s.

inductors contain series resistance, so rejection of the f_0 component is not perfect for actual circuits.

Example 7   Filter Design

Suppose that we need a filter that passes components higher in frequency than 1 kHz and rejects components lower than 1 kHz. Select a suitable second-order circuit configuration, choose $L = 50$ mH, and specify the values required for the other components.

Solution   We need to pass high-frequency components and reject low-frequency components. Therefore, we need a highpass filter. The circuit diagram for a second-order highpass filter is shown in Figure 35(a), and the corresponding transfer-function magnitude plots are shown in Figure 35(b). Usually, we want the transfer function to be approximately constant in the passband. Thus, we choose $Q_s \cong 1$. We select $f_0 \cong 1$ kHz, so the components above 1 kHz are passed, while

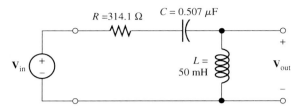

Figure 38 Filter designed in Example 7.

lower-frequency components are (at least partly) rejected. Solving Equation 30 for the capacitance and substituting values, we have

$$C = \frac{1}{(2\pi)^2 f_0^2 L} = \frac{1}{(2\pi)^2 \times 10^6 \times 50 \times 10^{-3}}$$
$$= 0.507 \ \mu F$$

Solving Equation 31 for the resistance and substituting values, we get

$$R = \frac{2\pi f_0 L}{Q_s} = \frac{2\pi \times 1000 \times 50 \times 10^{-3}}{1} = 314.1 \ \Omega$$

The circuit and values are shown in Figure 38. ∎

There are several reasons why we might not use the exact values that we calculated for the components in the last example. First, fixed-value capacitors and resistors are readily available only in certain standard values. Furthermore, the design called for a filter to reject components lower than 1 kHz and pass components higher than 1 kHz. We arbitrarily selected $f_0 = 1$ kHz. Depending on whether it is more important to reject the low frequencies or to pass the high frequencies without change in amplitude, a slightly higher or lower value for f_0 could be better. Finally, our choice of Q_s was somewhat arbitrary. In practice, we could choose variable components by using the calculations as a starting point. Then, we would adjust the filter experimentally for the most satisfactory performance.

Exercise 20 Suppose that we need a filter that passes components lower in frequency than 5 kHz and rejects components higher than 5 kHz. Select a suitable second-order circuit configuration, choose $L = 5$ mH, and specify the values required for the other components.
Answer See Figure 39. □

Exercise 21 Suppose that we want a filter that passes components between $f_L = 45$ kHz and $f_H = 55$ kHz. Higher and lower frequencies are to be rejected. Design a circuit using a 1-mH inductance.

Figure 39 Answer for Exercise 20.

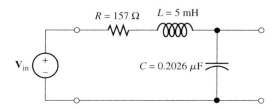

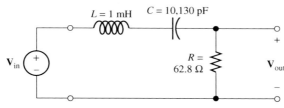

Figure 40 Answer for Exercise 21.

Answer We need a bandpass filter with $f_0 \cong 50$ kHz and $Q_s = 5$. The resulting circuit is shown in Figure 40.

□

9 TRANSFER FUNCTIONS AND BODE PLOTS WITH MATLAB

So far in this chapter, we have used manual methods to illustrate Bode-plot concepts for simple filters. While manual methods can be extended to more complex circuits, it is often quicker and more accurate to use computer software to derive transfer functions and produce Bode plots.

Because subtle programming errors can result in grossly erroneous results, it is good practice to employ independent checks on computer-generated Bode plots. For example, a complex circuit can often be readily analyzed manually at very high and at very low frequencies. At very low frequencies, the inductances behave as short circuits and the capacitances behave as open circuits. Thus, we can replace the inductances by shorts and the capacitances by opens and analyze the simplified circuit to determine the value of the transfer function at low frequencies, providing an independent check on the plots produced by a computer.

Similarly, at very high frequencies, the inductances become open circuits, and the capacitances become shorts. Next, we illustrate this approach with an example.

Manual analysis at dc and very high frequencies often provides some easy checks on computer-aided Bode plots.

Example 8   **Computer-Generated Bode Plot**

The circuit of Figure 41 is a notch filter. Use MATLAB to generate a magnitude Bode plot of the transfer function $H(f) = \mathbf{V}_{out}/\mathbf{V}_{in}$ with frequency ranging from 10 Hz to 100 kHz. Then, analyze the circuit manually at very high and very low frequencies to provide checks on the plot. Use the plot to determine the frequency of maximum attenuation and the value of the transfer function at that frequency.

Solution   Using the voltage-divider principle, we can write the transfer function for the filter as

$$H(f) = \frac{\mathbf{V}_{out}}{\mathbf{V}_{in}} = \frac{R_3}{R_1 + R_3 + 1/[j\omega C + 1/(R_2 + j\omega L)]}$$

A MATLAB m-file that produces the Bode plot is:

```
clear
% Enter the component values:
R1 = 90; R2 = 10; R3 = 100;
L = 0.1; C = 1e-7;
% The following command generates 1000 frequency values
% per decade, evenly spaced from 10^1 to 10^5 Hz
% on a logarithmic scale:
```

333

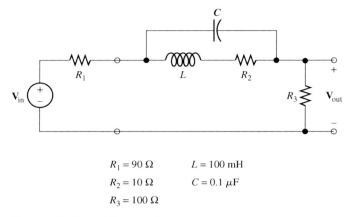

$$R_1 = 90\ \Omega \qquad L = 100\ \text{mH}$$
$$R_2 = 10\ \Omega \qquad C = 0.1\ \mu\text{F}$$
$$R_3 = 100\ \Omega$$

Figure 41 Filter of Example 8.

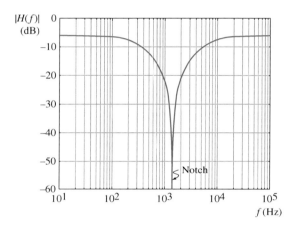

Figure 42 Bode plot for Example 8 produced using MATLAB.

```
f = logspace(1,5,4000);
w = 2*pi*f;
% Evaluate the transfer function for each frequency.
% As usual, we are using i in place of j:
H = R3./(R1+R3+1./(i*w*C + 1./(R2 + i*w*L)));
% Convert the magnitude values to decibels and plot:
semilogx(f,20*log10(abs(H)))
```

The resulting plot is shown in Figure 42. This circuit is called a notch filter because it strongly rejects components in the vicinity of 1591 Hz while passing higher and lower frequencies. The maximum attenuation is 60 dB.

The m-file is named Example_6_8 and appears in the MATLAB folder, and if you have access to MATLAB, you can run it to see the result. Then, you can use the toolbar on the figure screen to magnify a portion of the plot and obtain the notch frequency and maximum attenuation with excellent accuracy.

The command

```
f = logspace(1,5,4000)
```

generates an array of 4000 frequency values, starting at 10^1 Hz and ending at 10^5 Hz, evenly spaced on a logarithmic scale with 1000 points per decade. (Typically, we might start with 100 points per decade, but this transfer function changes very rapidly in the vicinity of 1590 Hz, so we increased the number of points to more accurately determine the location and depth of the notch.)

As a partial check on our analysis and program, we analyze the circuit at $f = 0$ (dc) to determine the transfer function at very low frequencies. To do so, we replace the inductance by a short and the capacitance by an open circuit. Then, the circuit becomes a simple resistive voltage divider consisting of R_1, R_2, and R_3. Therefore, we have

$$H(0) = \frac{\mathbf{V}_{out}}{\mathbf{V}_{in}} = \frac{R_3}{R_1 + R_2 + R_3} = 0.5$$

In decibels, this becomes

$$H_{dB}(0) = 20\log(0.5) = -6\text{ dB}$$

which agrees very well with the plotted value at 10 Hz.

For a second check, we replace the capacitance by a short circuit and the inductance by an open circuit to determine the value of the transfer function at very high frequencies. Then, the circuit again becomes a simple resistive voltage divider consisting of R_1 and R_3. Thus, we have

$$H(\infty) = \frac{R_3}{R_1 + R_3} = 0.5263$$

In decibels, this becomes

$$H_{dB}(\infty) = 20\log(0.5263) = -5.575\text{ dB}$$

which agrees very closely with the value plotted at 100 kHz. ∎

Using the Symbolic Toolbox to Derive Transfer Functions

In the previous example, we could readily write the transfer function by applying the voltage-divider principle. For more complex circuits, manual analysis can be very time consuming. An alternative is to use the MATLAB Symbolic Toolbox to help derive the desired transfer function. Assuming that the transfer function of interest is the output voltage divided by the input voltage, the step-by-step procedure is:

1. Set the input voltage $\mathbf{V}_{in}$ to 1 V.
2. Choose node-voltage variables for the circuit, including the output voltage $\mathbf{V}_{out}$ as one of the variables.
3. Write the node equations.
4. Use the solve command to solve for the output voltage $\mathbf{V}_{out}$ (which is actually equal to the transfer function, because we assumed that the input voltage is 1 V).
5. Define a row vector that contains the list of frequencies for which we want to evaluate the transfer function and use the subs command to substitute the frequency values into the transfer function.
6. Plot the results.

   (This procedure can be readily adapted to other transfer functions that may be of interest, such as output current divided by input current.) We illustrate the procedure with an example.

| Example 9 | Bode Plot Using the MATLAB Symbolic Toolbox |

Obtain a magnitude bode plot of the transfer function $H(f) = \mathbf{V}_{\text{out}}/\mathbf{V}_{\text{in}}$ for the circuit of Figure 43 with frequency ranging from 100 kHz to 10 MHz. Manually check the plotted values for high and low frequencies.

Solution We assume that the input voltage $\mathbf{V}_{\text{in}}$ is 1 V. Then, we choose node voltage variables $\mathbf{V}_1$, $\mathbf{V}_2$, and $\mathbf{V}_3$ as shown in the figure. Notice that $\mathbf{V}_3$ and $\mathbf{V}_{\text{out}}$ are the same voltage and are equal to the desired transfer function. The node equations are obtained by applying KCL at each node.

$$\frac{\mathbf{V}_1 - 1}{R_s} + j\omega C_1 \mathbf{V}_1 + \frac{\mathbf{V}_1 - \mathbf{V}_2}{j\omega L_1} = 0$$

$$\frac{\mathbf{V}_2 - \mathbf{V}_1}{j\omega L_1} + j\omega C_2 \mathbf{V}_2 + \frac{\mathbf{V}_2 - \mathbf{V}_3}{j\omega L_2} = 0$$

$$\frac{\mathbf{V}_3 - \mathbf{V}_2}{j\omega L_2} + j\omega C_3 \mathbf{V}_3 + \frac{\mathbf{V}_3}{R_L} = 0$$

An m-file that produces the desired Bode plot is:

```
clear
% Construct the symbolic objects that appear in the circuit:
syms V1 V2 V3
syms w Rs RL C1 C2 C3 L1 L2 real
% Notice that V1, V2 and V3 are complex quantities
% while w, Rs, etc. are real.
% Solve the node voltage equations for V1, V2, and V3:
% Use i rather than j.
[V1 V2 V3] = solve('(V1-1)/Rs + i*w*C1*V1 + (V1-V2)/(i*w*L1) = 0',...
          '(V2-V1)/(i*w*L1) + i*w*C2*V2 + (V2-V3)/(i*w*L2) = 0',...
          '(V3-V2)/(i*w*L2) + i*w*C3*V3 + V3/RL = 0',...
          'V1','V2','V3');
% Enter the component values:
C1 = 1.967e-9; C2 = 6.366e-9; C3 = 1.967e-9;
L1 = 12.88e-6; L2 = 12.88e-6; Rs = 50; RL = 50;
% Substitute the component values into the solution for V3
% and define result as the transfer function H:
H = subs(V3); % Recall that the transfer function is the same as the
% output voltage V3.
% Next, set up a row matrix of logarithmically equally spaced
% frequencies at 100 points per decade from 10^5 to 10^7 Hz:
f = logspace(5,7,200);
```

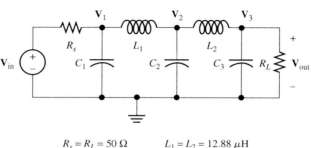

$$R_s = R_L = 50\ \Omega \qquad L_1 = L_2 = 12.88\ \mu\text{H}$$

$$C_1 = C_3 = 1967\ \text{pF} \qquad C_2 = 6366\ \text{pF}$$

Figure 43 Fifth-order Butterworth lowpass filter.

336

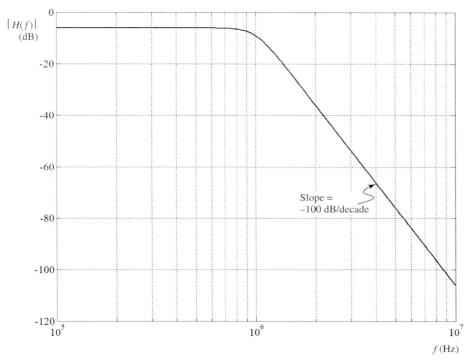

Figure 44 Bode plot for Example 9.

```
wn = 2*pi*f;
% Substitute the frequency values into the transfer function
% and convert to numeric form by using the double command:
H = double(subs(H,w,wn));
% Convert the transfer function magnitude to dB and plot:
HmagdB = 20*log10(abs(H));
semilogx(f,HmagdB)
```

The resulting plot is shown in Figure 44. The m-file is named Example_6_ 9 and can be found in the MATLAB folder.

To check the plotted transfer function at very low frequencies, we replace the inductances by shorts and the capacitors with opens. Then, the circuit becomes a simple voltage divider and the transfer function is

$$H(0) = \frac{R_L}{R_s + R_L} = 0.5$$

which is equivalent to −6 dB, agreeing very well with the value plotted at 100 kHz.

At very high frequencies, the capacitors become shorts and the inductors become opens. Then the output voltage tends toward zero, and the transfer function tends toward −∞ dB. This agrees with the trend of the plot at high frequencies. ■

The filter of the previous example is known as a fifth-order Butterworth lowpass filter. Books on radio-frequency design typically have component values for normalized versions of this and many other types of filters listed in design tables. The values from the tables can be scaled to obtain filters with the desired half-power frequencies and impedance levels. So in this case, the designer would know exactly what the transfer function should be before doing the analysis. However, the parasitic effects of the components can significantly change the performance in unpredictable ways. A designer could include these parasitics in the analysis and use a MATLAB analysis to see their effects. However, such detailed analysis is beyond the scope of this book. Our aim is to illustrate the power of computer-aided analysis.

Exercise 22 If you have access to MATLAB and the Symbolic Toolbox, run the m-files Example_6_8 and Example_6_9 that are contained in the MATLAB folder. (**Note:** We have run these files successfully with MATLAB versions R2008a and R2008b. However, they may not run with other versions.)
Answer The resulting plots should be very similar to Figures 42 and 44, respectively. □

10 DIGITAL SIGNAL PROCESSING

So far, we have introduced the concepts related to filters in the context of *RLC* circuits. However, many modern systems make use of a more sophisticated technology called **digital signal processing** (DSP). In using DSP to filter a signal, the analog input signal $x(t)$ is converted to digital form (a sequence of numbers) by an **analog-to-digital converter** (ADC). A digital computer then uses the digitized input signal to compute a sequence of values for the output signal. Finally, if desired, the computed values are converted to analog form by a **digital-to-analog converter** (DAC) to produce the output signal $y(t)$. The generic block diagram of a DSP system is shown in Figure 45.

Besides filtering, many other operations, such as speech recognition, can be performed by DSP systems. DSP was used in the early days of the Space Telescope to focus blurry images resulting from an error in the telescope's design. High-definition televisions, digital cell phones, and MP3 music players are examples of products that have been made possible by DSP technology.

DSP is a large and rapidly evolving field that will continue to produce novel products. We discuss digital filters very briefly to give you a glimpse of this exciting field.

Conversion of Signals from Analog to Digital Form

Analog signals are converted to digital form by a DAC in a two-step process. First, the analog signal is sampled (i.e., measured) at periodic points in time. Then, a code word is assigned to represent the approximate value of each sample. Usually, the code words consist of binary symbols. This process is illustrated in Figure 46, in which each sample value is represented by a three-bit code word corresponding to the amplitude zone into which the sample falls. Thus, each sample value is converted

Figure 45 Generic block diagram of a digital signal-processing (DSP) system.

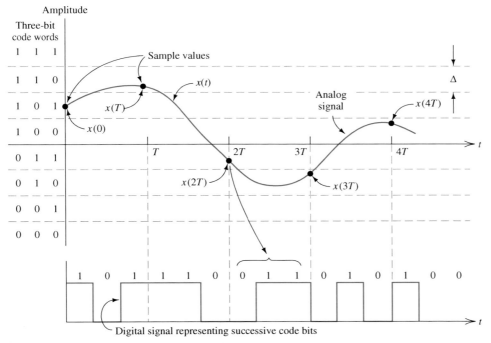

Figure 46 An analog signal is converted to an approximate digital equivalent by sampling. Each sample value is represented by a three-bit code word. (Practical converters use longer code words, and the width Δ of each amplitude zone is much smaller.)

into a code word, which in turn can be represented by a digital waveform as shown in the figure.

The rate f_s at which a signal must be sampled depends on the frequencies of the signal components. We have seen that all real signals can be considered to consist of sinusoidal components having various frequencies, amplitudes, and phases. If a signal contains no components with frequencies higher than f_H, the signal can (in theory) be exactly reconstructed from its samples, provided that the sampling frequency f_s is selected to be more than twice f_H:

$$f_s > 2f_H \qquad (48)$$

For example, high-fidelity audio signals have a highest frequency of about 15 kHz. Therefore, the minimum sampling rate that should be used for audio signals is 30 kHz. Practical considerations dictate a sampling frequency somewhat higher than the theoretical minimum. For instance, audio compact-disc technology converts audio signals to digital form with a sampling rate of 44.1 kHz. Naturally, it is desirable to use the lowest practical sampling rate to minimize the amount of data (in the form of code words) that must be stored or manipulated by the DSP system.

If a signal contains no components with frequencies higher than f_H, the signal can be exactly reconstructed from its samples, provided that the sampling rate f_s is selected to be more than twice f_H.

Of course, the interval between samples T is the reciprocal of the sampling rate:

$$T = \frac{1}{f_s} \qquad (49)$$

A second consideration important in converting analog signals to digital form is the number of amplitude zones to be used. Exact signal amplitudes cannot be

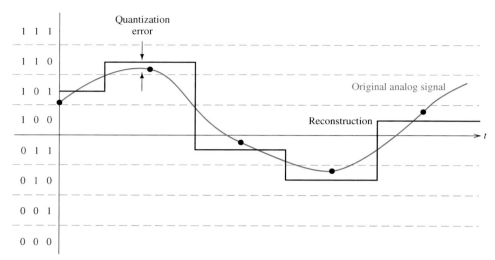

Figure 47 Quantization error occurs when an analog signal is reconstructed from its digital form.

represented, because all amplitudes falling into a given zone have the same code word. Thus, when a DAC converts the code words to recreate the original analog waveform, it is possible to reconstruct only an approximation to the original signal with the reconstructed voltage in the middle of each zone, which is illustrated in Figure 47. Thus, some **quantization error** exists between the original signal and the reconstruction. This error can be reduced by using a larger number of zones, which requires longer code words. The number N of amplitude zones is related to the number of bits k in a code word by

$$N = 2^k \qquad (50)$$

Hence, if we are using an 8-bit ($k = 8$) ADC, there are $N = 2^8 = 256$ amplitude zones. In compact-disc technology, 16-bit words are used to represent sample values. With this number of bits, it is very difficult for a listener to detect the effects of quantization error on the reconstructed audio signal.

Often, in engineering instrumentation, we need to determine the DAC specifications needed for converting sensor signals to digital form. For example, suppose that we need to digitize a signal that ranges from -1 to $+1$ V with a resolution of at most $\Delta = 0.5$ mV. (Δ is illustrated in the upper right-hand corner of Figure 46.) Then, the minimum number of zones is the total signal range (2 V) divided by Δ, which yields $N = 4000$. However, N must be an integer power of two. Thus, we require $k = 12$. (In other words, a 12-bit ADC is needed.)

In the remainder of this section, we will ignore quantization error and assume that the exact sample values are available to the digital computer.

Digital Filters

We have seen that ADCs convert analog signals into sequences of code words that can accurately represent the amplitudes of the signals at the sampling instants. Although the computer actually manipulates code words that represent signal amplitudes, it is convenient to focus on the numbers that the code words represent. Conceptually, the

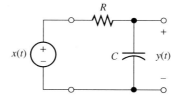

Figure 48 First-order *RC* lowpass filter.

signal $x(t)$ is converted into a list of values $x(nT)$ in which T is the interval between samples and n is a variable that takes on integer values. Often, we omit the sampling period from our notation and write the input and output samples simply as $x(n)$ and $y(n)$, respectively.

Digital Lowpass Filter

Digital filters can be designed to mimic the *RLC* filters that we discussed earlier in this chapter. For example, consider the first-order *RC* lowpass filter shown in Figure 48, in which we have denoted the input voltage as $x(t)$ and the output voltage as $y(t)$. Writing a Kirchhoff's current equation at the top node of the capacitance, we have

$$\frac{y(t) - x(t)}{R} + C\frac{dy(t)}{dt} = 0 \tag{51}$$

Multiplying each term by R and using the fact that the time constant is $\tau = RC$, we find that

$$y(t) - x(t) + \tau\frac{dy(t)}{dt} = 0 \tag{52}$$

We can approximate the derivative as

$$\frac{dy(t)}{dt} \cong \frac{\Delta y}{\Delta t} = \frac{y(n) - y(n-1)}{T} \tag{53}$$

and write the approximate equivalent to the differential equation

$$y(n) - x(n) + \tau\frac{y(n) - y(n-1)}{T} = 0 \tag{54}$$

This type of equation is sometimes called a **difference equation** because it involves differences between successive samples. Solving for the nth output value, we have

$$y(n) = ay(n-1) + (1-a)x(n) \tag{55}$$

in which we have defined the parameter

$$a = \frac{\tau/T}{1 + \tau/T} \tag{56}$$

Equation 55 defines the calculations that need to be carried out to perform lowpass filtering of the input $x(n)$. For each sample point, the output is a times the previous output value plus $(1 - a)$ times the present input value. Usually, we have $\tau \gg T$ and a is slightly less than unity.

| Example 10 | Step Response of a First-Order Digital Lowpass Filter |

Compute and plot the input and output samples for $n = 0$ to 20, given $a = 0.9$. The input is a step function defined by

$$x(n) = 0 \text{ for } n < 0$$
$$= 1 \text{ for } n \geq 0$$

Assume that $y(n) = 0$ for $n < 0$.

Solution   We have

$$y(0) = ay(-1) + (1 - a)x(0) = 0.9 \times 0 + 0.1 \times 1 = 0.1$$
$$y(1) = ay(0) + (1 - a)x(1) = 0.19$$
$$y(2) = ay(1) + (1 - a)x(2) = 0.271$$

$$\cdots$$

$$y(20) = 0.8906$$

Plots of $x(n)$ and $y(n)$ are shown in Figure 49.

Exercise 23   **a.** Determine the value of the time constant τ, in terms of the sampling interval T corresponding to $a = 0.9$. **b.** Recall that the time constant is the time required for the step response to reach $1 - \exp(-1) = 0.632$ times its final value. Estimate the value of the time constant for the response shown in Figure 49.
Answer   **a.** $\tau = 9T$; **b.** $\tau \cong 9T$. $\square$

Other Digital Filters

We could develop digital bandpass, notch, or highpass filters that mimic the behavior of the RLC filters discussed earlier in this chapter. Furthermore, high-order digital

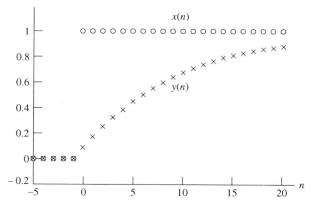

Figure 49 Step input and corresponding output of a first-order digital lowpass filter.

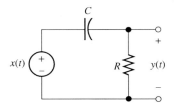

Figure 50 *RC* highpass filter. See
Exercise 24.

filters are possible. In general, the equations defining such filters are of the form

$$y(n) = \sum_{\ell=1}^{N} a_\ell y(n - \ell) + \sum_{k=0}^{M} b_k x(n - k) \tag{57}$$

The type of filter and its performance depend on the values selected for the coefficients a_ℓ and b_k. For the first-order lowpass filter considered in Example 10, the coefficients are $a_1 = 0.9, b_0 = 0.1$, and all of the other coefficients are zero.

Exercise 24 Consider the *RC* highpass filter shown in Figure 50. Apply the method that we used for the lowpass filter to find an equation having the form of Equation 57 for the highpass filter. Give expressions for the coefficients in terms of the time constant $\tau = RC$ and the sampling interval T.
Answer $y(n) = a_1 y(n - 1) + b_0 x(n) + b_1 x(n - 1)$ in which

$$a_1 = b_0 = -b_1 = \frac{\tau/T}{1 + \tau/T}$$

□

A Simple Notch Filter

A simple way to obtain a notch filter is to select $a_\ell = 0$ for all ℓ, $b_0 = 0.5, b_d = 0.5$, and to set the remaining b_k coefficients to zero. Then, the output of the digital filter is given by

$$y(n) = 0.5x(n) + 0.5x(n - d) = 0.5[x(n) + x(n - d)]$$

Thus, each input sample is delayed in time by Td and added to the current sample. Finally, the sum of the input and its delayed version is multiplied by 0.5. To see that this results in a notch filter, consider a sinewave delayed by an interval Td. We can write

$$A \cos[\omega(t - Td)] = A \cos(\omega t - \omega Td) = A \cos(\omega t - \theta)$$

Hence, a time delay of Td amounts to a phase shift of ωTd radians or $fTd \times 360°$. (Keep in mind that, in this discussion, T represents the interval between samples, *not the period of the sinewave*.) For low frequencies, the phase shift is small, so the low-frequency components of $x(n)$ add nearly in phase with those of $x(n - d)$. On the other hand, for the frequency

$$f_{\text{notch}} = \frac{1}{2Td} = \frac{f_s}{2d} \tag{58}$$

the phase shift is 180°. Of course, when we phase shift a sinewave by 180° and add it to the original, the sum is zero. Thus, any input component having the frequency f_{notch} does not appear in the output. The first-order lowpass filter and this simple notch filter are just two of many possible digital filters that can be realized by selection of the coefficient values in Equation 57.

Exercise 25 Suppose that the sampling frequency is $f_s = 10$ kHz, and we want to eliminate the 500-Hz component with a simple notch filter. **a.** Determine the value needed for d. **b.** What difficulty would be encountered if we wanted to eliminate the 300-Hz component?

Answer **a.** $d = 10$; **b.** Equation 58 yields $d = 16.67$, but d is required to be an integer value. ◻

Digital Filter Demonstration

Next, we will use MATLAB to demonstrate the operation of a digital filter. First, we will create samples of a virtual signal including noise and interference. The signal of interest consists of a 1-Hz sinewave and is representative of many types of real world signals such as delta waves contained in the electroencephalogram (EEG) of an individual in deep sleep, or the output of a pressure sensor submerged in the ocean with waves passing over. Part of the interference consists of a 60-Hz sinewave, which is a common real-world problem due to coupling between the ac power line and the signal sensor. The other part of the interference is random noise, which is also common in real-world data.

The MATLAB code that we use to create our simulated data is

```
t = 0:1/6000:2;
signal = cos(2*pi*t);
interference = cos(120*pi*t);
white_noise = randn(size(t));
noise = zeros(size(t));
for n = 2:12001
noise(n) = 0.25*(white_noise(n) - white_noise(n - 1));
end
x = signal + interference + noise; % This is the simulated data.
```

The first command generates a 12,001-element row vector containing the sample times for a two-second interval with a sampling frequency of $f_s = 6000$ Hz. The second and third commands set up row matrices containing samples of the signal and the 60-Hz interference. In the next line, the random-number generator feature of MATLAB generates "white noise" that contains components of equal amplitudes (on average) at all frequencies up to half of the sampling frequency. The white noise is then manipulated by the commands in the for-end loop, producing noise with components from dc to 3000 Hz peaking around 1500 Hz. Then, the signal, interference and noise are added to produce the simulated data $x(n)$. (Of course, in a real-world application, the data are obtained by applying the outputs of sensors, such as EEG electrodes, to analog-to-digital converters.)

Next, we use MATLAB to plot the signal, interference, noise, and the simulated data.

```
subplot(2,2,1)
plot(t, signal)
axis([0 2 -2 2])
subplot(2,2,2)
plot(t, interference)
axis([0 2 -2 2])
subplot(2,2,3)
plot(t,noise)
```

```
axis([0 2 -2 2])
subplot(2,2,4)
plot(t,x)
axis([0 2 -3 3])
```

The resulting plots are shown in Figure 51. The simulated data is typical of what is often obtained from sensors in real-world experiments. In a biomedical setting, for example, an electrocardiograph produces data that is the sum of the heart signal, 60-Hz power-line interference, and noise from muscle contractions, especially when the subject is moving, as in a stress test.

Actually, the plot of the 60-Hz interference appears a little uneven in Figure 51(b) because of finite screen resolution for the display. This is a form of distortion, called aliasing that occurs when the sampling rate is too low. If you run the commands on your own computer and use the zoom tool to expand the display horizontally, you will see a smooth plot of the 60-Hz sinewave interference. An m-file named DSPdemo that contains the commands used in this demonstration of a digital filter appears in the MATLAB folder.

What we need is a digital filter that processes the data $x(n)$ of Figure 51(d) and produces an output closely matching the signal in Figure 51(a). This filter should pass the signal (1-Hz sinewave), reject the 60-Hz interference, and reject the noise, which has its largest components in the vicinity of 1500 Hz.

To achieve this, we will use a digital notch filter to remove the 60-Hz sinewave interference cascaded with a lowpass filter to remove most of the noise. The conceptual diagram of the digital filter is shown in Figure 52.

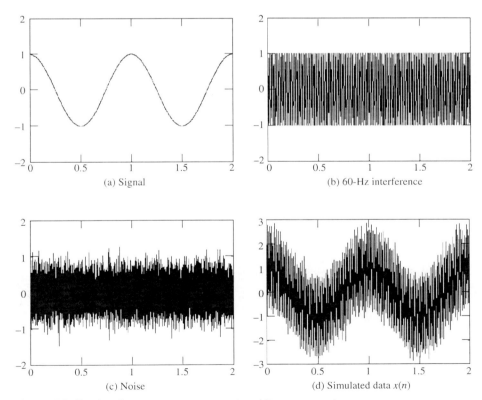

(a) Signal

(b) 60-Hz interference

(c) Noise

(d) Simulated data $x(n)$

Figure 51 Simulated pressure-sensor output and its components.

345

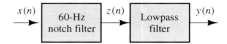

Figure 52 Digital filter.

Equation 58 reveals that by using $d = 50$ and $f_s = 6000$ Hz, we can realize a notch filter with zero gain at precisely 60 Hz. (If 60-Hz interference is a problem, it is a good idea to pick the sampling frequency to be an even integer multiple of 60 Hz, which is one reason we picked the sampling frequency to be 6000 Hz.) The output $z(n)$ of the notch filter is given in terms of the input data $x(n)$ as

$$z(n) = \frac{1}{2}[x(n) + x(n - 50)]$$

Also, we need a lowpass filter to eliminate the noise. We decide to use the first-order lowpass filter discussed earlier in this section. Because we do not want the lowpass filter to disturb the signal, we choose its break frequency to much higher than 1 Hz, say $f_B = 50$ Hz. For an RC lowpass filter, the break frequency is

$$f_B = \frac{1}{2\pi RC}$$

Solving for the time constant and substituting values, we have

$$\tau = RC = \frac{1}{2\pi f_B} = \frac{1}{2\pi(50)} = 3.183 \text{ ms}$$

The gain constant for the (approximately) equivalent digital filter is given by Equation 56 in which $T = 1/f_s = 1/6000$ s is the sampling interval. We then have

$$a = \frac{\tau/T}{1 + \tau/T} = 0.9503$$

Substituting this value into Equation 55 yields the equation for the present $y(n)$ output of the lowpass filter in terms of its input $z(n)$ and previous output $y(n - 1)$.

$$y(n) = 0.9503y(n - 1) + 0.0497z(n)$$

The MATLAB commands to filter the simulated data $x(n)$ and plot the output $y(n)$ are:

```
for n = 51:12001
z(n) = (x(n) + x(n - 50))/2; % This is the notch filter.
end
y = zeros(size(z));
for n = 2:12001
y(n) = 0.9503*y(n-1) + 0.0497*z(n); % This is the lowpass filter.
end
figure
plot(t,y)
```

The resulting plot is shown in Figure 53. As desired, the output is nearly identical to the 1-Hz sinewave signal. This relatively simple digital filter has done a very good job of eliminating the noise and interference because most of the noise and the interference have frequencies much higher than does the signal. When the frequencies of the signal are nearer to those of the noise and interference, we would need to resort to higher-order filters.

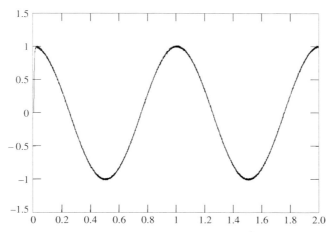

Figure 53 Output signal.

Comparison of Filter Technologies

We have discussed two ways to filter signals: RLC circuits and digital filters. There are a number of other filter types, such as **active filters** that are composed of resistances, capacitances and **operational amplifiers,** or **op amps.** Other filters are based on mechanical resonances in piezoelectric crystals, surface acoustic waves, the propagation of electric fields in wave guides, switched capacitor networks, and transmission lines.

In all cases, the objective of a filter is to separate a desired signal from noise and interference. Radio amateurs operating in the frequency band between 28 and 29.7 MHz often need to place a band reject filter between the transmitter and antenna to eliminate second-harmonic frequency components from reaching the antenna. If they are not removed, second-harmonic components can cause some very annoying interference on their neighbor's television screens. In this application, an RLC filter would be the technology of choice because of the large currents and voltages involved.

On the other hand, a sleep researcher may wish to filter brain waves to separate delta waves that appear at frequencies of 4 Hz or less from higher frequency brain waves. In this case, a digital filter is appropriate.

In summary, there are many applications for filters and many technologies for implementing filters. Most of the principles we have introduced in our discussion of RLC circuits and digital filters apply to filters based on other technologies.

> The objective of a filter is to separate a desired signal from noise and interference.

Summary

1. The fundamental concept of Fourier theory is that we can construct any signal by adding sinusoids with the proper amplitudes, frequencies, and phases.

2. In effect, a filter decomposes the input signal into its sinusoidal components, adjusts the amplitude and phase of each component, depending on its frequency, and sums the adjusted components to produce the output signal. Often, we need a filter that passes components in a given frequency range to the output, without change in amplitude

or phase, and that rejects components at other frequencies.

3. The transfer function of a filter circuit is the phasor output divided by the phasor input as a function of frequency. The transfer function is a complex quantity that shows how the amplitudes and phases of input components are affected when passing through the filter.

4. We can use circuit analysis with phasors and complex impedances to determine the transfer function of a given circuit.

5. A first-order filter is characterized by its half-power frequency f_B.

6. A transfer-function magnitude is converted to decibels by taking 20 times the common logarithm of the magnitude.

7. Two-port filters are cascaded by connecting the output of the first to the input of the second. The overall transfer function of the cascade is the product of the transfer functions of the individual filters. If the transfer functions are converted to decibels, they are added for a cascade connection.

8. On a logarithmic frequency scale, frequency is multiplied by a given factor for equal increments of length along the axis. A decade is a range of frequencies for which the ratio of the highest frequency to the lowest is 10. An octave is a two-to-one change in frequency.

9. A Bode plot shows the magnitude of a network function in decibels versus frequency, using a logarithmic scale for frequency.

10. The Bode plots for first-order filters can be closely approximated by straight-line asymptotes. In the case of a first-order lowpass filter, the transfer-function magnitude slopes downward at 20 dB/decade for frequencies that are higher than the half-power frequency. For a first-order highpass filter, the transfer-function magnitude slopes at 20 dB/decade below the break frequency.

11. At low frequencies, inductances behave as short circuits, and capacitances behave as open circuits. At high frequencies, inductances behave as open

circuits, and capacitances behave as short circuits. Often, RLC filters can be readily analyzed at low- or high-frequencies, providing checks on computer-generated Bode plots.

12. The key parameters of series and parallel resonant circuits are the resonant frequency and quality factor. The impedance of either type of circuit is purely resistive at the resonant frequency. High-quality-factor circuits can have responses that are much larger in magnitude than the driving source.

13. Filters may be classified as lowpass, highpass, bandpass, and band-reject filters. Ideal filters have constant (nonzero) gain (transfer-function magnitude) in the passband and zero gain in the stopband.

14. The series resonant circuit can be used to form any of the four filter types.

15. A second-order filter is characterized by its resonant frequency and quality factor.

16. MATLAB is useful in deriving and plotting network functions of complex RLC filters.

17. In using digital signal processing (DSP) to filter a signal, the analog input signal $x(t)$ is converted to digital form (a sequence of numbers) by an analog-to-digital converter (ADC). A digital computer uses the digitized input signal to compute a sequence of values for the output signal, and, finally, (if desired) the computed values are converted to analog form by a digital-to-analog converter (DAC) to produce the output signal $y(t)$.

18. If a signal contains no components with frequencies higher than f_H, the signal can be exactly reconstructed from its samples, provided that the sampling rate f_s is selected to be more than twice f_H.

19. Approximately equivalent digital filters can be found for RLC filters.

Note: You can check many of the Bode plots in this chapter by using a computer-aided circuit-analysis program such as Multisim from National Instruments or OrCAD Capture from Cadence Inc.

Problems

Section 1: Fourier Analysis, Filters, and Transfer Functions

P1. What is the fundamental concept of Fourier theory?

P2. The triangular waveform shown in Figure P2 can be written as the infinite sum

$$v_t(t) = 1 + \frac{8}{\pi^2} \cos(2000\pi t)$$

$$+ \frac{8}{(3\pi)^2} \cos(6000\pi t) + \cdots$$

$$+ \frac{8}{(n\pi)^2} \cos(2000n\pi t) + \cdots$$

in which n takes odd integer values only. Use MATLAB to compute and plot the sum through $n = 19$ for $0 \leq t \leq 2\,\text{ms}$. Compare your plot with the waveform shown in Figure P2.

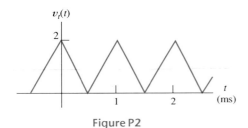

Figure P2

P3. The full-wave rectified cosine wave shown in Figure P3 can be written as

$$v_{\text{fw}} = \frac{2}{\pi} + \frac{4}{\pi(1)(3)} \cos(4000\pi t)$$

$$- \frac{4}{\pi(3)(5)} \cos(8000\pi t) + \cdots$$

$$+ \frac{4(-1)^{(n/2+1)}}{\pi(n-1)(n+1)} \cos(2000n\pi t) + \cdots$$

in which n assumes even integer values. Use MATLAB to compute and plot the sum

through $n = 60$ for $0 \leq t \leq 2\,\text{ms}$. Compare your plot with the waveform shown in Figure P3.

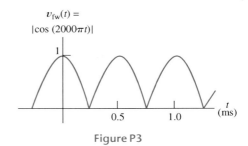

Figure P3

P4. The Fourier series for the **half-wave rectified cosine** shown in Figure P4 is

$$v_{\text{hw}}(t) = \frac{1}{\pi} + \frac{1}{2}\cos(2\pi t) + \frac{2}{\pi(1)(3)}\cos(4\pi t)$$

$$- \frac{2}{\pi(3)(5)}\cos(8\pi t) + \cdots$$

$$+ \frac{2(-1)^{(n/2+1)}}{\pi(n-1)(n+1)}\cos(2n\pi t) + \cdots$$

in which $n = 2, 4, 6$, etc. Use MATLAB to compute and plot the sum through $n = 4$ for $-0.5 \leq t \leq 1.5\,\text{s}$. Then plot the sum through $n = 50$. Compare your plots with the waveform in Figure P4.

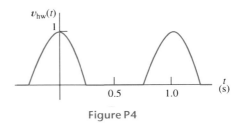

Figure P4

---

* Denotes that answers are contained in the Student Solutions files.

P5. Fourier analysis shows that the **sawtooth waveform** of Figure P5 can be written as

$$v_{st}(t) = 1 - \frac{2}{\pi} \sin(2000\pi t)$$

$$- \frac{2}{2\pi} \sin(4000\pi t) - \frac{2}{3\pi} \sin(6000\pi t)$$

$$- \cdots - \frac{2}{n\pi} \sin(2000 n\pi t) - \cdots$$

Use MATLAB to compute and plot the sum through $n = 3$ for $0 \le t \le 2$ ms. Repeat for the sum through $n = 50$.

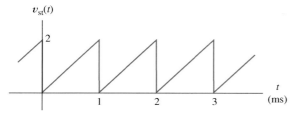

Figure P5

P6. What is the transfer function of a filter? Describe how the transfer function of a filter can be determined using laboratory methods.

P7. How does a filter process an input signal to produce the output signal in terms of sinusoidal components?

*P8. The transfer function $H(f) = \mathbf{V}_{out}/\mathbf{V}_{in}$ of a filter is shown in Figure P8. The input signal is given by

$$v_{in}(t) = 5 + 2\cos(5000\pi t + 30°)$$

$$+ 2\cos(15000\pi t)$$

Find an expression (as a function of time) for the steady-state output of the filter.

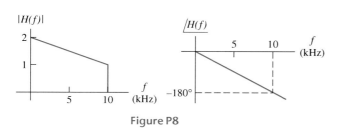

Figure P8

P9. Repeat Problem P8 for the input voltage given by

$$v_{in}(t) = 4 + 5\cos(10^4\pi t - 30°) + 2\sin(24000\pi t)$$

P10. Repeat Problem P8 for the input voltage given by

$$v_{in}(t) = 6 + 2\cos(6000\pi t) - 4\cos(12000\pi t)$$

*P11. The input to a certain filter is given by

$$v_{in}(t) = 2\cos\left(10^4\pi t - 25°\right)$$

and the steady-state output is given by

$$v_{out}(t) = 2\cos\left(10^4\pi t + 20°\right)$$

Determine the (complex) value of the transfer function of the filter for $f = 5000$ Hz.

*P12. The input and output voltages of a filter operating under sinusoidal steady-state conditions are observed on an oscilloscope. The peak amplitude of the input is 5 V and the output is 15 V. The period of both signals is 4 ms. The input reaches a positive peak at $t = 1$ ms, and the output reaches its positive peak at $t = 1.5$ ms. Determine the frequency and the corresponding value of the transfer function.

*P13. The triangular waveform of Problem P2 is the input for a filter with the transfer function shown in Figure P13. Assume that the phase of the transfer function is zero for all frequencies. Determine the steady-state output of the filter.

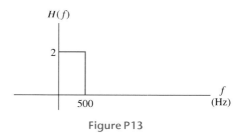

Figure P13

*P14. Consider a circuit for which the output voltage is the running-time integral of the input voltage, as illustrated in Figure P14. If the input voltage is given by $v_{in}(t) =$

$V_{\max}\cos(2\pi ft)$, find an expression for the output voltage as a function of time. Then, find an expression for the transfer function of the integrator. Plot the magnitude and phase of the transfer function versus frequency.

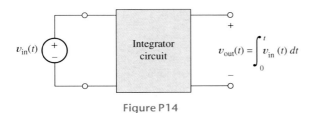

$$v_{\text{out}}(t) = \int_0^t v_{\text{in}}(t)\, dt$$

Figure P14

P15. The sawtooth waveform of Problem P5 is applied as the input to a filter with the transfer function shown in Figure P15. Assume that the phase of the transfer function is zero for all frequencies. Determine the steady-state output of the filter.

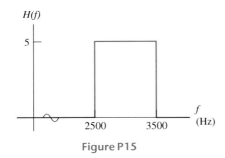

Figure P15

P16. Figure P16 shows the input and output voltages of a certain filter operating in steady state with a sinusoidal input. Determine the frequency and the corresponding value of the transfer function.

P17. List the frequencies in hertz for which the transfer function of a filter can be determined given that the input to the filter is

$$v_{\text{in}}(t) = 2 + 3\cos(1000\pi t) + 3\sin(2000\pi t)$$
$$+ \cos(3000\pi t)\ \text{V}$$

and the output is

$$v_{\text{out}}(t) = 3 + 2\cos(1000\pi t + 30°)$$
$$+ 3\cos(3000\pi t)\ \text{V}$$

Compute the transfer function for each of these frequencies.

P18. Consider a system for which the output voltage is $v_o(t) = v_{\text{in}}(t) + v_{\text{in}}(t - 10^{-3})$. (In other words, the output equals the input plus the input delayed by 1 ms.) Given that the input voltage is $v_{\text{in}}(t) = V_{\max}\cos(2\pi ft)$, find an expression for the output voltage as a function of time. Then, find an expression for the transfer function of the system. Use MATLAB to plot the magnitude of the transfer function versus frequency for the range from 0 to 2000 Hz. Comment on the result.

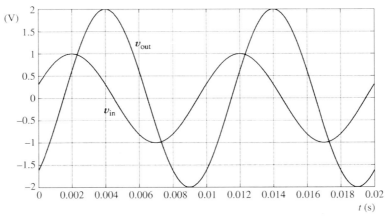

Figure P16

P19. Suppose we have a system for which the output voltage is

$$v_o(t) = 1000 \int_{t-10^{-3}}^{t} v_{in}(t)\,dt$$

Given the input voltage $v_{in}(t) = V_{max}\cos(2\pi ft)$, find an expression for the output voltage as a function of time. Then, find an expression for the transfer function of the system. Use MATLAB to plot the magnitude of the transfer function versus frequency for the range from 0 to 2000 Hz. Comment on the result.

P20. Suppose we have a circuit for which the output voltage is the time derivative of the input voltage, as illustrated in Figure P20. For an input voltage given by $v_{in}(t) = V_{max}\cos(2\pi ft)$, find an expression for the output voltage as a function of time. Then, find an expression for the transfer function of the differentiator. Plot the magnitude and phase of the transfer function versus frequency.

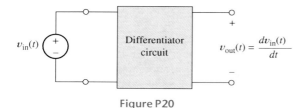

Figure P20

Section 2: First-Order Lowpass Filters

P21. Draw the circuit diagram of a first-order RC lowpass filter and give the expression for the half-power frequency in terms of the circuit components. Sketch the magnitude and phase of the transfer function versus frequency.

P22. Repeat Problem P21 for a first-order RL filter.

*P23. Consider a first-order RC lowpass filter. At what frequency (in terms of f_B) is the phase shift equal to $-1°$? $-10°$? $-89°$?

P24. You may be familiar with using the time constant to characterize first-order RC circuits. Find the relationship between the half-power frequency and the time constant.

*P25. An input signal given by

$$v_{in}(t) = 5\cos(500\pi t) + 5\cos(1000\pi t)$$
$$+ 5\cos(2000\pi t)$$

is applied to the lowpass RC filter shown in Figure P25. Find an expression for the output signal.

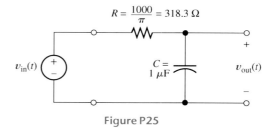

Figure P25

P26. The input signal of a first-order lowpass filter with the transfer function given by Equation 9 on page 296 and a half-power frequency of 200 Hz is

$$v_{in}(t) = 3 + 2\sin\left(800\pi t + 30°\right)$$
$$+ 5\cos\left(20 \times 10^3 \pi t\right)$$

Find an expression for the output voltage.

P27. Suppose that we need a first-order RC lowpass filter with a half-power frequency of 1 kHz. Determine the value of the capacitance, given that the resistance is 5 kΩ.

P28. The input signal to a filter contains components that range in frequency from 100 Hz to 50 kHz. We wish to reduce the amplitude of the 50-kHz component by a factor of 200 by passing the signal through a first-order lowpass filter. What half-power frequency is required for the filter? By what factor is a component at 2 kHz changed in amplitude in passing through this filter?

P29. Suppose we have a first-order lowpass filter that is operating in sinusoidal steady-state conditions at a frequency of 5 kHz. Using an oscilloscope, we observe that the positive-going zero crossing of the output is delayed by 30 μs compared with that of the input. Determine the break frequency of the filter.

*P30. Sketch the magnitude of the transfer function $H(f) = \mathbf{V}_{out}/\mathbf{V}_{in}$ to scale versus frequency for the circuit shown in Figure P30. What is the value of the half-power frequency? (*Hint:* Start by finding the Thévenin equivalent circuit seen by the capacitance.)

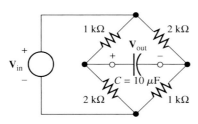

Figure P30

P31. In steady-state operation, a first-order RC lowpass filter has the input signal $v_{in}(t) = 5\cos(20 \times 10^3 \pi t)$ and the output signal $v_{out}(t) = 0.2\cos(20 \times 10^3 \pi t - \theta)$. Determine the break frequency of the filter and the value of θ.

P32. Consider the circuit shown in Figure P32(a). This circuit consists of a source having an internal resistance of R_s, an RC lowpass filter, and a load resistance R_L. **a.** Show that the transfer function of this circuit is given by

$$H(f) = \frac{\mathbf{V}_{out}}{\mathbf{V}_s} = \frac{R_L}{R_s + R + R_L} \times \frac{1}{1 + j(f/f_B)}$$

in which the half-power frequency f_B is given by

$$f_B = \frac{1}{2\pi R_t C} \quad \text{where} \quad R_t = \frac{R_L(R_s + R)}{R_L + R_s + R}$$

Notice that R_t is the parallel combination of R_L and $(R_s + R)$. [*Hint:* One way to make this problem easier is to rearrange the circuit as shown in Figure P32(b) and then to find the Thévenin equivalent for the source and resistances.] **b.** Given that $C = 0.2\,\mu\text{F}$, $R_s = 2\,\text{k}\Omega$, $R = 47\,\text{k}\Omega$, and $R_L = 1\,\text{k}\Omega$, sketch (or use MATLAB to plot) the magnitude of $H(f)$ to scale versus f/f_B from 0 to 3.

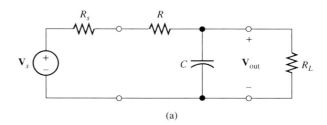

(a)

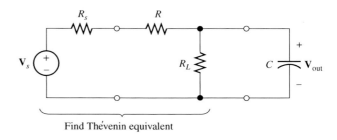

Find Thévenin equivalent

(b)

Figure P32

P33. **a.** Derive an expression for the transfer function $H(f) = \mathbf{V}_{out}/\mathbf{V}_{in}$ for the circuit shown in Figure P33. Find an expression for the half-power frequency. **b.** Given $R_1 = 50\,\Omega$, $R_2 = 50\,\Omega$, and $L = 15\,\mu\text{H}$, sketch (or use MATLAB to plot) the magnitude of the transfer function versus frequency.

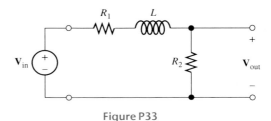

Figure P33

P34. We apply a 5-V-rms 20-kHz sinusoid to the input of a first-order RC lowpass filter, and the output voltage in steady state is 0.5 V rms. Predict the steady-state rms output voltage after the frequency of the input signal is raised to 150 kHz and the amplitude remains constant.

P35. Perhaps surprisingly, we can apply the transfer-function concept to mechanical systems. Suppose we have a mass m moving through a liquid with an applied force f and velocity v. The motion of the mass is described by the first-order differential equation

$$f = m\frac{dv}{dt} + kv$$

in which k is the coefficient of viscous friction. Find an expression for the transfer function

$$H(f) = \frac{\mathbf{V}}{\mathbf{F}}$$

Also, find the half-power frequency (defined as the frequency at which the transfer function magnitude is $1/\sqrt{2}$ times its dc value) in terms of k and m. [*Hint:* To determine the transfer function, assume a steady-state sinusoidal velocity $v = V_m \cos(2\pi ft)$, solve for the force, and take the ratio of their phasors.]

Section 3: Decibels, the Cascade Connection, and Logarithmic Frequency Scales

P36. What is a logarithmic frequency scale? A linear frequency scale?

P37. What is a notch filter? What is one application?

P38. What is the main advantage of converting transfer function magnitudes to decibels before plotting?

P39. What is the passband of a filter?

*P40. **a.** Given $|H(f)|_{dB} = -10\,dB$, find $|H(f)|$. **b.** Repeat for $|H(f)|_{dB} = 10\,dB$.

*P41. **a.** What frequency is halfway between 100 and 3000 Hz on a logarithmic frequency scale? **b.** On a linear frequency scale?

P42. Find the decibel equivalent for $|H(f)| = 0.5$. Repeat for $|H(f)| = 2$, $|H(f)| = 1/\sqrt{2} \cong 0.7071$, and $|H(f)| = \sqrt{2}$.

P43. Find the frequency that is **a.** one octave higher than 800 Hz; **b.** two octaves lower; **c.** two decades lower; **d.** one decade higher.

P44. Explain what we mean when we say that two filters are cascaded.

P45. We have a list of successive frequencies 2, f_1, f_2, f_3, 50 Hz. Determine the values of f_1, f_2, and f_3 so that the frequencies are evenly spaced on: **a.** a linear frequency scale, and **b.** a logarithmic frequency scale.

*P46. Two first-order lowpass filters are in cascade as shown in Figure P46. The transfer functions are

$$H_1(f) = H_2(f) = \frac{1}{1 + j(f/f_B)}$$

a. Write an expression for the overall transfer function. **b.** Find an expression for the half-power frequency for the overall transfer function in terms of f_B.

(*Comment:* This filter cannot be implemented by cascading two simple *RC* lowpass filters like the one shown in Figure 7 because the transfer function of the first circuit is changed when the second is connected. Instead, a buffer amplifier must be inserted between the *RC* filters.)

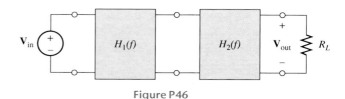

Figure P46

P47. How many decades are between $f_1 = 20\,Hz$ and $f_2 = 4.5\,kHz$? **b.** How many octaves?

P48. We have two filters with transfer functions $H_1(f)$ and $H_2(f)$ cascaded in the order 1–2. Give the expression for the overall transfer function of the cascade. Repeat if the transfer function magnitudes are expressed in decibels denoted as $|H_1(f)|_{dB}$ and $|H_2(f)|_{dB}$. What caution concerning $H_1(f)$ must be considered?

P49. Two filters are in cascade. At a given frequency f_1, the transfer function values are $|H_1(f_1)|_{dB} = -30$ and $|H_2(f_1)|_{dB} = +10$. Find the magnitude of the overall transfer function in decibels at $f = f_1$.

Section 4: Bode Plots

P50. What is a Bode plot?

P51. What is the slope of the high-frequency asymptote for the Bode magnitude plot for a first-order lowpass filter? The low-frequency asymptote? At what frequency do the asymptotes meet?

*P52. A transfer function is given by

$$H(f) = \frac{100}{1 + j(f/1000)}$$

Sketch the asymptotic magnitude and phase Bode plots to scale. What is the value of the half-power frequency?

P53. Suppose that three filters, having identical first-order lowpass transfer functions, are cascaded, what will be the rate at which the overall transfer function magnitude declines above the break frequency? Explain.

P54. Solve for the transfer function $H(f) = \mathbf{V}_{out}/\mathbf{V}_{in}$ and sketch the asymptotic Bode magnitude and phase plots to scale for the circuit shown in Figure P54.

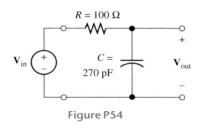

Figure P54

P55. A transfer function is given by

$$H(f) = \frac{10}{1 - j(f/500)}$$

Sketch the asymptotic magnitude and phase Bode plots to scale. What is the value of the half-power frequency?

P56. Consider a circuit for which

$$v_{out}(t) = v_{in}(t) - 200\pi \int_0^t v_{out}(t)dt$$

a. Assume that $v_{out}(t) = A\cos(2\pi ft)$, and find an expression for $v_{in}(t)$. **b.** Use the results of part (a) to find an expression for the transfer function $H(f) = \mathbf{V}_{out}/\mathbf{V}_{in}$ for the system. **c.** Draw the asymptotic Bode plot for the transfer function magnitude.

P57. Solve for the transfer function $H(f) = \mathbf{V}_{out}/\mathbf{V}_{in}$ and draw the asymptotic Bode magnitude and phase plots for the circuit shown in Figure P57.

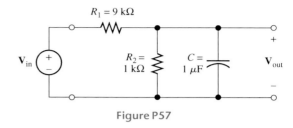

Figure P57

P58. Sketch the asymptotic magnitude and phase Bode plots to scale for the transfer function

$$H(f) = \frac{1 - j(f/100)}{1 + j(f/100)}$$

P59. Solve for the transfer function $H(f) = \mathbf{V}_{out}/\mathbf{V}_{in}$ and draw the Bode magnitude and phase plots for the circuit shown in Figure P59.

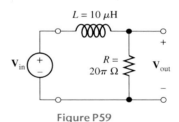

Figure P59

*P60. In solving Problem P14, we find that the transfer function of an integrator circuit is given by $H(f) = 1/(j2\pi f)$. Sketch the Bode magnitude and phase plots to scale. What is the slope of the magnitude plot?

P61. In solving Problem P20, we find that the transfer function of a differentiator circuit is given by $H(f) = j2\pi f$. Sketch the Bode magnitude and phase plots to scale. What is the slope of the magnitude plot?

Section 5: First-Order Highpass Filters

P62. Draw the circuit diagram of a first-order RC highpass filter and give the expression for the half-power frequency in terms of the circuit components.

P63. What is the slope of the high-frequency asymptote for the Bode magnitude plot for a first-order highpass filter? The low-frequency asymptote? At what frequency do the asymptotes meet?

*P64. Consider the circuit shown in Figure P64. Sketch the asymptotic Bode magnitude and phase plots to scale for the transfer function $H(f) = \mathbf{V}_{out}/\mathbf{V}_{in}$.

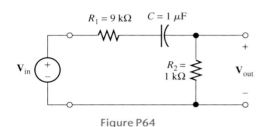

Figure P64

*P65. Consider the first-order highpass filter shown in Figure P65. The input signal is given by

$$v_{in}(t) = 5 + 5\cos(2000\pi t)$$

Find an expression for the output $v_{out}(t)$ in steady-state conditions.

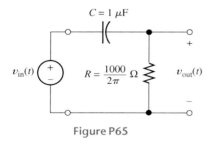

Figure P65

P66. Repeat Problem P65 for the input signal given by

$$v_{in}(t) = 10\cos(400\pi t) + 20\cos(4000\pi t)$$

P67. Suppose we need a first-order highpass filter (such as Figure 19) to attenuate a 60-Hz input component by 60 dB. What value is required for the break frequency of the filter? By how many dB is the 600-Hz component attenuated by this filter? If $R = 5\,\text{k}\Omega$, what is the value of C?

P68. Consider the circuit shown in Figure P68. Sketch the Bode magnitude and phase plots to scale for the transfer function $H(f) = \mathbf{V}_{out}/\mathbf{V}_{in}$.

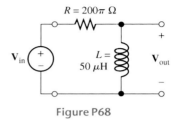

Figure P68

P69. Consider the circuit shown in Figure P69. Sketch the Bode magnitude and phase plots to scale for the transfer function $H(f) = \mathbf{V}_{out}/\mathbf{V}_{in}$.

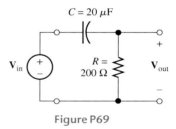

Figure P69

Section 6: Series Resonance

P70. What can you say about the impedance of a series RLC circuit at the resonant frequency? How are the resonant frequency and the quality factor defined?

P71. What is a *bandpass filter*? How is its bandwidth defined?

*P72. Consider the series resonant circuit shown in Figure P72, with $L = 20\,\mu\text{H}$, $R = 14.14\,\Omega$,

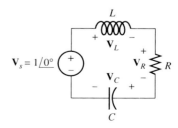

Figure P72

and $C = 1000$ pF. Compute the resonant frequency, the bandwidth, and the half-power frequencies. Assuming that the frequency of the source is the same as the resonant frequency, find the phasor voltages across the elements and sketch a phasor diagram.

P73. Work Problem P72 for $L = 80\,\mu H$, $R = 14.14\,\Omega$, and $C = 1000$ pF.

P74. Suppose we have a series resonant circuit for which $B = 30\,kHz$, $f_0 = 300\,kHz$, and $R = 40\,\Omega$. Determine the values of L and C.

*P75. At the resonant frequency $f_0 = 1\,MHz$, a series resonant circuit with $R = 50\,\Omega$ has $|\mathbf{V}_R| = 2\,V$ and $|\mathbf{V}_L| = 20\,V$. Determine the values of L and C. What is the value of $|\mathbf{V}_C|$?

P76. Suppose we have a series resonant circuit for which $f_0 = 12\,MHz$ and $B = 600\,kHz$. Furthermore, the minimum value of the impedance magnitude is $20\,\Omega$. Determine the values of R, L, and C.

P77. Derive an expression for the resonant frequency of the circuit shown in Figure P77. (Recall that we have defined the resonant frequency to be the frequency for which the impedance is purely resistive.)

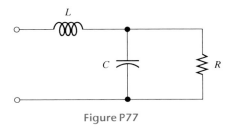

Figure P77

Section 7: Parallel Resonance

P78. What can you say about the impedance of a parallel RLC circuit at the resonant frequency? How is the resonant frequency defined? Compare the definition of quality factor for the parallel resonant circuit with that for the series resonant circuit.

*P79. A parallel resonant circuit has $R = 5\,k\Omega$, $L = 50\,\mu H$, and $C = 200\,pF$. Determine the resonant frequency, quality factor, and bandwidth.

P80. A parallel resonant circuit has $f_0 = 20\,MHz$ and $B = 200\,kHz$. The maximum value of

$|Z_p|$ is $5\,k\Omega$. Determine the values of R, L, and C.

P81. Consider the parallel resonant circuit shown in Figure 29. Determine the L and C values, given $R = 1\,k\Omega$, $f_0 = 10\,MHz$, and $B = 500\,kHz$. If $\mathbf{I} = 10^{-3}\angle 0°$, draw a phasor diagram showing the currents through each of the elements in the circuit at resonance.

P82. A parallel resonant circuit has $f_0 = 100\,MHz$, $B = 5\,MHz$, and $R = 2\,k\Omega$. Determine the values of L and C.

Section 8: Ideal and Second-Order Filters

P83. Name four types of ideal filters and sketch their transfer functions.

*P84. An ideal bandpass filter has cutoff frequencies of 9 and 11 kHz and a gain magnitude of two in the passband. Sketch the transfer-function magnitude to scale versus frequency. Repeat for an ideal band-reject filter.

P85. An ideal lowpass filter has a cutoff frequency of 10 kHz and a gain magnitude of two in the passband. Sketch the transfer-function magnitude to scale versus frequency. Repeat for an ideal highpass filter.

P86. Each AM radio signal has components ranging from 10 kHz below its carrier frequency to 10 kHz above its carrier frequency. Various radio stations in a given geographical region are assigned different carrier frequencies so that the frequency ranges of the signals do not overlap. Suppose that a certain AM radio transmitter has a carrier frequency of 980 kHz. What type of filter should be used if we want the filter to pass the components from this transmitter and reject the components of all other transmitters? What are the best values for the cutoff frequencies?

P87. In an electrocardiograph, the heart signals contain components with frequencies ranging from dc to 100 Hz. During exercise on a treadmill, the signal obtained from the electrodes also contains noise generated by muscle contractions. Most of the noise components have frequencies exceeding 100 Hz. What type of filter should be used to reduce the noise? What cutoff frequency is appropriate?

*P88. Draw the circuit diagram of a second-order highpass filter. Suppose that $R = 1\,\text{k}\Omega$, $Q_s = 1$, and $f_0 = 100\,\text{kHz}$. Determine the values of L and C.

P89. Draw the circuit diagram of a second-order highpass filter. Given that $R = 50\,\Omega$, $Q_s = 0.5$, and $f_0 = 30\,\text{MHz}$, determine the values of L and C.

P90. Suppose that sinewave interference has been inadvertently added to an audio signal that has frequency components ranging from 20 Hz to 15 kHz. The frequency of the interference slowly varies in the range 950 to 1050 Hz. A filter that attenuates the interference by at least 20 dB and passes most of the audio components is desired. What type of filter is needed? Sketch the magnitude Bode plot of a suitable filter, labeling its specifications.

Section 9: Transfer Functions and Bode Plots with MATLAB

P91. Consider the filter shown in Figure P91. **a.** Derive an expression for the transfer function $H(f) = \mathbf{V}_{\text{out}}/\mathbf{V}_{\text{in}}$. **b.** Use MATLAB to obtain a Bode plot of the transfer-function magnitude for $R_1 = 9\,\text{k}\Omega$, $R_2 = 1\,\text{k}\Omega$, and $C = 0.01\,\mu\text{F}$. Allow frequency to range from 10 Hz to 1 MHz. **c.** At very low frequencies, the capacitance becomes an open circuit. In this case, determine an expression for the transfer function and evaluate for the circuit parameters of part (b). Does the result agree with the value plotted in part (b)? **d.** At very high frequencies, the capacitance becomes a short circuit. In this case, determine an

expression for the transfer function and evaluate for the circuit parameters of part (b). Does the result agree with the value plotted in part (b)?

P92. Repeat Problem P91 for the circuit of Figure P92.

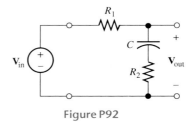

Figure P92

P93. Suppose that we need a filter with the Bode plot shown in Figure P93(a). We decide to cascade a highpass circuit and a lowpass circuit as shown in Figure P93(b). So that the second (i.e., right-hand) circuit looks like an approximate open circuit across the output of the first (i.e., left-hand) circuit, we choose $R_2 = 100R_1$. **a.** Which of the components form the lowpass filter? Which form the

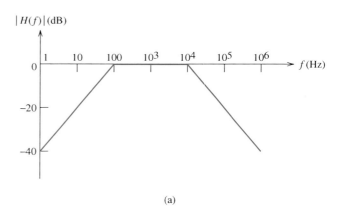

(a)

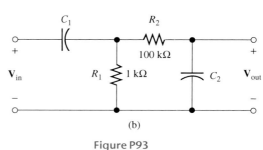

(b)

Figure P93

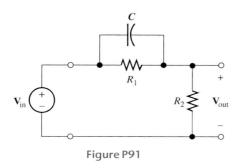

Figure P91

highpass filter? **b.** Compute the capacitances needed to achieve the desired break frequencies, making the approximation that the left-hand circuit has an open-circuit load. **c.** Write expressions that can be used to compute the exact transfer function $H(f) = \mathbf{V}_{out}/\mathbf{V}_{in}$ and use MATLAB to produce a Bode magnitude plot for f ranging from 1 Hz to 1 MHz. The result should be a close approximation to the desired plot shown in Figure P93(a).

P94. Suppose that we need a filter with the Bode plot shown in Figure P93(a). We decide to cascade a highpass circuit and a lowpass circuit, as shown in Figure P94. So that the second (i.e., right-hand) circuit looks like an approximate open circuit across the output of the first (i.e., left-hand) circuit, we choose $C_2 = C_1/100$. **a.** Which of the components form the lowpass filter? Which form the highpass filter? **b.** Compute the resistances needed to achieve the desired break frequencies, making the approximation that the left-hand circuit has an open-circuit load. **c.** Write expressions that can be used to compute the exact transfer function $H(f) = \mathbf{V}_{out}/\mathbf{V}_{in}$ and use MATLAB to produce a Bode magnitude plot for f ranging from 1 Hz to 1 MHz. The result should be a close approximation to the desired plot shown in Figure P93(a).

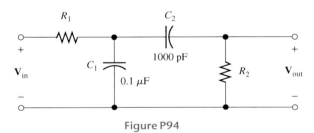

Figure P94

P95. Other combinations of R, L, and C have behaviors similar to that of the series resonant circuit. For example, consider the circuit shown in Figure P95. **a.** Derive an expression for the resonant frequency of this circuit. (We have defined the resonant frequency to be the frequency for which the impedance is purely resistive.) **b.** Compute the resonant frequency, given $L = 1 \text{ mH}$, $R = 1000 \ \Omega$, and $C = 0.25 \ \mu\text{F}$. **c.** Use

MATLAB to obtain a plot of the impedance magnitude of this circuit for f ranging from 95 to 105 percent of the resonant frequency. Compare the result with that of a series RLC circuit.

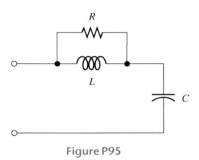

Figure P95

P96. Consider the circuit of Figure P77 with $R = 1 \text{ k}\Omega$, $L = 1 \text{ mH}$, and $C = 0.25 \ \mu\text{F}$. **a.** Using MATLAB, obtain a plot of the impedance magnitude of this circuit for f ranging from 9 to 11 kHz. **b.** From the plot, determine the minimum impedance, the frequency at which the impedance is minimum, and the bandwidth (i.e., the band of frequencies for which the impedance is less than $\sqrt{2}$ times the minimum value). **c.** Determine the component values for a series RLC circuit having the same parameters as those found in part (b). **d.** Plot the impedance magnitude of the series circuit on the same axes as the plot for part (a).

P97. Other combinations of R, L, and C have behaviors similiar to that of the parallel circuit. For example, consider the circuit shown in Figure P97. **a.** Derive an expression for the resonant frequency of this circuit. (We have defined the resonant frequency to be the frequency for which the impedance is purely resistive. However, in this case you may find the algebra easier if you work with admittances.) **b.** Compute the resonant frequency, given $L = 1 \text{ mH}$, $R = 1 \ \Omega$, and $C = 0.25 \ \mu\text{F}$. **c.** Use MATLAB to obtain a plot of the impedance magnitude of this circuit for f ranging from 95 to 105 percent of the resonant frequency. Compare the result with that of a parallel RLC circuit.

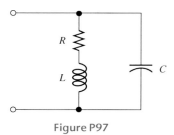

Figure P97

P98. Consider the filter shown in Figure P98. **a.** Derive an expression for the transfer function $H(f) = \mathbf{V}_{out}/\mathbf{V}_{in}$. **b.** Use MATLAB to obtain a Bode plot of the transfer function magnitude for $R = 10\ \Omega$, $L = 10\ \text{mH}$, and $C = 0.02533\ \mu\text{F}$. Allow frequency to range from 1 kHz to 100 kHz. **c.** At very low frequencies, the capacitance becomes an open circuit and the inductance becomes a short circuit. In this case, determine an expression for the transfer function and evaluate for the circuit parameters of part (b). Does the result agree with the value plotted in part (b)? **d.** At very high frequencies, the capacitance becomes a short circuit and the inductance becomes an open circuit. In this case, determine an expression for the transfer function and evaluate for the circuit parameters of part (b). Does the result agree with the value plotted in part (b)?

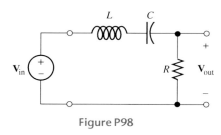

Figure P98

P99. Repeat Problem P98 for the circuit of Figure P99.

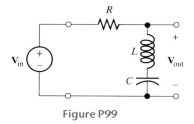

Figure P99

P100. Use the method of Example 9 to obtain a magnitude bode plot of the transfer function $H(f) = \mathbf{V}_{out}/\mathbf{V}_{in}$ for the lowpass filter of Figure P100 with frequency ranging from 100 kHz to 10 MHz. Manually verify the plotted values for high and low frequencies. Also, determine the half-power frequency for this filter.

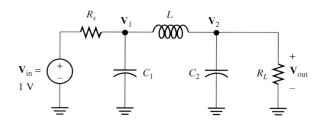

$$C_1 = C_2 = 3.1831 \times 10^{-9}\,\text{F} \qquad L = 15.915\,\mu\text{H}$$
$$R_s = R_L = 50\ \Omega$$

Figure P100

P101. Repeat Problem P100 for the highpass filter shown in Figure P101.

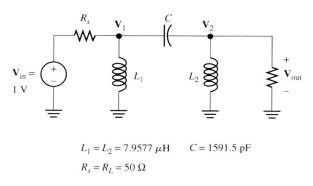

$$L_1 = L_2 = 7.9577\,\mu\text{H} \qquad C = 1591.5\,\text{pF}$$
$$R_s = R_L = 50\ \Omega$$

Figure P101

Section 10: Digital Signal Processing

P102. Develop a digital filter that mimics the action of the RL filter shown in Figure P102. Determine expressions for the coefficients in terms of the time constant and sampling interval T. (*Hint:* If your circuit equation contains an integral, differentiate with respect to time to obtain a pure differential equation.) **b.** Given $R = 10\ \Omega$ and $L = 200\ \text{mH}$, sketch the step response of the circuit to scale. **c.** Use MATLAB to determine and plot the step response of the digital filter for several time constants. Use the time constant of part (b) and $f_s = 500$ Hz. Compare the results of parts (b) and (c).

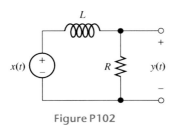

Figure P102

P103. Repeat Problem P102 for the filter shown in Figure P103.

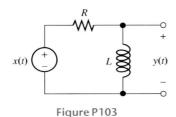

Figure P103

*P104. Consider the second-order bandpass filter shown in Figure P104. **a.** Derive expressions for L and C in terms of the resonant frequency ω_0 and quality factor Q_s. **b.** Write the KVL equation for the circuit and use it to develop a digital filter that mimics the action of the RLC filter. Use the results of part (a) to write the coefficients in terms of the resonant frequency ω_0, circuit quality factor Q_s, and sampling interval T. (*Hint:* The circuit equation contains an integral, so differentiate with respect to time to obtain a pure differential equation.)

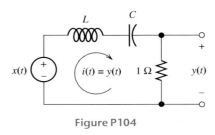

Figure P104

Practice Test

Here is a practice test you can use to check your comprehension of the most important concepts in this chapter. Answers can be found at the end of this chapter and complete solutions are included in the Student Solutions files.

T1. What is the basic concept of Fourier theory as it relates to real-world signals? How does the transfer function of a filter relate to this concept?

T2. An input signal given by

$$v_{in}(t) = 3 + 4\cos(1000\pi t)$$
$$+ 5\cos(2000\pi t - 30°)$$

is applied to the RL filter shown in Figure T2. Find the expression for the output signal $v_{out}(t)$.

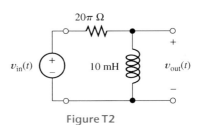

Figure T2

T3. Consider the Bode magnitude plot for the transfer function of a certain filter given by

$$H(f) = \frac{\mathbf{V}_{out}}{\mathbf{V}_{in}} = 50\frac{j(f/200)}{1 + j(f/200)}$$

a. What is the slope of the low-frequency asymptote?

b. What is the slope of the high-frequency asymptote?

c. What are the coordinates of the point at which the asymptotes meet?

d. What type of filter is this?

e. What is the value of the break frequency?

T4. A series resonant circuit has $R = 5\ \Omega$, $L = 20\,\text{mH}$, and $C = 1\,\mu\text{F}$. Determine the values of:

a. the resonant frequency in Hz.

b. Q.

c. bandwidth in Hz.

d. the impedance of the circuit at the resonant frequency.

e. the impedance of the circuit at dc.

f. the impedance of the circuit as the frequency approaches infinity.

T5. Repeat question T4 for a parallel resonant circuit with $R = 10\,\text{k}\Omega$, $L = 1\,\text{mH}$, and $C = 1000\,\text{pF}$.

T6. Consider the transfer function $\mathbf{V}_{\text{out}}/\mathbf{V}_{\text{in}}$ for each of the circuits shown in Figure T6. Classify each circuit as a first-order low-pass filter, second-order bandpass filter, etc. Justify your answers.

T7. Give a list of MATLAB commands to produce the magnitude Bode plot for the transfer function of question T3 for frequency ranging from 10 Hz to 10 kHz.

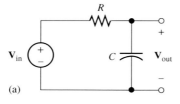

(a)

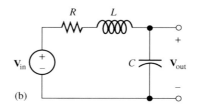

(b)

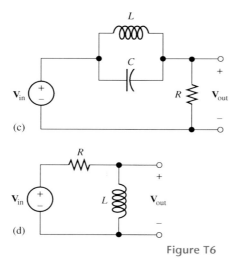

(c)

(d)

Figure T6

Answers for the Practice Test

T1. All real-world signals (which are usually time-varying currents or voltages) are sums of sinewaves of various frequencies, amplitudes, and phases. The transfer function of a filter is a function of frequency that shows how the amplitudes and phases of the input components are altered to produce the output components.

T2. $v_{out}(t) = 1.789 \cos(1000\pi t - 63.43°) + 3.535 \cos(2000\pi t + 15°)$

T3. **a.** The slope of the low-frequency asymptote is $+20$ dB/decade. **b.** The slope of the high-frequency asymptote is zero. **c.** The coordinates at which the asymptotes meet are $20 \log(50) = 34$ dB and 200 Hz. **d.** This is a first-order highpass filter. **e.** The break frequency is 200 Hz.

T4. **a.** 1125 Hz; **b.** 28.28; **c.** 39.79 Hz; **d.** $5\ \Omega$; **e.** infinite impedance; **f.** infinite impedance.

T5. **a.** 159.2 kHz; **b.** 10.0; **c.** 15.92 kHz; **d.** 10 kΩ; **e.** zero impedance; **f.** zero impedance.

T6. **a.** First-order lowpass filter; **b.** second-order lowpass filter; **c.** second-order band-reject (or notch) filter; **d.** first-order highpass filter.

T7. One set of commands is:

```
f = logspace(1,4,400);
H = 50*i*(f/200)./(1 + i*f/200);
semilogx(f,20*log10(abs(H)))
```

Other sets of commands will also work. Check to see if your commands produce a plot equivalent to the one produced by the set given above.

Complex Numbers

Sinusoidal steady-state analysis is greatly facilitated if the currents and voltages are represented as complex numbers known as **phasors**. In this appendix, we review complex numbers.

Basic Complex-Number Concepts

Complex numbers involve the imaginary number $j = \sqrt{-1}$. (Electrical engineers use j to represent the square root of -1 rather than i, because i is often used for currents.) Several examples of complex numbers are

$$3 + j4 \quad \text{and} \quad -2 + j5$$

We say that a complex number $Z = x + jy$ has a **real part** x and an **imaginary part** y. We can represent complex numbers by points in the **complex plane**, in which the real part is the horizontal coordinate and the imaginary part is the vertical coordinate. We often show the complex number by an arrow directed from the origin of the complex plane to the point defined by the real and imaginary components. This is illustrated in Figure 1.

A **pure imaginary number**, $j6$ for example, has a real part of zero. On the other hand, a **pure real number**, such as 5, has an imaginary part of zero.

We say that complex numbers of the form $x + jy$ are in **rectangular form**. The **complex conjugate** of a number in rectangular form is obtained by changing the sign of the imaginary part. For example, if

$$Z_2 = 3 - j4$$

then the complex conjugate of Z_2 is

$$Z_2^* = 3 + j4$$

(Notice that we denote the complex conjugate by the symbol *.)

We add, subtract, multiply, and divide complex numbers that are in rectangular form in much the same way as we do algebraic expressions, making the substitution $j^2 = -1$.

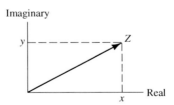

Figure 1 Complex plane.

From Appendix A of *Electrical Engineering: Principles and Applications*, Fifth Edition, Allan R. Hambley. Copyright © 2011 by Pearson Education, Inc. Published by Pearson Prentice Hall. All rights reserved.

| **Example 1** | Complex Arithmetic in Rectangular Form |

Given that $Z_1 = 5 + j5$ and $Z_2 = 3 - j4$, reduce $Z_1 + Z_2$, $Z_1 - Z_2$, $Z_1 Z_2$, and Z_1/Z_2 to rectangular form.

Solution For the sum, we have

$$Z_1 + Z_2 = (5 + j5) + (3 - j4) = 8 + j1$$

Notice that we add (algebraically) real part to real part and imaginary part to imaginary part.

The difference is

$$Z_1 - Z_2 = (5 + j5) - (3 - j4) = 2 + j9$$

In this case, we subtract each part of Z_2 from the corresponding part of Z_1.

For the product, we get

$$
\begin{aligned}
Z_1 Z_2 &= (5 + j5)(3 - j4) \\
&= 15 - j20 + j15 - j^2 20 \\
&= 15 - j20 + j15 + 20 \\
&= 35 - j5
\end{aligned}
$$

Notice that we expanded the product in the usual way for binomial expressions. Then, we used the fact that $j^2 = -1$.

To divide the numbers, we obtain

$$\frac{Z_1}{Z_2} = \frac{5 + j5}{3 - j4}$$

We can reduce this expression to rectangular form by multiplying the numerator and denominator by the complex conjugate of the denominator. This causes the denominator of the fraction to become pure real. Then, we divide each part of the numerator by the denominator. Thus, we find that

$$
\begin{aligned}
\frac{Z_1}{Z_2} &= \frac{5 + j5}{3 - j4} \times \frac{Z_2^*}{Z_2^*} \\
&= \frac{5 + j5}{3 - j4} \times \frac{3 + j4}{3 + j4} \\
&= \frac{15 + j20 + j15 + j^2 20}{9 + j12 - j12 - j^2 16} \\
&= \frac{15 + j20 + j15 - 20}{9 + j12 - j12 + 16} \\
&= \frac{-5 + j35}{25} \\
&= -0.2 + j1.4
\end{aligned}
$$
∎

Exercise 1 Given that $Z_1 = 2 - j3$ and $Z_2 = 8 + j6$, reduce $Z_1 + Z_2$, $Z_1 - Z_2$, $Z_1 Z_2$, and Z_1/Z_2 to rectangular form.

Answer $Z_1 + Z_2 = 10 + j3$, $Z_1 - Z_2 = -6 - j9$, $Z_1 Z_2 = 34 - j12$, $Z_1/Z_2 = -0.02 - j0.36$.
□

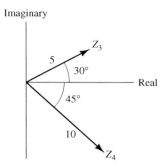

Figure 2 Complex numbers in polar form.

Complex Numbers in Polar Form

Complex numbers can be expressed in **polar form** by giving the length of the arrow that represents the number and the angle between the arrow and the positive real axis. Examples of complex numbers in polar form are

$$Z_3 = 5\underline{/30^\circ} \quad \text{and} \quad Z_4 = 10\underline{/-45^\circ}$$

These numbers are shown in Figure 2. The length of the arrow that represents a complex number Z is denoted as $|Z|$ and is called the **magnitude** of the complex number.

Complex numbers can be converted from polar to rectangular form, or vice versa, by using the fact that the magnitude $|Z|$, the real part x, and the imaginary part y form a right triangle. This is illustrated in Figure 3. Using trigonometry, we can write the following relationships:

$$|Z|^2 = x^2 + y^2 \tag{1}$$

$$\tan(\theta) = \frac{y}{x} \tag{2}$$

$$x = |Z|\cos(\theta) \tag{3}$$

$$y = |Z|\sin(\theta) \tag{4}$$

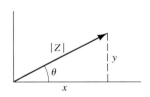

Figure 3 Complex number representation.

These equations can be used to convert numbers from polar to rectangular form, or vice versa.

Example 2 | Polar-to-Rectangular Conversion

Convert $Z_3 = 5\underline{/30^\circ}$ to rectangular form.

Solution   Using Equations 3 and 4, we have

$$x = |Z|\cos(\theta) = 5\cos(30^\circ) = 4.33$$

and

$$y = |Z|\sin(\theta) = 5\sin(30^\circ) = 2.5$$

Thus, we can write

$$Z_3 = 5\underline{/30^\circ} = x + jy = 4.33 + j2.5$$　∎

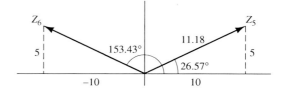

Figure 4 Complex numbers of Example 3.

Example 3   Rectangular-to-Polar Conversion

Convert $Z_5 = 10 + j5$ and $Z_6 = -10 + j5$ to polar form.

Solution   The complex numbers are illustrated in Figure 4. First, we use Equation 1 to find the magnitudes of each of the numbers. Thus,

$$|Z_5| = \sqrt{x_5^2 + y_5^2} = \sqrt{10^2 + 5^2} = 11.18$$

and

$$|Z_6| = \sqrt{x_6^2 + y_6^2} = \sqrt{(-10)^2 + 5^2} = 11.18$$

To find the angles, we use Equation 2.

$$\tan(\theta_5) = \frac{y_5}{x_5} = \frac{5}{10} = 0.5$$

Taking the arctangent of both sides, we have

$$\theta_5 = \arctan(0.5) = 26.57°$$

Thus, we can write

$$Z_5 = 10 + j5 = 11.18\underline{/26.57°}$$

This is illustrated in Figure 4.

Evaluating Equation 2 for Z_6, we have

$$\tan(\theta_6) = \frac{y_6}{x_6} = \frac{5}{-10} = -0.5$$

Now if we take the arctan of both sides, we obtain

$$\theta_6 = -26.57°$$

However, $Z_6 = -10 + j5$ is shown in Figure 4. Clearly, the value that we have found for θ_5 is incorrect. The reason for this is that the arctangent function is multivalued. The value actually given by most calculators or computer programs is the principal value. *If the number falls to the left of the imaginary axis (i.e., if the real part is negative), we must add (or subtract) 180° to* $\arctan(y/x)$ *to obtain the correct angle.* Thus, the true angle for Z_6 is

$$\theta_6 = 180 + \arctan\left(\frac{y_6}{x_6}\right) = 180 - 26.57 = 153.43°$$

Finally, we can write

$$Z_6 = -10 + j5 = 11.18\underline{/153.43°} \qquad \blacksquare$$

The procedures that we have illustrated in Examples 2 and 3 can be carried out with a relatively simple calculator. However, if we find the angle by taking the arctangent of y/x, we must consider the fact that the principal value of the arctangent is the true angle only if the real part x is positive. If x is negative, we have

$$\theta = \arctan\left(\frac{y}{x}\right) \pm 180° \qquad (5)$$

Many scientific calculators are capable of converting complex numbers from polar to rectangular, and vice versa, in a single operation. Practice with your calculator to become proficient using this feature. *It is always a good idea to make a sketch of the number in the complex plane as a check on the conversion process.*

Exercise 2 Convert the numbers $Z_1 = 15\underline{/45°}$, $Z_2 = 10\underline{/-150°}$, and $Z_3 = 5\underline{/90°}$ to rectangular form.
Answer $Z_1 = 10.6 + j10.6$, $Z_2 = -8.66 - j5$, $Z_3 = j5$. □

Exercise 3 Convert the numbers $Z_1 = 3 + j4$, $Z_2 = -j10$, and $Z_3 = -5 - j5$ to polar form.
Answer $Z_1 = 5\underline{/53.13°}$, $Z_2 = 10\underline{/-90°}$, $Z_3 = 7.07\underline{/-135°}$. □

Euler's Identities

You may have been wondering what complex numbers have to do with sinusoids. The connection is through Euler's identities, which state that

$$\cos(\theta) = \frac{e^{j\theta} + e^{-j\theta}}{2} \qquad (6)$$

and

$$\sin(\theta) = \frac{e^{j\theta} - e^{-j\theta}}{2j} \qquad (7)$$

Equations 6 through 9 are the bridge between sinusoidal currents or voltages and complex numbers.

Another form of these identities is

$$e^{j\theta} = \cos(\theta) + j\sin(\theta) \qquad (8)$$

and

$$e^{-j\theta} = \cos(\theta) - j\sin(\theta) \qquad (9)$$

Thus, $e^{j\theta}$ is a complex number having a real part of $\cos(\theta)$ and an imaginary part of $\sin(\theta)$. This is illustrated in Figure 5. The magnitude is

$$|e^{j\theta}| = \sqrt{\cos^2(\theta) + \sin^2(\theta)}$$

By the well-known identity $\cos^2(\theta) + \sin^2(\theta) = 1$, this becomes

$$|e^{j\theta}| = 1 \qquad (10)$$

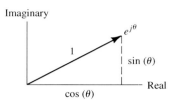

Figure 5 Euler's identity.

Furthermore, the angle of $e^{j\theta}$ is θ. Thus, we can write

$$e^{j\theta} = 1\underline{/\theta} = \cos(\theta) + j\sin(\theta) \qquad (11)$$

Similarly, we have

$$e^{-j\theta} = 1\underline{/-\theta} = \cos(\theta) - j\sin(\theta) \qquad (12)$$

Notice that $e^{-j\theta}$ is the complex conjugate of $e^{j\theta}$.

A complex number such as $A\underline{/\theta}$ can be written as

$$A\underline{/\theta} = A \times (1\underline{/\theta}) = Ae^{j\theta} \qquad (13)$$

We call $Ae^{j\theta}$ the **exponential form** of a complex number. Hence, a given complex number can be written in three forms: the rectangular form, the polar form, and the exponential form. Using Equation 11 to substitute for $e^{j\theta}$ on the right-hand side of Equation 13, we obtain the three forms of a complex number:

$$A\underline{/\theta} = Ae^{j\theta} = A\cos(\theta) + jA\sin(\theta) \qquad (14)$$

| **Example 4** | **Exponential Form of a Complex Number** |

Express the complex number $Z = 10\underline{/60°}$ in exponential and rectangular forms. Sketch the number in the complex plane.

Solution Conversion from polar to exponential forms is based on Equation 13. Thus, we have

$$Z = 10\underline{/60°} = 10e^{j60°}$$

The rectangular form can be found by using Equation 8:

$$Z = 10 \times (e^{j60°})$$
$$= 10 \times [\cos(60°) + j\sin(60°)]$$
$$= 5 + j8.66$$

The graphical representation of Z is shown in Figure 6. ∎

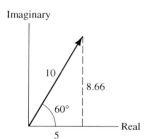

Figure 6 See Example 4.

Exercise 4 Express $Z_1 = 10 + j10$ and $Z_2 = -10 + j10$ in polar and exponential forms.

Answer $Z_1 = 14.14\underline{/45°} = 14.14e^{j45°}$, $Z_2 = 14.14\underline{/135°} = 14.14e^{j135°}$. □

Arithmetic Operations in Polar and Exponential Form

To add (or subtract) complex numbers, we must first convert them to rectangular form. Then, we add (or subtract) real part to real part and imaginary to imaginary.

Consider two complex numbers in exponential form given by

$$Z_1 = |Z_1|e^{j\theta_1} \quad \text{and} \quad Z_2 = |Z_2|e^{j\theta_2}$$

The polar forms of these numbers are

$$Z_1 = |Z_1|\angle{\theta_1} \quad \text{and} \quad Z_2 = |Z_2|\angle{\theta_2}$$

For multiplication of numbers in exponential form, we have

$$Z_1 \times Z_2 = |Z_1|e^{j\theta_1} \times |Z_2|e^{j\theta_2} = |Z_1||Z_2|e^{j(\theta_1+\theta_2)}$$

As usual, in multiplying exponentials, we add the exponents. In polar form, this is

$$Z_1 \times Z_2 = |Z_1|\angle{\theta_1} \times |Z_2|\angle{\theta_2} = |Z_1||Z_2|\angle{\theta_1 + \theta_2}$$

Thus, to multiply numbers in polar form, we multiply the magnitudes and add the angles.

Now consider division:

$$\frac{Z_1}{Z_2} = \frac{|Z_1|e^{j\theta_1}}{|Z_2|e^{j\theta_2}} = \frac{|Z_1|}{|Z_2|}e^{j(\theta_1-\theta_2)}$$

As usual, in dividing exponentials, we subtract the exponents. In polar form, this is

$$\frac{Z_1}{Z_2} = \frac{|Z_1|\angle{\theta_1}}{|Z_2|\angle{\theta_2}} = \frac{|Z_1|}{|Z_2|}\angle{\theta_1 - \theta_2}$$

Thus, to divide numbers in polar form, we divide the magnitudes and subtract the angle of the divisor from the angle of the dividend.

Example 5 **Complex Arithmetic in Polar Form**

Given $Z_1 = 10\angle{60°}$ and $Z_2 = 5\angle{45°}$, find $Z_1 Z_2$, Z_1/Z_2, and $Z_1 + Z_2$ in polar form.

Solution   For the product, we have

$$Z_1 \times Z_2 = 10\angle{60°} \times 5\angle{45°} = 50\angle{105°}$$

Dividing the numbers, we have

$$\frac{Z_1}{Z_2} = \frac{10\angle{60°}}{5\angle{45°}} = 2\angle{15°}$$

Before we can add (or subtract) the numbers, we must convert them to rectangular form. Using Equation 14 to convert the polar numbers to rectangular, we get

$$Z_1 = 10\angle{60°} = 10\cos(60°) + j10\sin(60°)$$
$$= 5 + j8.66$$
$$Z_2 = 5\angle{45°} = 5\cos(45°) + j5\sin(45°)$$
$$= 3.54 + j3.54$$

Now, we can add the numbers. We denote the sum as Z_s:

$$Z_s = Z_1 + Z_2 = 5 + j8.66 + 3.54 + j3.54$$
$$= 8.54 + j12.2$$

Next, we convert the sum to polar form:

$$|Z_s| = \sqrt{(8.54)^2 + (12.2)^2} = 14.9$$
$$\tan \theta_s = \frac{12.2}{8.54} = 1.43$$

Taking the arctangent of both sides, we have

$$\theta_s = \arctan(1.43) = 55°$$

Because the real part of Z_s is positive, the correct angle is the principal value of the arctangent (i.e., $55°$ is the correct angle). Thus, we obtain

$$Z_s = Z_1 + Z_2 = 14.9 \underline{/55°} \qquad \blacksquare$$

Exercise 5   Given $Z_1 = 10\underline{/30°}$ and $Z_2 = 20 \underline{/135°}$, find $Z_1 Z_2$, Z_1/Z_2, $Z_1 - Z_2$, and $Z_1 + Z_2$ in polar form.
Answer $Z_1 Z_2 = 200\underline{/165°}$, $Z_1/Z_2 = 0.5\underline{/-105°}$, $Z_1 - Z_2 = 24.6\underline{/-21.8°}$, $Z_1 + Z_2 = 19.9\underline{/106°}$. □

Summary

1. Complex numbers can be expressed in rectangular, polar, or exponential forms. Addition, subtraction, multiplication, and division of complex numbers are necessary operations in solving steady-state ac circuits by the phasor method.

2. Sinusoids and complex numbers are related through Euler's identities.

Problems*

P1.   Given that $Z_1 = 2 + j3$ and $Z_2 = 4 - j3$, reduce $Z_1 + Z_2$, $Z_1 - Z_2$, $Z_1 Z_2$, and Z_1/Z_2 to rectangular form.

P2.   Given that $Z_1 = 1 - j2$ and $Z_2 = 2 + j3$, reduce $Z_1 + Z_2$, $Z_1 - Z_2$, $Z_1 Z_2$, and Z_1/Z_2 to rectangular form.

P3.   Given that $Z_1 = 10 + j5$ and $Z_2 = 20 - j20$, reduce $Z_1 + Z_2$, $Z_1 - Z_2$, $Z_1 Z_2$, and Z_1/Z_2 to rectangular form.

P4.   Express each of these complex numbers in polar form and in exponential form: **a.** $Z_a = 5 - j5$; **b.** $Z_b = -10 + j5$; **c.** $Z_c = -3 - j4$; **d.** $Z_d = -j12$.

*   Solutions for these problems are contained in the Student Solutions files.

P5. Express each of these complex numbers in rectangular form and in exponential form: **a.** $Z_a = 5\angle 45°$; **b.** $Z_b = 10\angle 120°$; **c.** $Z_c = -15\angle -90°$; **d.** $Z_d = -10\angle 60°$.

P6. Express each of these complex numbers in rectangular form and in polar form: **a.** $Z_a = 5e^{j30°}$; **b.** $Z_b = 10e^{-j45°}$; **c.** $Z_c = 100e^{j135°}$; **d.** $Z_d = 6e^{j90°}$.

P7. Reduce each of the following to rectangular form:

a. $Z_a = 5 + j5 + 10\angle 30°$

b. $Z_b = 5\angle 45° - j10$

c. $Z_c = \dfrac{10\angle 45°}{3 + j4}$

d. $Z_d = \dfrac{15}{5\angle 90°}$

Index